Larger Moths
of Surrey

Larger Moths
of Surrey

GRAHAM A. COLLINS

SURREY WILDLIFE TRUST

Cover illustration: Heart Moth, by Jim Porter

ISBN 0 9526065 2 6

British Library Cataloguing-in-Publication Data.
A catalogue record for this book is available
from the British Library.

First published 1997
by Surrey Wildlife Trust
School Lane, Pirbright, Woking, Surrey GU24 0JN.

Printed and bound in Great Britain by
Biddles Ltd, Guildford and King's Lynn

FOREWORD

Surrey has a long and distinguished entomological history, figuring prominently in the works of Stephens in the early nineteenth century, through Barrett to the lepidopterists of the present century. Surprisingly, it has taken until now before the appearance of a complete county fauna for the larger moths. With the publication of this work we now have an up-to-date, authoritative account of the county's moth population, which, while principally considering the current status and distribution of Surrey's moth species, also relies on this wealth of historical data to put the present situation into context.

I first started studying moths over 40 years ago, and since then Surrey has changed considerably. The population has increased significantly, and much moth habitat has been lost to housing and road building. Land use has altered as a result of increased efficiency in farming techniques, and we have also seen such changes as the reduction in rabbit population following the introduction of myxomatosis in the 1950s and the wholesale loss of large elms caused by Dutch elm disease in the 1970s. All these changes have had their effects on the county's moths, but it is encouraging to see that a number of species have in fact become commoner and more widespread in recent years.

This volume, the third in a series of county faunal works for Surrey, will establish a baseline against which future changes in distribution can be judged, and will be invaluable to entomologists, conservationists and land owners. The inclusion of distribution maps, and detailed records for the scarcer species, will enable individuals to understand better the significance of any records that they may make.

Over 90 recorders have contributed data to this book, which stands as a testament to their combined efforts. The author, who has devoted over 12 years to the project, is to be congratulated on a fine achievement.

BERNARD SKINNER

CONTENTS

Appendices

Index

PREFACE

Surrey ranks among the best counties for larger moths in Britain, and yet, until now, there has been no attempt to publish details of the distribution, ecology, and phenology of this group for the county as a whole. The only work thus far produced covering the whole of our area is the *Victoria County History*, published at the turn of the century, and comprising little more than a list of species together with a handful of localities. This current work arose from a need to update the macrolepidoptera list for north-east Surrey (Evans, 1973), and the opportunity was taken to extend the coverage to the whole of the vice-county of Surrey, at the same time providing ecological data and distribution maps. The principal criterion for the list was scientific accuracy, and the utmost care has been taken in accepting records only from recorders of known competence; dubious records without voucher specimens, and records of species requiring dissection where this has not been done, have mostly not been accepted.

The order lepidoptera (butterflies and moths) is divided somewhat unscientifically into the larger species (macrolepidoptera), and the smaller species (microlepidoptera). The species covered by this volume are the macrolepidoptera in the sense used by authors from South (1907) to the modern day, i.e. Skinner (1984), the butterflies having already been covered in a companion volume (Collins, 1995). Most of the microlepidoptera have not been studied in sufficient detail to make their inclusion in a county list a possibility at this time, although it would be nice to see this done in the future.

This volume is the third in a series of county lists covering various invertebrate groups, in which the authors have given freely of their time and often made considerable financial input into the researching and recording of their subject. The costs of actually publishing their work are however far too great for any individual to bear, and the successful production of this volume has only been possible through the great kindness of the bodies listed below.

British Entomological & Natural History Society
Corporation of London
Butterfly Conservation (Surrey branch)

I am also extremely grateful for the assistance of the following: Martin Newman and staff (Surrey Wildlife Trust) for help in raising finances, supporting the Surrey Invertebrate Atlas Project, and acting as publishers; Clare Windsor (Surrey Wildlife Trust) for the design and typesetting, and for organizing the printing; Dr. Peter Sutcliffe for the chapter on geology; Colin Plant (London Natural History Society) for providing records relating to the London area of Surrey; Bernard Skinner for refereeing the species accounts; Roger Hawkins for proof-reading; and all the many individuals who have supported the project by providing records of moths – their names are listed separately.

The following have provided photographic slides for the colour illustrations – Graham A. Collins, Jim Porter. The plate of set moths was photographed by David Wilson.

The distribution maps in this book have been produced by the DMAP program (in its Windows version) written by Dr Alan Morton of Imperial College at Silwood Park. For further information about the program and its implementation see Morton and Collins (1992).

GRAHAM A. COLLINS

SURREY – THE STUDY AREA

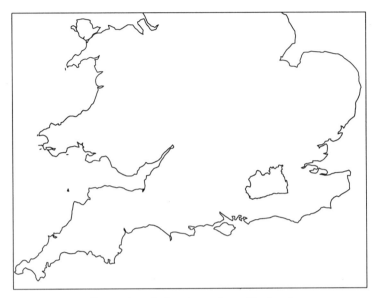

Surrey in relation to southern England

The boundary of the current county is a political boundary as ephemeral as the scientific names of many of the insects described in these volumes, and consequently wholly unsuited to the recording of any biological group over any period of time. For this a stable boundary is necessary and exists in the form of the vice-county, a division originally proposed by H.C. Watson in 1852 in order to provide a set of unit areas of roughly similar dimensions for botanical recording. The system was rapidly adopted by botanists and supported by the forerunners of the Botanical Society of the British Isles, and has since been in use by many zoologists. Since the introduction of this system the political boundary of Surrey has changed several times, and the sense of using the fixed boundary of the vice-county can immediately be seen. The whole vice-county system is explained in text and maps in Dandy (1969).

The vice-county of Surrey differs from the current administrative county principally in its northern boundary which is marked by the course of the River Thames thus including the boroughs of the south-western quadrant of Greater London. The southern boundary differs slightly in that it runs almost east-west in the vicinity of Horley and so includes the area occupied by Gatwick airport which is currently in West Sussex, and on the western boundary an area of approximately one square kilometre to the south of the village of Batt's Corner and part of present day Surrey is excluded. The other major exclusion is the district of Spelthorne, which only became attached to Surrey in 1965, and in fact belongs principally to the vice-county of Middlesex. The actual boundary and that of the adjacent vice-counties is shown on the accompanying map.

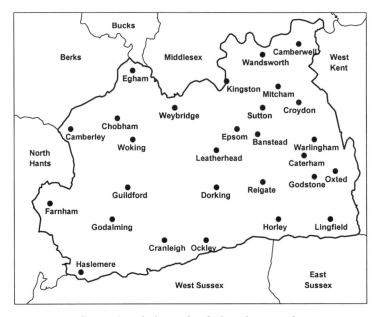

Surrey in relation to bordering vice-counties

GEOLOGY OF SURREY

by Dr P J C Sutcliffe
School of Geological Sciences, Kingston University

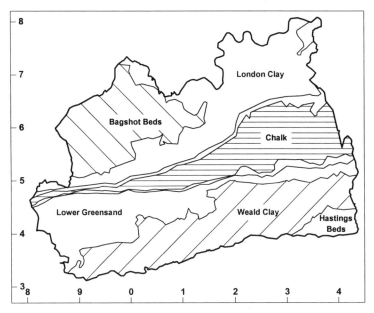

Solid geology of Surrey, after 'Butterflies of Surrey'.

The county of Surrey is situated on the northern limb of a large geological fold structure, the Wealden Anticline, which forms the backbone of south-east England. This heavily eroded upright, arched form passes to the north into the associated London Valley Syncline (the London Basin). These structures, which are elongated in an east-west direction, were developed in the late Tertiary Period (between 6 and 23 million years ago) during the Alpine Orogeny. This orogeny, or "mountain-building period", was caused by the northward motion of the African Continental Plate against the European Plate. The northward motion caused the rocks in the south-east England area to buckle to produce the fold structures.

All the solid rocks exposed in Surrey, and underlying the superficial soils and gravels, are of Cretaceous and Tertiary age (between 2 and 145 million years old) and are dominantly of marine or coastal plain origin. The scattered superficial deposits are predominantly Pleistocene in age and glacial in origin, or are Holocene river gravels. Within Surrey, the oldest solid rocks occur to the south of the county, with the rocks younging and dipping towards the north at a low angle (~2°).

The oldest rocks exposed in the southern part of the county are the Hastings Beds (alternating sands and clays, found in the Burstow, Lingfield and Dormansland areas) which tend to produce thin, well-drained acidic sandy soils covered with scrub by heathland. The broad expanse of younger Weald Clay (in the Outwood, Crowhurst area) is predominantly poorly drained marshy 'wetland'.

The Lower Greensand, so called because of its high content of *glauconite* (a dark green, iron silicate mineral, typical of sediments formed in a marine environment), is very variable in thickness and composition. The main component units or beds are the Atherfield Clay, Hythe Beds, Sandgate Beds and Folkestone Sands. Whilst these beds vary in grain size and composition, most are orange-brown in colour, due to the oxidized state of the constituent iron minerals. The sandy units (Sandgate Beds and Folkestone Sands) are well-drained, porous sediments, often used as a building-sand source as at Albury and Buckland. Sometimes the sands are so pure (white in colour), as in the Buckland area, that they can be used for glass-making or foundry-moulding sand. Within the Sandgate Beds near Redhill, seams of "fuller's earth" occur. This is a fine clay, rich in the clay mineral, *montmorillonite*, which has strong adsorptive properties. *Montmorillonite* is the decomposed residuum of volcanic ash, from an ancient volcano, possibly situated off the Cornish coast, which fell into the shallow seas and lagoons that covered south-east England in Lower Cretaceous times. Fuller's earth was used for cleaning or 'fulling' woollen cloth before the use of detergents. This early practice led to the names of many of the villages reflecting this trade, eg Woolpits (pits for bleaching wool) and Bletchingley (from Blaecon, to bleach, and ley, a field). It is now extensively utilized in refining syrups and oils, water purification, and in the oil industry as a lubricant used in the drilling of oil and gas wells. Fuller's earth has been extracted in the Reigate and Godstone area since Roman times, the main quarry at present being at Nutfield. In recent years, some of the worked-out pits have been turned into nature reserves and others used as landfill sites.

One of the most characteristic features of the Lower Greensand scenery is the high escarpment which it forms. Leith Hill, at 249 metres, is the highest point of the Weald. The Hythe Beds produce deep fertile soils, owing to the clay-rich nature of this sandy unit.

The Gault Clay outcrop occupies a narrow flat belt of intensively cultivated land adjacent to the Lower Greensand hills. The heavy wet soils are capable of supporting a thriving natural or economically-harvested flora.

The Chalk escarpment of the North and South Downs is one of the most prominent features of south-east England, forming a rim around the Weald.

The escarpment owes its existence to the relative compositional homogeneity of Chalk and to its facility for water to move freely through joints in the rock. These properties give the Chalk a higher resistance to erosion than the looser, softer sands and clays in the rest of the sequence.

The Chalk is a fine white limestone, composed of microscopic marine algal fragments (coccoliths). The Chalk sequence is divisible into three units. The Lower Chalk is the least pure, containing a moderate admixture of clay, giving it a grey coloration. The Middle Chalk is harder, whiter and more nodular in character, whilst the Upper Chalk contains abundant dark grey or black flint nodules. The Chalk is used extensively in the manufacture of cement or as a source of lime for agricultural purposes. Disused Chalk pits are commonplace in Surrey, but few working quarries remain. Soils in the Chalk downland areas are usually very thin and poor, unless the Chalk is covered by sandy superficial sediments.

After the deposition of the Chalk, the Wealden area underwent gradual uplift, raising the whole area above sea level. Much of the Chalk sediments were eroded before the later Tertiary sediments were laid down mainly in the London Basin area, on the northern flanks of the Weald. The London Clay is a dense, grey clay of marine origin, showing that the sea had partially re-invaded this area. The heavy clay is poorly drained and supported a woodland flora before much of this area became part of the urban jungle.

The Bagshot Beds are typified by well-drained, sandy gravels which support a heathland vegetation. Wisley Gardens shows that these beds can sustain a very varied range of plant life.

The superficial sediments of Surrey, such as the Netley Heath Beds around Newlands Corner, sit unconformably on the older units, and are usually composed of sandy gravels with variable amounts of clay.

MOTH HABITATS IN SURREY

Surrey is a very rich county with many examples of most types of habitat to be found in the south-east of England. The principal exception to this is the obvious lack of coastal habitats, but even here many species of moth which are found in such areas can also be found in Surrey in alternative habitats such as chalk downland or sandy heathland. The variety and quality of habitat types means that Surrey is also very rich in invertebrates; applying the criteria for resident species used in this list gives a total of some 540 resident moths, which exceeds the number for all adjacent vice-counties and is scarcely less than for, say, the whole of Sussex, Kent, or Hampshire. There are however no species which occur solely in Surrey.

Deciduous woodland is a widespread and common habitat in Surrey, from the oakwoods of the weald and London clay to the beech woods of the North Downs. Tree species are utilized as foodplants by a considerable number of lepidopterous larvae, but woodland is also home to species which are associated with plants growing in rides and clearings, and species which are found most commonly when trees are cut down, such as the Yellow-legged and Large Red-belted Clearwings. The woodland around Chiddingfold in the south-west of the county, which is known to be one of the richest areas in Surrey for butterflies, is also very rich in moth species. Several, such as the Small Black Arches and the Broad-bordered Bee Hawk, are virtually confined to this area, and a number of other species have their biggest populations here. Other woodlands worthy of note are Staffhurst Wood, Limpsfield, and Glovers Wood, Charlwood, both also on the weald, and Bookham Common near Leatherhead, also the woods of the greensand ridge with their bilberry understorey, home to such species as the Bilberry Pug, Little Thorn and Beautiful Snout. Beech woods are commonest on the chalk, but individual trees occur widely throughout the county and the moths associated with beech are equally widespread. Alder woodland is rare, but again small groups of trees are found along most of Surrey's watercourses together with their associated species.

Conifers occur in Surrey as plantations, in domestic gardens, and on heathland where the Scots pine regenerates freely. Moths whose larvae feed on conifers are usually widespread in the county and may be expected to occur on most site lists. Some species such as Blair's Shoulder-knot and Freyer's Pug occur principally in domestic gardens on alien hostplants, although the pug has also been recorded from native juniper.

Parkland, characterized by widely-spaced ancient trees, usually oaks, interspersed with grassland and scrub, is an important habitat in Surrey. Richmond Park supports a large colony of the Double Line in its last remaining site in the east of England. Parkland is also home to the Heart Moth, which is probably commoner in Surrey than anywhere else.

Heathland is well represented in Surrey. Chobham Common and Thursley Common, both National Nature Reserves, are probably the best known areas, but there are equally good areas around Pirbright, Ash, Puttenham and Frensham which would all repay further investigation. These heaths occur on both the Bagshot beds and the greensand, and, with the possible exception of the Heath Rustic, appear to be home to a similar range of heathland species.

Grassland occurs in many forms, the most important of which is calcareous grassland on the chalk of east Surrey. Here the chalk forms a band some 10 km wide with a south-facing scarp slope and a north facing dip slope dissected by many dry valleys. Many of the chalk specialities, such as the Lace Border, Chalk Carpet, Straw Belle and Light Feathered Rustic, are currently to be found on the scarp sites such as Mickleham, Box Hill and Betchworth being renowned for their richness.

Wetland areas are scarce in Surrey. In particular, reedbeds, home to so many wainscot species, are very poorly represented, the only decent examples being at Frensham, Milford, Esher Common, Thorpe and along the Wey Navigation. Reed-feeders such as the Brown-veined and Twin-spotted Wainscots, Southern and Obscure Wainscots, and the Silky Wainscot are all resident in Surrey but each at only a handful of sites and all must be considered threatened. Other species associated with damp habitats such as the Lesser Cream Wave, Oblique Carpet and Dentated Pug are similarly very localized.

Domestic gardens form the principal habitat for a number of species whose larvae feed mainly on alien plants. Mention has already been made of Blair's Shoulder-knot and Freyer's Pug. The Golden Plusia and Varied Coronet are also garden species, the latter having established itself in Surrey within the last forty years. The Cypress Pug is apparently attempting to follow suit, and if successful will also become a garden species.

COLLECTING AND CONSERVATION

There can be little doubt that the south-east of England is under threat from the increasing number of people living there. Housing development, road building and more efficient farming practices have all had an important impact on our county, and since the middle of the present century over one dozen species or subspecies of larger moth have become extinct in Surrey, and a number of other ones are under threat. However, the picture is not entirely black. There are almost as many moths that have increased from comparative rarity to become common and widespread species in the same period, and during the survey additional species have been added to the list of Surrey residents. In many cases we do not understand why these changes have occurred, but it is fair to say that, without exception, none of these declines have been as a result of amateur collectors taking specimens for collections; most of these specimens are taken at light traps or bred from the early stages. The population dynamics of insects, together with their behaviour at light, means that collecting removes either male adults or larvae, many of which would die or be predated in nature, and in relation to the total population of a species the number taken by collectors at any one time is infinitesimal. On the other hand, the vast majority of our knowledge about moths, their distribution and habits, and the bulk of data on which this book is based has been gathered by amateur entomologists.

Conservation of our moths must be habitat-based. This involves not only protecting moth habitats but also managing them. In the period 1975-85, 7% of Surrey's woodland, 16% of heathland, and 25% of unimproved grassland has been lost (Lindley [1985]). Much of this loss was due to agriculture and housing, but a considerable proportion, over 20% in the case of high-value habitats, was due to natural change. Woodland must be considered the natural climax community in much of Surrey and habitats such as downland, grassland and heathland are in danger of becoming low-grade secondary woodland unless they are actively managed. The public perception of the value of trees is an obstacle to this aim. In a number of instances there has been public outcry at the removal of trees and scrub which is necessary to maintain more open habitats which, as mentioned earlier, are considerably more threatened than woodland. Occasionally, over-management can also be a problem; over-severe and inappropriate grazing on the North Downs has resulted in a reduction in the population of the Five-spot Burnet, and clearance of birch to extend heathland has resulted in the loss of trees utilized by a population of the Goat Moth. The current theme in conservation is biodiversity, and management of a site purely for a single species without regard to the other inhabitants is counterproductive. Of course it is also necessary to study the ecological requirements of individual species, but in most cases we simply do not have the knowledge to apply suitable management at this level.

Species which have become extinct since 1950, or are probably extinct

Zygaena trifolii decreta	Five-spot Burnet (marsh form)	early 1960s
Eupithecia irriguata	Marbled Pug	1972
Trichopteryx polycommata	Barred Tooth-striped	1960
Cleorodes lichenaria	Brussels Lace	early 1950s (but see text)
Hemaris tityus	Narrow-bordered Bee Hawk	1953
Parasemia plantaginis	Wood Tiger	1951
Spilosoma urticae	Water Ermine	1959
Pachetra sagittigera britannica	Feathered Ear	1960
Heliophobus reticulata marginosa	Bordered Gothic	1964
Mniotype adusta	Dark Brocade	1968
Jodia croceago	Orange Upperwing	1984
Cosmia diffinis	White-spotted Pinion	1979
Tyta luctuosa	Four-spotted	1984

Species which have seriously declined, 1950-96

Cyclophora porata	False Mocha
Gnophos obscurata	Annulet

Species which have significantly increased, 1950-96

Idaea vulpinaria atrosignaria	Least Carpet
Xanthorhoe biriviata	Balsam Carpet
Chloroclysta siterata	Red-green Carpet
Hyloicus pinastri	Pine Hawk
Furcula bicuspis	Alder Kitten
Euproctis chrysorrhoea	Brown-tail
Rhyacia simulans	Dotted Rustic
Hadena compta	Varied Coronet
Cucullia absinthii	Wormwood Shark
Lithophane ornitopus lactipennis	Grey Shoulder-knot
Lithophane leautieri hesperica	Blair's Shoulder-knot
Parascotia fuliginaria	Waved Black

Species recently discovered to be resident, or probably resident

Eupithecia egenaria	Pauper Pug
Eupithecia millefoliata	Yarrow Pug
Stilbia anomala	Anomalous

STUDYING MOTHS

The following abbreviations are used frequently throughout this book:

mvl	–	mercury vapour light
acl	–	actinic light
RES	–	Rothamsted Experimental Station trap

Moths are 'attracted' to various light sources and entomologists have long made use of this phenomenon to capture their specimens. Mercury-vapour light traps produce considerable quantities of ultra-violet radiation, a wavelength to which the eyes of moths are strongly sensitive. The technique is comparatively recent, and did not gain wide acceptance until the early 1950's; this should be borne in mind when comparing the earlier lists with the later ones. The lights require mains voltage to operate and consequently their use in the field is limited by the need to carry a portable generator. Also, because of their great efficiency they are excellent recording tools but do tend to discourage the use of other field techniques which are far more appropriate for finding a limited number of species, which are thus probably now under-recorded. Actinic lights are fluorescent tubes that are coated to emit ultra-violet light. They can be run from 12V DC batteries and so are more portable than mvl, but their catch is considerably less. The Rothamsted traps use an incandescent bulb within an omnidirectional trap and form a national network of traps used, initially, to track the progress of pest species. Comparison of the catches with those of ultra-violet based traps shows that in general much lower numbers of moths are encountered; some species of larger and faster-flying moths are infrequently captured, but on the other hand some of the more delicate species such as Waves of the genera *Scopula* and *Idaea* are seen in much greater numbers at Rothamsted traps than at any other type. An inventory of Rothamsted traps operated in Surrey during the survey period is given in the appendix.

The vast majority of records presented in this book have been made by light trapping, but there are other field techniques by which one may locate lepidoptera, and for some species these can be more efficient than light.

sugar Sugar is essentially a substitute for naturally occurring adult food sources, and in its usual form consists of a sticky mess of treacle and brown sugar spread onto the trunks of trees, fence posts etc. The moths may be observed as they alight to feed. An alternative presentation is in the form of sugar ropes – rope such as sash cord which is steeped in a mixture of sugar and wine and draped over suitable vegetation. Recipes and techniques can be found in Dickson (1976).

assembling Female moths attract mates by the use of scent, and if a freshly emerged female is placed in a cage she may be used to lure males. This technique is mainly of use with day-flying species such as the Emperor and various Eggars.

beating   The use of light traps has meant that techniques for finding the early stages have been largely ignored. A glance at the species accounts later in this book shows many common species for which the feral foodplant in our county remains unrecorded. Beating involves tapping larvae from trees and shrubs onto a tray.

sweeping   Sweeping is the equivalent technique used for species feeding on low-growing plants. A strong calico net bag is swept vigorously through such plants as heather and grass.

gen. det.   Genitalia determinations. Most moths can be adequately identified, with sufficient experience, by examining the wing pattern, but there are a number of species which are sufficiently similar to need structural examination to be reliably named. The most suitable structures of the insects are the hard chitinous parts of the reproductive organs, which must be prepared and examined under reasonable magnification. The Moths and Butterflies of Great Britain and Ireland, currently under production, illustrates most of the species for which this is necessary. The technique is relatively simple and can certainly be undertaken by anyone who can set a moth. The reluctance of most entomologists to undertake this task has resulted in the exclusion of a number of records from the present work.

HISTORY OF PUBLISHED WORKS

The only list of lepidoptera to include the whole of the county is that which appears in the *Victoria County History* of 1902 (referred to as the *VCH* in the species accounts) and is indeed little more than a list of species together with a handful of sites from which they were then known. It contains contributions from such well known entomologists of the day as Herbert Goss, Charles Barrett, and Sydney Webb, and provides a useful starting point against which to compare the current fauna of the county.

The London area, an area of twenty miles radius with its centre at St. Paul's Cathedral utilized by the London Natural History Society, was the subject of various papers by Baron de Worms which appeared in the London Naturalist from 1949 to 1959. This area and the vice-county of Surrey overlap, the arc of its boundary passing through Weybridge, Mickleham, Nutfield and Limpsfield. Around the same time Russell Bretherton was compiling his list of the macrolepidoptera of north-west Surrey, an area he defined as being bounded to the west and north by the county boundaries and to the south and east by the railways from Guildford to, respectively, Ash Vale and Woking through to Weybridge. This list is notable for including the results of a number of static mercury-vapour traps, the use of which as a method of sampling nocturnal lepidoptera had only just been discovered, and also in attempting to apply a statistical analysis to these results.

The next major list to appear was that for Croydon and north-east Surrey (Evans, 1973), an area broadly similar in size to the north-west Surrey survey. This list was described at the time by its reviewer as "the best authenticated and most attractively presented local list we have seen", and included information such as voltinism, habits and for many species a complete listing of records. In addition a limited number of distribution maps were provided. It was this work and the guidance of its author, Ken Evans, which steered me through my formative years in entomology, and the desire to update and expand the list that led directly to the formation of the current recording scheme.

More recently the London lists of de Worms have been updated by Colin Plant, to include many more modern records together with distribution maps for nearly all the species.

In addition to the these lists which cover a major portion of the county, there have been a number of lists covering much more restricted areas or even single sites. In the early years of this century the Haslemere Natural History Society produced its list of the Lepidoptera occurring within six miles of Haslemere (Oldaker, 1913). This is little more than a list, and, most unfortunately, gives no indication to which of the three possible vice-counties the various records pertain. The nomenclature was modernized in the second edition of 1951 but there was some confusion of the synonymy which resulted in the inclusion of two species which have never been recorded from Surrey (Large Thorn and Marsh Moth, q.v.). Bookham Common, the London Natural History Society's special survey area, was the subject of a list published in 1955 (Wheeler, 1955). Recording with mercury vapour light came in just too late for this survey and more recent work there with mv traps has revealed the presence of many species not on the list, although it must be said that some species recorded in the 1950s have not been seen recently. A more recent list presenting comprehensive records for a single site is that for Mitcham Common (Morris, 1984); these records, with minor corrections, are all included in the present work.

The publication of this work is not, of course, the end of the story. Moth populations are dynamic, responding to changes in land use and other factors which we often do not understand. As already discussed, even in a relatively short period some species have declined from relative abundance to near extinction while other species have increased very considerably. Who, in the middle of this century, would have been concerned about the future of such species as the White-spotted Pinion or the False Mocha, and who could have predicted that Blair's Shoulder-knot or the Red-green Carpet would have become common back-garden moths? It is only by constant monitoring of the status and distribution of our county's moths, as well as studying their ecology and habits, that we stand any chance of being able to take corrective measures to safeguard our fauna. I shall continue to maintain a database of Surrey macrolepidoptera, and would welcome the continued support of those who have made this book possible.

PUBLISHED SURREY LISTS

Goss, H., 1902.
>Butterflies and moths. *A history of the county of Surrey,* **3** *Zoology.* Constable, London. (*VICTORIA COUNTY HISTORY*).

de Worms, C.G.M., 1954-58.
>The moths of London and its surroundings. *Lond. Nat.* **33**:101-146; **34**:66-107; **35**:33-76; **36**:59-99; **37**:136-178.

Bretherton, R.F., 1957.
>A list of the macrolepidoptera and Pyralidina of north-west Surrey. *Proc. S. Lond. ent. nat. Hist. Soc.* **1955**:94-151.

Bretherton, R.F., 1965.
>Additions to the list of macrolepidoptera and Pyralidina of north-west Surrey. *Proc. S. Lond. ent. nat. Hist. Soc.* **1965**:18-30.

Evans, L.K., and Evans, K.G.W., 1973.
>A survey of the macrolepidoptera of Croydon and north-east Surrey. *Proc. Croydon Nat. Hist. Sci. Soc.* **XIV**:273-408.

Plant, C.W., 1993.
>*Larger moths of the London area.* London Natural History Society.

CURRENT PUBLISHED LISTS FOR ADJOINING VICE-COUNTIES

KENT

Chalmers-Hunt, J.M., 1962-67.
The butterflies and moths of Kent, **2**. Arbroath and London.

Chalmers-Hunt, J.M., 1968-81.
The butterflies and moths of Kent, **3**. Arbroath and London.

SUSSEX

Pratt, C., 1981.
A history of the butterflies and moths of Sussex. Booth Museum, Brighton.

NORTH HANTS.

Goater, B., 1974.
The butterflies and moths of Hampshire and the Isle of Wight. Classey, Faringdon.

Goater, B., 1992.
The butterflies and moths of Hampshire and the Isle of Wight: additions and corrections. Joint Nature Conservation Committee.

BERKS.

Baker, B.R., 1994.
The butterflies and moths of Berkshire. Hedera Press, Uffington.

BUCKS.

Ansorge, E., 1969.
The macrolepidoptera of Buckinghamshire. Bucks Archaeological Society, Aylesbury.

MIDDLESEX

Plant, C.W., 1993.
Larger moths of the London area. London Natural History Society. [Includes the whole of VC21 (Middlesex), plus part of Surrey.]

EXPLANATION OF SPECIES ACCOUNTS

The following accounts contain details of all the species of larger moths recorded in Surrey as reported to me or published in the various journals or textbooks. Published records of doubtful status or those published in error are surrounded by square brackets. The principal concern of the book is to establish the present status of each species occurring in Surrey, and for this a period of twenty years, often mentioned as the survey period, has been used. All information, except where otherwise stated, relates to this period and all data is based on observations made in the county of Surrey. Each species has a summary of its status, habitat preferences, distribution within the county and frequency, its voltinism and flight periods, and the feral foodplants from which its larvae have been noted. Those species with comparatively few records have these records listed in full; usually these are arranged more or less geographically from south-west to north-east, but occasionally they are chronological. Migrant records are listed chronologically. Nomenclature follows Emmet (1991) except where more recent names are available, in which case the older name is given as a synonym.

The following definitions are used.

STATUS

Resident   Species which have been noted breeding or have occurred in sufficient numbers to indicate breeding within the last twenty years, and whose existence does not rely on migration. This is the only group for which conservation measures need be considered.

Extinct   Species formerly resident, but which have not been recorded within the last twenty years. While there are a few British species which have been lost for a hundred years before being rediscovered, a period of twenty years absence in a well-worked county is considered sufficient grounds for considering a species extinct.

Migrant   Species which occur in the county solely by virtue of their passage from continental Europe or North Africa, such passage being, as far as can reasonably be determined, under their own power. These species may breed, some regularly, but cannot survive the winter except on rare occasion and would die out without continual replenishment from foreign stock.

Vagrant   Species whose presence in the county cannot be explained by either residency or migration. This includes species that may have been transported with garden plants, agricultural produce, or even unwittingly by other entomologists, as well as species not generally considered to be migratory.

Status uncertain   A few species have insufficient records to be positively assigned to one of the above classes.

Doubtful   A category reserved for older records of species which are unlikely to have occurred in the county and which now cannot be confirmed.

Erroneous   Species which have not occurred in the county where there are published records resulting from errors of a taxonomic or clerical nature.

DISTRIBUTION

Widespread   Species occurring throughout most of the county, without particular preference for habitat or soil type.

Restricted   Species occurring fairly widely but nevertheless absent from large areas often as a result of habitat requirement.

Local   Species recorded from only a few sites, although these sites themselves may be widespread.

Very local   Species recorded from very few sites, often in the same general area or geological formation.

FREQUENCY

The frequency of a species is necessarily subjective, depending on a particular recorder's methods and experience. Some fairly common species are reluctant to come to light traps, the sole recording method of a number of recorders, whereas they may occur at sugar or flowers, or may be netted at dusk. Similarly some species are rather uncommon as adults but can be found much more easily and in greater numbers as larvae. The frequency is thus estimated from all sources and is given on a sliding scale as follows:

Common/Fairly common/Uncommon/Scarce/Rare

NATIONAL STATUS

Resident or potentially resident moths that qualify for a national status of Notable or even RDB classification are so indicated. The status follows Waring (1992b) and must be considered provisional. It should also be noted that species that are classified as nationally notable can be common and widespread at a local level, and, likewise, species that are rare in or absent from Surrey may be common in other parts of the country. The groups are classified according to the number of 10 km squares in Great Britain from which they have been recorded since 1980, as follows:

Notable   Species recorded from more than 15 squares, but not more than 100. They are further subdivided into **Notable/Nb** (31-100 squares) and **Na** (16-30 squares).

RDB   Red Data Book species are those recorded from 15 or fewer 10 km squares, and are divided into classes based on the perceived degree of threat: **RDB3**, rare; **RDB2**, vulnerable; and **RDB1**, endangered.

VOLTINISM

The voltinism or "broodedness" of many species is complicated and not easy to determine due to the comparative paucity of larval records. It may be **univoltine**, with a single brood of adults occurring in any one year, or **bivoltine**, with two broods, offspring of the first contributing wholly and completely to adults of the second. In some species the second brood is only partial, some pupae lying over to produce adults of the first brood of the following year; the offspring of the second brood may survive to the following year or they may die from lack of food and cold as the winter progresses. Species in which the second brood is only very small and occasional are considered to be univoltine, but these exceptions are mentioned in the text.

FLIGHT PERIOD

The flight period stated is that time in which most of the adults are to be found and refers to Surrey data obtained during the last twenty years. Extremely early or late individuals are excluded.

FOODPLANT

The list of foodplants refers wholly to Surrey data, and mostly includes plants that are native, agricultural crops, or escaped garden plants. Plants of domestic gardens are generally excluded except in cases where a garden plant forms a major, or indeed the only, recorded foodplant. The names of plants are given in English; a list of scientific names is given in the appendices. The following definitions are used:

Foodplant   where listed indicates that it has been utilized as a foodplant during the last twenty years.

[Foodplant] a foodplant in brackets indicates that there is insufficient evidence to indicate that the food was used, but where probability suggests that it has. For example where a pupa has been dug from the base of a particular tree.

(Foodplant) a foodplant in parentheses indicates that there are old records, but that the particular plant has not been recorded as being used during the last twenty years.

{Foodplant} a foodplant in braces indicates that the plant is a native to Britain but not to Surrey.

REFERENCES TO PUBLICATIONS

Some of the information in this book has been derived from data already published in other books or the entomological journals. Where the reference contains more detailed or related information, the full source is listed in the reference section of the appendixes. Where, however, the reference is merely in confirmation of a record, an abbreviated form is given in the text. The abbreviations and their full names are as follows:

Bull. AES	*Bulletin of the Amateur Entomologists' Society*
Ent.	*The Entomologist*
Ent. Gaz.	*Entomologist's Gazette*
E.M.M.	*Entomologist's Monthly Magazine*
Ent. Rec.	*Entomologist's Record and Journal of Variation*
L.N.	*London Naturalist*
Proc. BENHS	*Proceedings and Transactions of the British Entomological and Natural History Society*
Proc. SLENHS	*Proceedings and Transactions of the South London Entomological and Natural History Society*
Ent. Ann.	*Entomologist's Annual*
Ent. Wkly. Intell.	*Entomologist's Weekly Intelligencer*
VCH	*Victoria County History*
Week. Ent.	*Weekly Entomologist*

EXPLANATION OF DISTRIBUTION MAPS

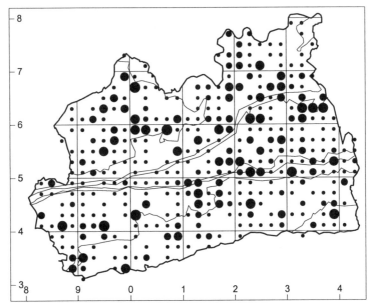

Coverage of moth records 1976-96. The larger the dot, the greater the number of species recorded in that tetrad.

The accounts of most resident species are accompanied by a distribution map which shows from which tetrads that particular moth has been recorded since 1976, a tetrad being an area 2 km square. The national grid lines are also shown, allowing the location of sites using the grid references given in the gazetteer, as are the boundaries of the principal geological formations.

A round symbol represents a record of an adult, and a square one a record of one of the early stages, indicating breeding. The coverage is necessarily more patchy than could be achieved with such groups as butterflies or plants, since many visits to a particular site are needed before even a fraction of the total moth list can be recorded there; the maps should be viewed as a graphical representation of the distribution as described in the species accounts and list of records. The map above shows recording coverage, with the day-flying species excluded, and shows some bias towards the north-east together with poor coverage from the Guildford area, although there is at least one well-recorded site in each 10 km square. These limitations should be borne in mind when consulting individual distribution maps. Maps for migrant species are not included, although most species show a bias towards the south-west or the east depending on their continental origin.

The maps were prepared with the DMAP program written by Alan Morton of Imperial College at Silwood Park.

LIST OF RECORDERS

The following individuals have contributed records, and where records are given in the text the recorder is indicated by their initials. Recorders are listed in alphabetical order of his or her initials to enable easy identification.

A&OH	A. and O. Hall	Mugswell
AG	A. Gange	Virginia Water
AJ	A. Jenkins	
AJH	A.J. Halstead	Wisley RES
AJW	A.J. Wren	
AMD	A.M. Davis	
AMJ	A.M. Jones	
ASW	A.S. Wheeler	Ashtead
BC	B. Chesney	Norbury
BG	B. Grabaskey	Epsom Downs
BH	W.R.B. Hynd	Boundstone
BS	B. Skinner	Addington
CGMdeW	C.G.M. de Worms	Horsell
CH	C. Hart	Buckland
CT	C. Thain	
CWP	C.W. Plant	
D. Couzens	D. Couzens	East Sheen
DAT	D.A. Trembath	Dorking
DC	D. Coleman	Carshalton
DCL	D.C. Lees	Purley
DWB	D.W. Baldock	Milford
DY	D. Young	
ED	E. Dennison	Pirbright RES
EE	E. Emmett	Haslemere
EHW	E.H. Wild	Selsdon
GAC	G.A. Collins	South Croydon
GBC	G.B. Collins	
GG	G. Geen	Ashtead
GJ	G. Jeffcoate	
GM	G. Martin	Camberwell
HM-P	H. Mackworth-Praed	Headley
ID	I. Dodd	Buckland
J. Pontin	J. Pontin	Woking
JAB	J.A. Bailey	Windlesham RES

JACG .... J.A.C. Greenwood .... Pyrford
JBS .... J.B. Steer .... Horley
JC .... J. Clarke .... Lingfield
JDH .... J.D. Holloway .... Wotton
JHFC .... Juniper Hall Field Centre
JKH .... J.K. Hatto .... Rowhills
JLM .... J.L. Messenger .... Wormley
JP .... J. Porter .... Tolworth/Surbiton/
                                                 Chessington
JTS .... J.T. Scanes .... Surbiton/Tolworth
JVD .... J.V. Dacie .... Wimbledon
KGWE .... K.G.W. Evans .... Addiscombe
KMG .... K.M. Gravener .... Shirley
KNAA .... K.N.A. Alexander
LJDW .... L.J.D. Wakely .... East Horsley
LKE .... L.K. Evans
M&JH .... M. and J. Halsey
MB .... M. Boyle
ME .... M. Enfield
MH .... M. Harvey
MP .... M. Parsons .... Raynes Park
MR .... M. Reed .... Ewhurst
MRH .... M.R. Honey
PAC .... P.A. Cordell .... Nutfield
PAD .... P.A. Davey .... Rushmoor
PAM .... P.A. Martin .... Mitcham
PAS .... P.A. Sokoloff
PC .... P. Cattermole .... Cranleigh
PJB .... P.J. Baker .... Thorpe
PJS .... P.J. Sellar .... Purley
PMS .... P.M. Stirling .... Purley/Coulsdon
RAC .... R.A. Cramp .... Reigate
RDH .... R.D. Hawkins
RF .... R. Fairclough .... Leigh
RFB .... R.F. Bretherton .... Bramley
RFMcC .... R.F. McCormick .... North Cheam
RGS .... R.G. Shotter .... South Norwood
RKAM .... R.K.A. Morris .... Mitcham

RMP .... R.M. Palmer .... Caterham
RWP .... R.W. Parfitt
SBRC .... Surrey Biological Records Centre
SC .... S. Clancey .... Wallington
SCP .... S.C. Pittis .... Woking
SFI .... S.F. Imber .... Ewhurst
SHC .... S.H. Church
SWG .... S.W. Gale .... Banstead
TD .... T. Dillon .... Oxted
TGW .... T.G. Winter .... Haslemere RES
TJD .... T.J. Daley
WJ .... W. James .... Leatherhead
WL .... W. Lockyer

Also   C.B. Ashby
           P.F. Collins
           A.H. Dobson
           A. Morris
           G. Revill
           M. Singleton

and   A.M. Riley and
                I. Woiwod .... Rothamsted
           J. Bebbington............... Juniper Hall
           D. and M. Pearce .... Pirbright
           M. Youlton .... Guildford
           B. and J. Garson .... Normandy
           V. Wallace .... Shirley
           R. Lawson .... Gomshall
           P. Lawson .... Pirbright

HEPIALIDAE – The Swifts

A family of very primitive moths, the adults of which are strongly crepuscular; indeed a moth trap started after dark will only attract the occasional specimen whereas one started at dusk may reveal the moths to be common. The adults are medium to large sized moths with elongate wings and very short antennae. The eggs are small and are scattered by the female in flight. The larvae are whitish but are adorned with chitinized prothoracic plates and pinacula. They are subterranean, feeding on the roots of ferns and herbaceous plants, and may take several years to reach maturity. There are five British species, all of which are resident in Surrey.

Hepialus humuli (Linnaeus, 1758)   Ghost Swift

ssp. *humuli* (Linnaeus, 1758)

Resident; woodland, wooded commons, downland; widespread and fairly common.

Univoltine; June and July.

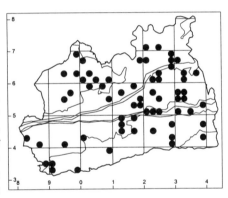

The Ghost Swift is a fairly common species that is found in suitable habitat throughout the county. The rather more patchy distribution in the west of the county may be due to the species' apparent dislike of heathland. The records received are usually either of females at light traps or of males flying at dusk; the hovering flight of the white males gives rise to the popular name.

Hepialus sylvina (Linnaeus, 1761)   Orange Swift

Resident; woodland, grassland, heathland; widespread and fairly common.

Univoltine; August to early September.

Another fairly common species found over most of the county with the exception of the more built-up areas of south London, the Orange Swift flies later in the year than the other species of this family but otherwise has similar habits.

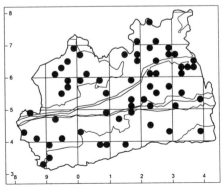

Hepialus hecta (Linnaeus, 1758)   Gold Swift

Resident; woodland, wooded commons; restricted but fairly common.

Univoltine; June to mid-July.

Foodplant – bracken.

The Gold Swift is rather more restricted in its distribution than the other common swifts, preferring open wooded habitats on lighter soils. It is probably genuinely absent from much of the weald and suburban London, and only occasional on heathland. Where it is found, however, it often occurs in good numbers.

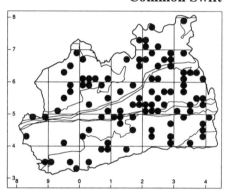

Hepialus lupulinus (Linnaeus, 1758)   Common Swift

Resident; grassland, open woodland, heathland; widespread and common.

Univoltine; May to mid-July.

The Common Swift is the commonest member of the family, found in a wide range of habitats and often swarming at dusk.

Hepialus fusconebulosa (DeGeer, 1778)   Map-winged Swift

Resident; woodland; local but sometimes fairly common.

Univoltine; late May and June.

Foodplant – (bracken).

The Map-winged Swift is certainly the least common member of the family in Surrey, and has a strong preference for habitats of some altitude on the chalk and greensand. At Hindhead Common, 1.6.1994, a female was observed ovipositing at the base of bracken stems (AMD). Only four individuals have been recorded outside these areas: Thorpe,

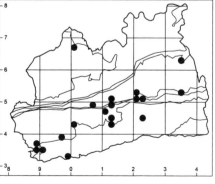

15.5.1984, 11.6.1989 (PJB); Leigh, 29.5.1987 (RF); and Tugley Wood, 7.6.1987 (SCP).

COSSIDAE – Leopards and Goat Moth

The Cossidae is a primitive family of moths with larvae that feed internally in the wood or pith of trees and reeds. The adults are nocturnal but are only weakly attracted to light and rarely seen otherwise as they do not feed. Two species are resident in Surrey.

Phragmataecia castaneae (Hübner, 1790)   Reed Leopard

Vagrant, or extinct resident; a single record.

A male specimen of the Reed Leopard was recorded as being found on a fence in Sutton on 23.6.1884 (*Ent.* **17**:184). As the species occurs only in East Anglia and Dorset this individual was probably a vagrant. However, the occurrence of two other specimens in the London area (Plant, 1993) suggests the possibility of the Reed Leopard being a former resident of the marshy areas of London.

Zeuzera pyrina (Linnaeus, 1761)   Leopard Moth

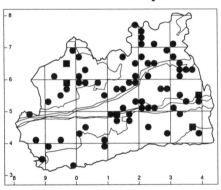

Resident; gardens, woodland, downland; widespread and fairly common.

Univoltine; late June and July.

Foodplant – sallow, wayfaring tree, crab apple, (pear, lilac, honeysuckle, oak, birch).

A fairly common species, especially so in suburban gardens. It is usually only the male that is seen at light traps and females are rarely encountered; two females were found on the same day at Chessington in 1996 (JP), the only time that the recorder had seen this sex. The larva feeds in the wood of deciduous trees and is most often encountered when searching for the larvae of clearwings in early spring.

Cossus cossus (Linnaeus, 1758)   PLATES 2,11   Goat Moth

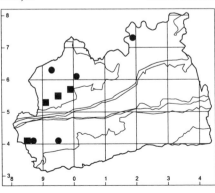

Notable/Nb

Resident; heathland; very local.

Univoltine; late June and early July.

Foodplant – birch, (Lombardy poplar, willow, oak, elm, ash).

The exact status of this species is hard to discern as the adults do not respond well to light traps, and the larvae are only occasionally found as they wander from their host tree in the autumn, a journey of a few minutes out of a larval lifespan of several years. The impression is of a rather reduced species, both locally and nationally. The *VCH* gives it as generally distributed and destructive in the larval stage; it was more recently found in south London (Evans, 1973) and areas of north-west Surrey (Bretherton, 1957). With the exception of an example from south-west London it is currently known principally from heathland where the larvae are associated with birch. The biggest known colony is on army land where it has been known for over 40 years; the land use is probably beneficial, preventing development for housing and access from the public, but occasional fires may pose a threat. First-year larvae feed in the layer between the bark and the wood, from one to three feet above ground level, and are quite common as often several larvae may be found under a piece of bark the size of one's hand. Fully grown larvae progress downwards until they tunnel into the wood at ground level and burrow into the roots. At least some leave the tree in the autumn to overwinter elsewhere. The larval burrow, especially in the autumn, smells of fermenting sap and is attractive to wasps and butterflies such as the Red Admiral; to my mind there is no smell of goat, and in captivity they are virtually odourless. There are a handful of records of larvae, and of adults at light, in areas of similar habitat and the moth is probably more widespread than the map suggests.

RECORDS – **Frensham Common**, 2.83 larva in birch (M. Tickner per DCL); **Rushmoor**, 17.6.84 (PAD); **Milford**, 6.7.91 (DWB); **Wyke Common**, larva (PJS), 27.9.91 larvae in birch, 7.3.92 larvae, 4.5.96 larvae (GAC); **Pirbright**, 18.8.88 full-grown larva (AJH); **Mayford**, 9.8.85 larva (J. Pontin); **Horsell**, 7.7.78 (CGMdeW); **Lightwater**, 1.7.84 at light (J. Pontin); **Richmond Park**, 5.7.95 (MP).

ZYGAENIDAE – Foresters and Burnets

A family of brightly coloured, day-flying moths, the Burnets are familiar even to most non-entomologists. The larvae of the Foresters are cryptically coloured and, in their earlier instars, mine the leaves of their foodplants, while those of the Burnets are aposematic, feeding openly. Pupation occurs in a tough silken cocoon which may, depending on species, be either hidden amongst vegetation or placed high on a grass stem or similar support. One species of Forester and three Burnets have been recorded in Surrey in recent years. Identification of the five-spotted moths of the genus *Zygaena* (Burnet moths) can cause considerable problems, especially between *Z. lonicerae* and *Z. trifolii* subspecies *decreta*; the latter subspecies is not considered to be currently resident in Surrey, but some of the earlier published records are open to doubt; vouchers of this taxon should be retained. The earlier flight period and restricted habitat of *Z. trifolii* subspecies *palustrella* should preclude confusion.

Adscita statices (Linnaeus, 1758)   Forester

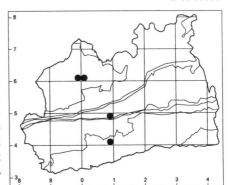

Notable/Nb

Resident; damp meadows, downland; very local and scarce.

Univoltine; June and July.

Evidently a rather reduced species, being recorded from only four sites in the last two decades. In the nineteenth century it was known from Leith Hill, Reigate Hill, Claygate and Haslemere (*VCH*), and Surbiton and Headley Lane (Tutt, 1899). It was taken at Cutt Mill, 21.6.1936 (*Proc. SLENHS* **1936-37**:18); Durfold Wood, 7.6.1950 (Howard, BENHS coll.); Chobham Common, 1952 (at mvl, EHW); and at Bookham Common, 22.6.1952 (Richardson, *Proc. SLENHS* **1952-53**:81) and 9.6.1956 (Wakely, *Ent. Rec.* **69**:155). Bretherton (1957 and 1965) gives a number of sites, and Evans (1973) gives Ashtead Common, 1947, adding that the site had now been drained and the insect not seen since. This is a difficult species to locate as the colonies can be extremely local, and it is possible that the Forester is more widespread in Surrey than the records suggest.

RECORDS – **Horsell Birch**, 20.6.92, 7.7.96 (J. Pontin); **Bonsey's Bridge**, 14.6.96 (GAC); **Ewhurst**, 18.6.87 (MR); **Hackhurst Downs**, one in about 1983 or 84 (PMS), 7.90 (J. Pontin).

[*Adscita geryon* (Hübner, 1813)   Cistus Forester

Doubtful.

The Cistus Forester was recorded from Box Hill in 1868 by W. West (*Ent. Rec.* **18**:170), a record not repeated in the *VCH*, Barrett (1895), or Tutt (1899). Box Hill, together with Mickleham, is given in de Worms (1954-58) as being "seen" in those localities "about" 1900 (by Barnett, not Barrett as stated in Plant (1993)), a wholly unsatisfactory record. The moth cannot be accepted on the county list without further evidence.]

[*Adscita globulariae* (Hübner, 1793)   Scarce Forester

Doubtful.

Listed from Reigate by de Mattos in Tutt (1899), who gave the record as one of many that were "probably erroneous, and want confirmation". There is no other evidence that this moth, the rarest of the three *Adscita* species, has ever occurred in our county.]

[*Zygaena viciae* ([Denis & Schiffermüller], 1775)   New Forest Burnet

Two Burnets taken by E.E. Green near Camberley, 20.8.1914, were shown at a meeting of the Entomological Society of London, and were accepted as *viciae* by the president and other members (*Ent.* **48**:91). A further specimen was said to have been taken in the "Haslemere district" by J. Hawkins, 29.7.1925 (Oldaker, *Ent.* **59**:37) [this district covers Surrey, West Sussex and North Hants.]. The only certain locality for this species in England was the New Forest (Hampshire) where it was discovered in 1872 and last seen in 1927, but there are unconfirmed records for Tilgate Forest (Sussex). In view of the late date of the Camberley specimens they must have been somewhat worn and they were almost certainly misidentified – Tremewan considered them to have probably been *Z. trifolii*.]

Zygaena filipendulae (Linnaeus, 1758)   **Six-spot Burnet**
ssp. *stephensi* Dupont, 1900

Resident; chalk downland, grassland, roadsides; widespread and common.

Univoltine; July and August.

Foodplant – bird's-foot trefoil, large bird's-foot trefoil.

The Six-spot Burnet is the commonest of the three Zygaena species occurring in Surrey, being found in open, grassy habitats everywhere, and is especially common on the chalk.

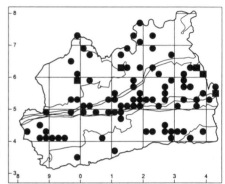

Zygaena trifolii (Esper, 1783)   PLATE 1   **Five-spot Burnet**
ssp. *decreta* Verity, 1926

Extinct.

Foodplant – (large bird's-foot trefoil).

This subspecies of *trifolii* and *lonicerae* are frequently confused and the only acceptable records of *trifolii decreta* are those where voucher specimens exist. Tremewan (1980) examined those in the national collection and confirmed the following records: Camberley, 1915; Byfleet, 1916-25; Chobham, 1922; West End (Esher), 1922-34; Normandy, 1929; Godalming, 1930; and Chiddingfold, 1931. He also had specimens from Bagshot, July 1957 and confirmed the records from Henley Gate, Pirbright, "14.6.1959 and later years" (Bretherton, 1965). It is now certainly extinct in Surrey and Tremewan (*loc. cit.*) considered that *lonicerae* had replaced it in both biotope and foodplant.

ssp. *palustrella* Verity, 1926

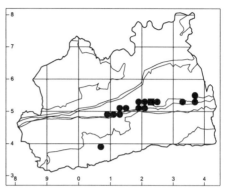

Resident; chalk downland; local but sometimes fairly common.

Univoltine; late May and early June.

Foodplant – bird's-foot trefoil.

This, the rarest of our three *Zygaena* species, is more or less confined to the scarp slope of the North Downs, where it can on occasion be common, although it has suffered a decline as a result of overgrazing at some sites. Off the chalk a few examples were recorded near Cranleigh in 1991 and again in 1994 (DWB), probably just a temporary establishment. Unlike the other species which are rather invariable, the Five-spot Burnet shows considerable variation in the degree of confluence of the spotting. A bilateral gynandromorph was taken on the downs, June 1986 (Tremewan, BENHS exhibition), and the yellow-spotted form, ab. *lutescens* Cockerell, was found at Caterham, 1989-90, at which point the site was destroyed and the strain lost (PAC, *pers. com.*).

Zygaena lonicerae (Scheven, 1777) PLATE 2 **Narrow-bordered Five-spot Burnet**
ssp. *latomarginata* Tutt, 1899

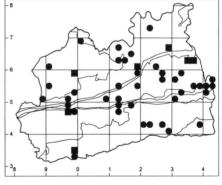

Resident; grassland, roadsides; widespread and fairly common.

Univoltine; July.

Foodplant – large bird's-foot trefoil (meadow vetchling, clover).

Although perhaps less widely distributed than *filipendulae*, the Narrow-bordered Five-spot Burnet is found throughout much of Surrey, frequently very commonly. It readily colonizes recently created habitat such as roadside verges. Confusion within the various five-spotted Burnets obscures the history of this species in Surrey, but it would appear to have increased greatly this century and to have replaced *trifolii decreta*. Variation in this species is rare, but a single example of the yellow-spotted form was taken at Claygate, 2.7.1988 (AMJ).

LIMACODIDAE

The Limacodidae is a family of world-wide distribution, of which only two rather atypical examples occur in Britain. The larvae are rather slug-like and have reduced thoracic legs and no prolegs; progress is made by means of ventral suckers on the abdominal segments. They feed on trees, but are rather difficult to dislodge by beating. Pupation takes place in an oval papery cocoon.

Apoda limacodes (Hufnagel, 1766)   PLATE 2   Festoon

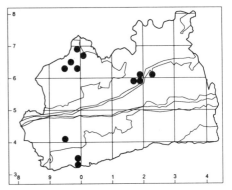

Notable/Nb

Resident; woodland; very local and scarce.

Univoltine; June and July.

Foodplant – (oak, beech).

A species of parkland and extensive oak woodland of some age, the Festoon is still surprisingly scarce in Surrey, being known from only three areas. There is some evidence that it has been increasing in recent years, i.e. Milford trap results.

RECORDS – **Tugley Wood**, 10.7.86 (2) (SCP), 14.7.90 (GAC), 19.7.91 (DY); **Canterbury Copse**, 4.7.85 (AJ); **Milford**, 29.7.80, 1984 (2), 85 (2), 86 (2), 87 (4), 90 (1), 91 (3), 92 (4), 93 (9), 94 (8), 95 (14), 96 (20) (DWB); **Ashtead**, 10.7.87 (GG); **Ashtead Common**, 16.7.77 (PAM), 1981-82 (BS), 8-12.7.83 (GAC), 10.7.85 (JP); 12.7.86 (AJ), 6.7.89, 26.6.90 (RFMcC), 26.6.93, 9.7.96 (DC); **Ashtead Forest**, 10.7.91 (JC); **Banstead**, 25-26.6.93 (2) (SWG); **Virginia Water**, 6.7.82 (AG); **Thorpe**, 27.6.76 (PJB); **Windlesham RES**, 1979 (1) (JAB); **Chobham Common**, 22.6.87 (AJ), 3.7.91, 9.6.93 (RFMcC).

Heterogenea asella ([Denis & Schiffermüller], 1775)   Triangle

Status uncertain.

The Triangle was recorded by Sheldon in an old London list (Buckell and Prout, 1898) as being local near Croydon . Tutt (1899) gives Horsell, recorded by Tugwell. A specimen was recorded from the Rothamsted trap at Alice Holt, North Hampshire, on 25.7.1985 (Winter, *Ent. Rec.* **98**:210), a site less than a mile from the Surrey boundary. This record supports the Surrey ones and suggests that the species may just possibly remain overlooked in the county.

SESIIDAE – Clearwing Moths

The Sesiidae is a family of day-flying moths which have scale-free areas within the wings and hence resemble members of the Hymenoptera. Despite this protective resemblance the adults are seldom seen, and, combined with a larval habit of feeding internally in trees and shrubs often leaving little or no evidence of their presence, it is probable that most species are severely under-recorded. This is reflected in the distribution maps. They do, however, tend to be colonial, and where one specimen is found it is likely that others will be present. All except three of the 14 accepted resident species have been found recently in Surrey; the remaining three are most unlikely to occur.

Sesia apiformis (Clerck, 1759)   PLATES 3,16   Hornet Clearwing

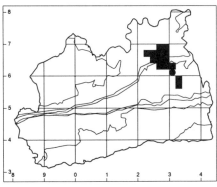

Notable/Nb

Resident; commons, suburban streets; very local but fairly common.

Univoltine; late June and early July.

Foodplant – hybrid black poplar.

Until recently the Hornet Clearwing was known from only a handful of records, but recent systematic fieldwork in the streets of south London has revealed it to be locally common. Although probably overlooked, this species has never had much of a history in Surrey, being known only from Kingston in the *VCH*, and Sutton (Evans, 1973). Hybrid black poplar is the foodplant in Surrey and likely looking trees should be searched for exit holes at any time of the year and for the exuviae during the flight period, these being found near ground level.

RECORDS – **Purley**, one found dead 1980 (DCL); **Coulsdon Common**, 1986 workings (GAC); **Whyteleafe**, 1986-87 (JC), exuviae 1991 (DCL); **Mitcham Common**, colony in hybrid black poplar 1990, 91 (DCL), 1994 (3), 22.6.95 (DC); **Dale Park**, 1994-6 exuviae and adults (DC); **Hackbridge**, 1994 exuviae (DC); **Wilderness Island**, 1994 exuviae (DC); **Beddington Park**, 1994-5 exuviae and adults (DC); **Banstead**, 1994, 96 exuviae (DC); **Rosehill Park**, 1994 exuviae (DC); **Roundshaw Park**, 1994 exuviae (DC); **Morden Hall Park**, 1995 exuviae (MB); **Motspur Park**, 1995 exuviae (MB); **Culvers Island**, 1995-6 exuviae (DC); **North Cheam**, 4.7.95 (1) (DC); **Roundshaw**, 1996 exuviae (DC).

Sesia bembeciformis (Hübner, 1797)   Lunar Hornet Clearwing

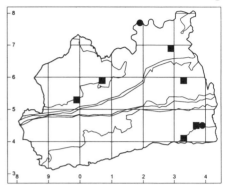

Resident; commons; very local.

June and August.

Foodplant – sallow.

The Lunar Hornet Clearwing is currently known from eight sites, although it is likely that it would be found to be much more widespread if searched for diligently. It was unrecorded in Evans (1973), but a handful of sites are listed in Bretherton (1957 and 1965), and the *VCH* described it as generally distributed. Tenanted living sallows are difficult to locate, but where ground has been cleared, sallow stumps, usually those over 75 mm in diameter, frequently contain the central borings of this species – these records have not been accepted without further confirmatory evidence.

RECORDS – **Mitcham Common**, 4.2.89 larvae (RKAM), 1990, 91 (DCL); **Kew Gardens**, 22.8.84 (R. Hastings per CWP); **Wisley Gardens**, larvae in sallow, reared 3.6.77 (AJH); **Stringers Common**, 1.4.89 larval workings in sallow (GAC); **Burstow**, 24.2.94 larva (JC); **Lingfield**, 15.6.96 (JC); **Blindley Heath**, 5.91 larvae in sallow, 26.2.94 larvae (JC), 23.4.93 pupa (GAC); **Riddlesdown Quarry**, larvae in sallow 1984, 91 (DCL).

Synanthedon tipuliformis (Clerck, 1759)   Currant Clearwing

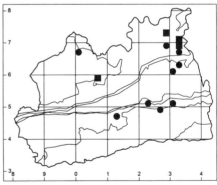

Notable/Nb

Resident; gardens; local.

Univoltine; late June and early July.

Foodplant – red currant, gooseberry.

The Currant Clearwing is the most widely recorded of this group, possibly because it is found principally in domestic gardens. The larva feeds internally in species of *Ribes*, and may be threatened by the use of pesticide sprays. The adult has been recorded on the flowers of ground-elder (GAC).

RECORDS – **Purley**, 2.7.78 (PMS); **South Croydon**, 23.6.76, 4.7.85 (GAC); **Mitcham**, 2.7.85 (RKAM); **Thornton Heath**, 22.6.76 (PAM); **South Norwood**, 1983 larvae in red currant and gooseberry, adult reared (RGS); **West Norwood**, on currant since 1983 (BS); **Wandsworth**, 11.94 larva in red currant, adult reared (DWB); **Wotton**, 16.6.90 (JDH); **Buckland**, 6.86 (1) (CH); **Earlswood**, 30.6.87 two pairs in copula (CH); **Nutfield**, 4.7.76 (PAC); **Thorpe**, 1977, 79, 84 (PJB); **Wisley Gardens**, larvae regular in currants (AJH).

Synanthedon vespiformis (Linnaeus, 1761) PLATE 9 Yellow-legged Clearwing

Notable/Nb

Resident; woodland, parkland; local.

Univoltine; late June to August.

Foodplant – oak, sweet chestnut, beech.

The Yellow-legged Clearwing is another species which is almost certainly rather more widespread than the records suggest. It is most easily found as a larva or pupa in recently cut stumps but will use intact trees as well, as at Richmond Park where the adult has been observed flying around bosses on large oak trunks (DC).

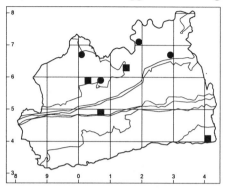

RECORDS – **Pyrford**, 1976 larvae in oak trunk (JACG); **Thorpe**, 17.7.78, 13.7.95 on thyme flowers (PJB); **Wisley Gardens**, 9.8.84, 6.7.92 (AJH); **Oxshott**, 18.4.97 larvae in oak stumps (GAC); **Ham Common**, 28.8.85 (RKAM); **Richmond Park**, 20.6.82 (KNAA), 3.7.93 (MP), 22.7.95 (GAC); **Mitcham Common**, 6.90, 26.6.91 (DCL), 2.8.91 (RKAM); **Dormansland**, 18.5.91 larvae and pupae common in sweet chestnut (JC), 18.4.92 larvae (RFMcC); **Silent Pool**, 16.5-13.6.92 larvae in beech stump (GAC).

Synanthedon spheciformis ([Denis & Schiffermüller], 1775) White-barred Clearwing

Notable/Nb

Resident; heathland, woodland; local.

Univoltine; June.

Foodplant – birch, alder.

The White-barred Clearwing is a rather local species showing, from these records and those of Bretherton (1957 and 1965), a distinct preference for heathland where the larva feeds inside birch, but also found in alder as along the River Wey. The trees used are often as thin as 3 cm in diameter and the larval mine is usually placed centrally (*q.v. culiciformis*).

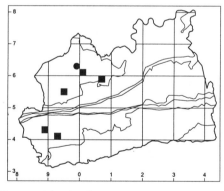

Adults have been found by beating birch and by sweeping heather.

RECORDS – **Chobham Common**, 11.6.82 adult swept (JP); **Horsell Common**, 12.5.93 pupa (J. Pontin); **Pirbright**, 9.5.92 pupa in birch (GAC); **Witley Common**, 4.94 larvae, eight adults reared (DWB), 21.4.95 larvae (GAC); **Wisley Common**, 19.6.80 (2), 15.6.85 (1) beaten from birch (P. Hodge), 11.6.82, 3.7.86 (AJH), 25.4.92 larvae in birch, 20.4.94 larva (GAC); **Thundry Meadows**, 6.5.96 pupa in alder (GAC).

Synanthedon flaviventris (Staudinger, 1883)   **Sallow Clearwing**

Notable/Nb

Resident; heathland, open woodland; restricted.

Foodplant – sallow.

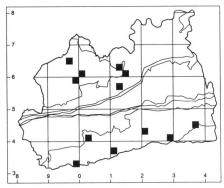

A rather local species, the Sallow Clearwing is best known from the north-west of the county, although recent fieldwork has revealed it to be widespread on the weald too. The larval galls may be found on sallow, smaller bushes being easier to search, but only in the spring of even years, a rather unusual situation which is reflected nationally. The galls are rather similar to those produced by the longhorn beetle *Saperda populnea* (L.) but are generally smaller and lack the horse-shoe shaped scar caused by the beetle's ovipositor. The adult moth remains undetected.

RECORDS – **Chobham Common**, 2.1.78 (3) larvae (JP), 27.2.88 galls on sallow (GAC); **Horsell Common**, 20.2.82 larvae (RFMcC); **Horsell Birch**, 21.2.90 galls on sallow (GAC); **Bookham Common**, 27.2.88 galls on sallow, 4.2.94 galls (GAC); **Esher Common**, 1976 reared from sallow (BS); **Prince's Coverts**, 2.82 larvae in sallow (JP); **Oaken Wood**, 15.3.96 larvae (GAC); **Run Common**, 1.3.96 larvae (GAC); **Somersbury Wood**, 1.3.96 larvae (GAC); **Newdigate**, 1.3.96 larvae (GAC); **Horley**, 11.2.94 galls on sallow (GAC); **Blindley Heath**, 1.2.94 larva, adult reared (JC).

Synanthedon andrenaeformis (Laspeyres, 1801)   PLATE 14   **Orange-tailed Clearwing**

Notable/Nb

Resident; chalk downland; very local.

July.

Foodplant – wayfaring-tree.

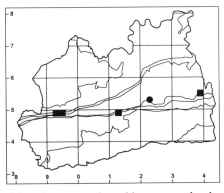

The Orange-tailed Clearwing is a very local species confined to the chalk of the North Downs and currently very difficult to obtain, the ratio of old workings to new mines being very high. Records in Evans (1973) suggest that it was once commoner. The full-grown larva produces a cap 6 mm in diameter through which it will eventually emerge, and I have only reared adults from such stems although uncapped workings may also be productive (BS, *pers. com.*). The adult, rarely taken in the wild, has been found twice (e.g. Collins, 1987).

RECORDS – **Oxted Downs**, 9.1.77 capped mines, parasitized (PMS); **Buckland Hills**,

21.6.76 (PAC); **Westcott Downs**, 22.1.77 larvae (JP), 16.7.86 (GAC); **White Downs**, 29.1.77 two larvae (JP), 23.3.85 capped mine on wayfaring-tree (RKAM), 19.2.94 capped mines (GAC); **Hog's Back**, 2.85 larvae (RFMcC), 27.3.93 capped mines, adults reared (GAC).

Synanthedon myopaeformis (Borkhausen, 1789)   Red-belted Clearwing

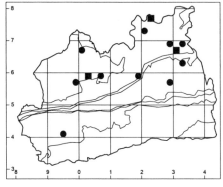

Notable/Nb

Resident; gardens, commons; local.

Univoltine; late June to August.

Foodplant – ornamental cherry, (crab apple, apple).

Like the Currant Clearwing, the Red-belted Clearwing is recorded mainly in suburban gardens and avenues. At one site a few trees were riddled with larval workings while other nearby trees were apparently untouched. Tenanted trees usually have frass coming from the bark, although this is also a feature of trees harbouring the Tortricid moth *Enarmonia formosana* (Scopoli). The adult has been recorded on the flowers of ground-elder (GAC).

RECORDS – **Milford**, 4.8.96 (DWB); **Thorpe**, 27.6.77 (PJB); **Mayford**, 11.8.84 (AJH); **Woking**, colony in ornamental cherry, adults 18.6-22.7.96 (SCP); **Wisley Gardens**, 8.7.83 (AJH); **Ashtead Common**, 29.6.76 (ASW); **Hooley**, 18.7.80 (CH); **Thornton Heath**, 8.7.77 (4) (PAM); **South Norwood**, 19-21.8.87, 5.7.89, 29.6.92 (RGS); **South Croydon**, 15.7.85 (GAC); **Mitcham Common**, 5.8.90 (RKAM), 19.8.91 (DCL); **Barnes**, 29.4.93 larvae in ornamental cherries (GAC); **Richmond Park**, 1996 (MP).

Synanthedon formicaeformis (Esper, 1783)   Red-tipped Clearwing

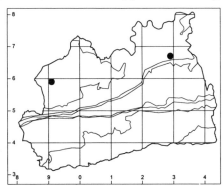

Notable/Nb

Resident; heathland, commons; very local and rare.

June and August.

Foodplant – (sallow).

Two individuals of the Red-tipped Clearwing taken recently at two widely separated sites were the first Surrey records for nearly 40 years. The species is clearly very uncommon as the only previous records known were of larvae and pupae at Wyke in 1946 (Parfitt in Bretherton, 1957), and larvae at Mitcham Common in 1950 (Wild in Evans, 1973).

RECORDS – **Frith Hill**, 15.6.88 (GAC); **Mitcham Common**, 6.8.91 (DCL).

Synanthedon culiciformis (Linnaeus, 1758) **Large Red-belted Clearwing**

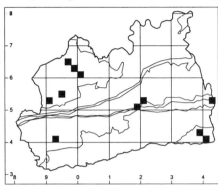

Notable/Nb

Resident; heathland, open woodland; local.

May and June.

Foodplant – birch.

As with most members of this family most of the records of the Large Red-belted Clearwing are of the early stages, the larva inhabiting birch where it usually feeds just below the bark (*q.v. spheciformis*). It is almost certainly widespread and recently cut birch stumps should be examined in the following spring. The adult has been recorded feeding at hawthorn blossom (GAC).

RECORDS – **Horsell Common**, 14.8.94 larvae (GAC); **Chobham Common**, 7.6.86 at hawthorn blossom, 20.2.94 larvae (GAC); **Gracious Pond**, 18.8.95 larvae (GAC); **Pirbright**, 9.5.92 exuviae, 3.9.95 larvae (GAC); **Wyke Common**, 19.5.92 pupa (JC); **Mare Hill Common**, 1993 exuviae (DWB); **Headley Heath**, bred 1981, 16.6.86 (RF), 7-14.5.95 (DC); **Box Hill**, 18.6.91 (4) exuviae in birch stump (JC); **Limpsfield Chart**, 1.3.94 larvae (JC); **Dormansland**, 1993 pupae (JC); **Lingfield**, 1990,91 pupae in birch stump (JC).

Bembecia scopigera (Scopoli, 1763) **Six-belted Clearwing**

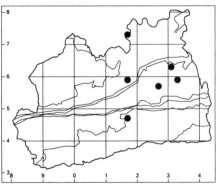

Notable/Nb

Resident; chalk grassland; very local.

Univoltine; July.

Only a very few records of the Six-belted Clearwing have been made, but again it is likely to be under-recorded. It ought to occur along the scarp of the North Downs, but has not been recorded there recently. A number of records are from areas where there has been disturbance, such as disused chalk and brick pits. The adult may be found by sweeping, or observed flying low around plants of bird's-foot trefoil.

RECORDS – **Ham**, 8.1977 (per CWP); **Riddlesdown Quarry**, 30.6.84, 1985, 86 swept (DCL), 2.7.90 (JC); **Chipstead Valley** 25.7.90, 21.7.91 (DC); **Roundshaw**, 11.7.96 (per CWP); **Ashtead Common**, 21.7.90 (AJH); **North Holmwood**, 26.7.96 (GJ).

LASIOCAMPIDAE – Eggars

The Lasiocampidae is a family of medium to very large sized moths. Two species, both of which occur in Surrey, have day-flying males; the rest are nocturnal. The adults are attracted to light, but have vestigial mouthparts and so do not feed at flowers or come to sugar. Males of most species can be readily assembled to virgin females. The larvae are densely hairy and feed on trees or grasses. Seven species are resident in Surrey.

Poecilocampa populi (Linnaeus, 1758)   December Moth

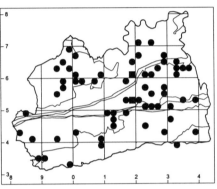

Resident; woodland, wooded downs and commons; widespread and common.

Univoltine; late October to December.

Foodplant – oak, silver birch, lime, (hawthorn).

The December Moth is a common species found throughout the county, except perhaps the more built-up parts of London. The flight period is rather late in the year and consequently the moth is probably under-recorded, although a light trap operated in suitable habitat will usually produce numbers of individuals.

Trichiura crataegi (Linnaeus, 1758)   Pale Eggar

Resident; wooded commons, woodland; restricted and generally scarce.

Univoltine; September.

Foodplant – (hawthorn, birch, sallow, aspen).

The current distribution of the Pale Eggar seems to be more or less restricted to the weald where it is scarce to very scarce; it does not seem to have been recorded recently in the larval state.

RECORDS – **Milford**, 1.9.83, 25.9.83 (DWB); **Canterbury Copse**, 14.9.86, 23.8.89 (AJ); **Bramley**, 11.9.77, 83 (3) (RFB); **Ewhurst**, 1-5.9.76, 9.9.79, 6.9.82 (SFI), 7.9.86 (MR); **Dorking**, 21.9-3.10.86 (2), 8.9.87 (DAT); **Buckland**, 18.9.84, 16.9.85, 13-20.9.87 (CH); **Leigh**, fairly common 1986-91 (RF); **Horley**, 6.9.88 (JBS); **Lingfield**, 4-17.9.95 (JC).

Eriogaster lanestris (Linnaeus, 1758)   PLATE 1   Small Eggar

Extinct.

Around the turn of the century the Small Eggar was described as "common locally; Epsom, Sutton, Haslemere" (*VCH*). Tutt (1900) adds Box Hill [and Aldworth – presumably a geographical error; there is an Aldworth in Berkshire]. At this time the species was apparently widespread in southern England. By the 1950's de Worms was only able to give one Surrey record: reared from Caterham in 1932 (P. Bell, in de Worms, *L.N.* **33**). Bretherton (1957) and Evans (1973) were unable to add any further records. The dot on the distribution map in Emmet (1991) is for a record which was later withdrawn and is undoubtedly an error. Until very recently this decline was a national one, but in the last few years the species seems to be making a comeback, the larval nests being reported as common in several counties; it is certainly resident in East Sussex, and may once again be found in Surrey.

Malacosoma neustria (Linnaeus, 1758)   PLATE 3   Lackey

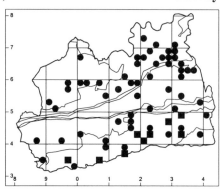

Resident; woodland, wooded commons, gardens; widespread and common.

Univoltine; June to August.

Foodplant – hazel, elm, bramble, (oak, aspen, sloe, sallow, laurel).

The Lackey moth seems to show a preference for clay soils, and is regular on both the weald and the London clay; elsewhere on sandy and chalk soils it can only be described as scarce. The larva probably feeds on many tree species, and, possibly when dislodged, on shrubs below.

Lasiocampa quercus (Linnaeus, 1758)   Oak Eggar

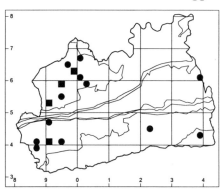

ssp. *quercus* (Linnaeus, 1758)

Resident; heathland, grassland; restricted but fairly common.

Univoltine; July and early August.

Foodplant – heather, bramble, (birch).

The vast majority of records of this species in Surrey are from the heathland of the Bagshot beds and the greensand, the males flying wildly on hot sunny days, the females at light traps, and the larvae swept from heather in the autumn and spring. Elsewhere there are records from: Lingfield, 18-21.7.1990, 14.7.1991 (JC), and Leigh, 1977, 1985, 1987, 21.7.1990 (3), 1991 (RF); all females at mvl. Also in the Addington area, 4.7.1989, 2.7.1993, and 22.7.1996 (AJW).

Macrothylacia rubi (Linnaeus, 1758) Fox Moth

Resident; heathland, grassland; local but often common as larvae.

Univoltine; late May and June.

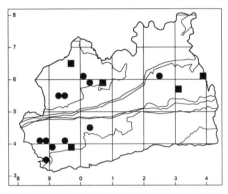

The Fox Moth is a rather local species which is currently known from heathland north and south of the Hog's Back, and from chalk grassland at Addington, Banstead Downs and Farthing Downs. On the heaths at least the larvae are often fairly common in the autumn and again in the spring, disappearing to pupate after the first few warm and sunny days.

RECORDS – **Addington**, 13.9.93 larvae (AJW); **Farthing Downs**, 5.9.85 larva (RKAM); **Banstead Downs**, 16.6.86 males (RFMcC), 23.5.89 (1), 10.6.90 (3), 2.6.92 (5) (DC); **Wisley Common**, larvae common, 14.6.86 (AJH), 8.6.88, 11.6.89 (SCP), 19.6.89 ova (JP); **Horsell**, 29.5.76 (CGMdeW); **Pyrford**, 1976-77 (JACG); **Chobham Common**, 4.9.82 larvae (SHC), 23.8.83 larvae, 17.9.88 larvae (GAC), 26.5.85 (AJH), 7.9.85 larvae, 3.7.91, 9.6.93 (RFMcC); **Pirbright**, 8.6.96 (GAC); **Pirbright Common**, 1983 (PC); **Blackheath**, 22.5.92 (DC); **Rushmoor**, 1983-4 (PAD); **Milford**, 11.6.92 (DWB); **Thursley Common**, 1.6.90, 28.5.92 (AJ), 7.6.96 (RMP); **Devil's Jumps**, 1.7.89 old, parasitized larva (RKAM); **Hindhead Common**, 10.5.93 (AMD) .

Euthrix potatoria (Linnaeus, 1758) Drinker

Resident; wetland, grassland, grassy rides in woods; fairly widespread and common.

Univoltine; mid-June to mid-August.

Foodplant – yellow iris.

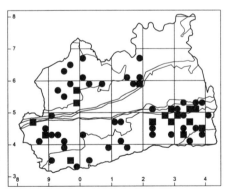

The Drinker is a rather widespread species, with the proviso that it is seemingly absent from the chalk and from suburban London. The moth's preference is for a damp habitat, which helps to explain this absence. Elsewhere both the moth and its larva are a common sight.

Gastropacha quercifolia (Linnaeus, 1758)   **Lappet**

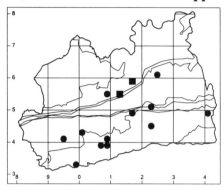

Resident; woodlands, scrubby grassland; local and scarce.

Univoltine; late June and July.

Foodplant – sloe, hawthorn, buckthorn, (sallow, alder buckthorn).

The Lappet moth can at best be described as locally fairly common, with regular records only from Banstead, Ashtead, and Ewhurst. Otherwise its appearance is only sporadic with even the most regularly run moth traps only attracting occasional individuals. It may be that the adult only responds weakly to light; at Bookham Common the moth was not seen in five years of trapping, but on 29.4.1992 a larva was found there on sloe; on the other hand I have seen three or four moths in a single trap at Banstead. The larva is evidently not too fussy in its choice of foodplant and the moth's localization is difficult to explain.

SATURNIIDAE – Emperors

The Saturniidae is a family of principally tropical moths, one example of which occurs in Britain. The male is day-flying, and the female is crepuscular but will come to light on occasion.

Pavonia pavonia (Linnaeus, 1758)   PLATE 3   **Emperor Moth**

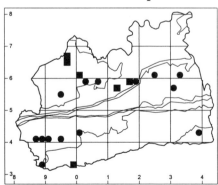

Resident; heathland, woodland, downland; restricted but probably fairly common.

Univoltine; April and May.

Foodplant – heather, sallow, bramble, hazel, (meadowsweet, oak, alder buckthorn).

In Surrey the Emperor is primarily a moth of heathland, where its larva is associated with heather. It has also occurred in woodland, for example at Fisherlane Wood, a larva on hazel, 11.6.1978 (RFB), and larvae on sallow, 16.6.1979 (PC), and in grassland, as at Ashtead and Banstead, where the larva feeds on bramble. The females will on occasion come to moth traps but the males are diurnal and may be assembled to a virgin female.

ENDROMIDAE – Kentish Glory

A family containing only one species, long since extinct in Surrey. The adults are large robust moths, the males being day-flying. The larva is glabrous with a posterior pyramidal hump, and the pupa is enclosed in a silken cocoon spun amongst debris on the ground.

Endromis versicolora (Linnaeus, 1758)   Kentish Glory

Extinct resident and introduction.

Foodplant – (garden privet).

The Kentish Glory was no doubt at one time resident in Surrey, although its presence is rather overshadowed by its more widely known occurrence in the neighbouring counties of Kent and Sussex. Barrett (1896) says "probably in Surrey, though the one specimen seen was not captured", and Tutt (1902) writing only a few years later gives Haslemere (Barrett), and Coombe Wood (Stephens). It was also recorded at Dulwich Wood (Stainton, *Ent. Wkly. Intell.* **2**:10). In Kent it became extinct about 1868, and in Sussex in about 1892. Since then it has occasionally been recorded, almost certainly as the result of deliberate or accidental introductions, as follows: Oxshott Common, prior to 1939, possibly introduced (CGMdeW); Addiscombe, a half-grown larva found on a privet hedge, July 1959, a female reared to later that year (Evans, 1973); Ashtead Common, attempted introduction 1970s. The record is further confused, as it has been nationally, by the presence of specimens labelled with the place of rearing rather than the original locality: a dangerous and unnecessary practice. The presence of specimens in the Liverpool museum labelled Ashtead is explained thus.

DREPANIDAE – Hook-tips

The Drepanidae is a family of medium sized moths with slender bodies and ample wings. Most of them have the apex of the forewing extended into a hook giving rise to the English name. The larvae feed on trees and lack anal claspers, these being modified to form a raised anal point. Five species are resident in Surrey.

Falcaria lacertinaria (Linnaeus, 1758)   Scalloped Hook-tip

Resident; woodland, heathland, commons; widespread and common.

Bivoltine; May, and August.

Foodplant – birch.

The Scalloped Hook-tip is a common species in suitable habitat everywhere, the adults being regular attendees at the moth trap, and the larvae being frequently encountered when beating birch, especially in the autumn.

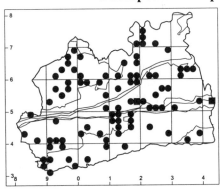

Drepana binaria (Hufnagel, 1767)   PLATE 3   Oak Hook-tip

Resident; woodland, heathland, commons; widespread and common.

Bivoltine; late May and June, and mid-July to August.

Foodplant – oak.

The Oak Hook-tip is the most widespread and common species of the genus in Surrey, occurring right into London where it depends on oaks in parkland and large gardens.

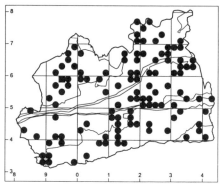

Drepana cultraria (Fabricius, 1775)   Barred Hook-tip

Resident; woodland; widespread and fairly common.

Bivoltine; May and June, and mid-July to August.

Foodplant – beech.

Although not seen in the same numbers as its congeners, the Barred Hook-tip is still fairly widespread in Surrey. As it is dependent on beech it is commonest on the North Downs, the extreme north-west, and in the Haslemere area. There are very few records from the weald, but this may be due to under-recording.

Drepana falcataria (Linnaeus, 1758)   Pebble Hook-tip
ssp. *falcataria* (Linnaeus, 1758)

Resident; heathland, woodland, wooded commons; widespread and common.

Bivoltine; late May and June, and late July and August.

Foodplant – birch, alder.

The Pebble Hook-tip is another very common hook-tip found throughout the county. The ground colour of the wings varies from quite a dusky brown through to a pale shade – almost as pale but not so contrasty as the Scottish subspecies *scotica* Bytinski-Salz.

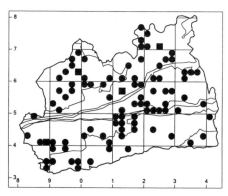

Cilix glaucata (Scopoli, 1763)

Chinese Character

Resident; woodland, commons; widespread and fairly common.

Bivoltine; late May and June, and late July and August.

Foodplant – (sloe, hawthorn).

Although found over most of the county, the Chinese Character gives the impression of being somewhat of an urban moth. Many rural traps record only a few specimens each year, whereas a trap on the edge of Mitcham Common averaged 27 specimens a year in the early 1980s (RKAM).

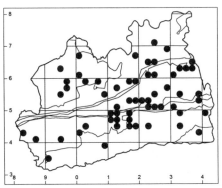

THYATIRIDAE – Lutestrings

The Thyatiridae is a small family, represented in Britain by nine species all of which occur in Surrey. The larvae have a full complement of prolegs and, with the exception of *batis* and *pyritoides*, feed between spun leaves of various trees.

Thyatira batis (Linnaeus, 1758)

Peach Blossom

Resident; woodland, wooded commons; widespread and fairly common.

Univoltine; June and July.

Foodplant – bramble.

The Peach Blossom is a very attractive species that is fairly common throughout the county including the London area. The larva has been found on bramble in a garden at South Croydon (GAC) in a year in which it was not recorded at the regularly run moth trap.

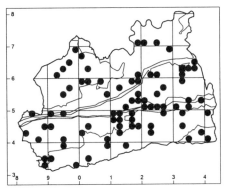

Habrosyne pyritoides (Hufnagel, 1766)   Buff Arches

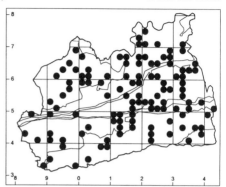

Resident; woodland, wooded commons; widespread and common.

Univoltine; July.

Foodplant – bramble.

The Buff Arches is a very common species almost everywhere. It is frequently encountered in numbers; trap counts at Bramley show 362 individuals were trapped in 1986 (RFB). The larva has been found on bramble at Mitcham Common (BS).

Tethea ocularis (Linnaeus, 1767)   Figure of Eighty
ssp. *octogesimea* (Hübner, 1786)

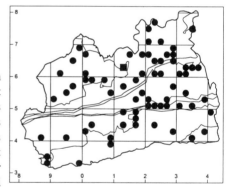

Resident; woodland, wooded commons; widespread and fairly common.

Univoltine; June and July.

Foodplant – aspen, (hybrid black poplar).

The Figure of Eighty is a fairly common species, especially at mercury vapour light where annual trap counts in double figures are the norm. The earlier entomologists regarded it as much less common, and it is not mentioned in the *VCH*, neither does it appear to have been known to Barrett or Newman as a Surrey moth, nor is it mentioned in the first edition of the Haslemere list (Oldaker, 1913). Early records for Surrey are of one taken at Witley, 2.7.1914 (Tullett, *Ent. Rec.* **32**:55), Dormansland, July 1922 (coll. H. Jeddere-Fisher), one at Godalming in 1924 (Wyatt, *Ent.* **58**:40), and another at Tooting, 10.6.1926 (Hawkins, *Proc. SLENHS* **1926-27**).

Tethea or ([Denis & Schiffermüller], 1775)

Poplar Lutestring

ssp. *or* ([Denis & Schiffermüller], 1775)

Resident; woodland; fairly widespread but generally uncommon.

Univoltine; June and July.

Foodplant – (aspen).

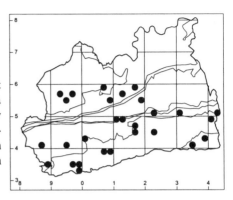

The Poplar Lutestring is certainly the scarcest species of this family in Surrey with only a few records from each site. It is apparently absent from the north-eastern and north-western corners of our county, but can otherwise be found in most areas where aspen occurs.

Tetheella fluctuosa (Hübner, 1803)

Satin Lutestring

Notable/Nb

Resident; woodland, wooded commons; fairly widespread and fairly common.

Univoltine; June and July.

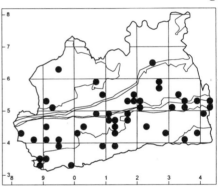

In the southern part of the county the Satin Lutestring is a fairly common and widely distributed species; north of the chalk, however, it is more localized. The melanic ab. *unicolor* Lempke, first recorded in East Kent, has been taken at Caterham, 12.6.1989 (GAC), and Nutfield, 21.7.1995 (PAC).

Ochropacha duplaris (Linnaeus, 1761)

Common Lutestring

Resident; woodland, wooded commons, heathland; widespread and fairly common.

Univoltine; July and August.

Foodplant – birch, (alder).

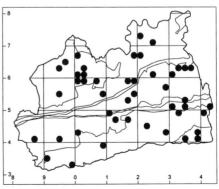

The Common Lutestring is quite a common species occurring throughout the county including suburban London. The form normally encountered is the melanic f. *obscura* Tutt.

Cymatophorima diluta ([Denis & Schiffermüller], 1775)   Oak Lutestring
ssp. *hartwiegi* (Reisser, 1927)

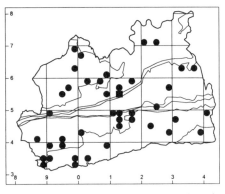

Resident; woodland, wooded commons; fairly widespread and often common.

Univoltine; late August and September.

Foodplant – oak.

The Oak Lutestring is rather widely distributed with the exception of the chalk where it is virtually unrecorded. Ab. *nubilata* Robson is stated to be frequent in Surrey (Skinner, 1984), but the only published references are to a few at New Haw, 1948 (Bretherton, 1957), and at Givons Grove (Evans, 1973); there is a specimen in the Messenger collection: Wormley, 13.9.1978 (JLM), and one was taken at Canterbury Copse, 18.9.1989 (AJ).

Achlya flavicornis (Linnaeus, 1758)   Yellow Horned
ssp. *galbanus* (Tutt, 1891)

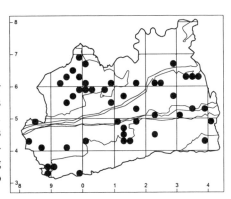

Resident; heathland, wooded commons; widespread and often common.

Univoltine; March to mid-April.

Foodplant – birch.

The Yellow Horned is a characteristic early spring species found where birch is encroaching on heathland and grassland. Fairly widespread throughout the county it is nevertheless absent from much of the built-up areas of south London. It has a strong affinity for mercury vapour light but can also be found at rest on birch trunks and twigs.

Polyploca ridens (Fabricius, 1787) PLATE 4 Frosted Green

Resident; woodland; restricted but fairly common.

Univoltine; mid-April to mid-May.

Foodplant – oak.

The distribution of the Frosted Green, as reference to its map shows, is restricted, it being absent from several rather large areas of north-east and western Surrey. Nevertheless it is often fairly common in suitable mature oak woodland. An extreme melanic, ab. *fumosa* Warnecke, was taken at Woking, 1976 (RCK coll.), and most Surrey examples are referable to f. *unicolor* Cockayne.

GEOMETRIDAE

The Geometridae is the second largest family of the macrolepidoptera with more than 300 British species. Only a few species are regular migrants. The adults come to light but are also frequently found flying at dusk or disturbed during the day. The larvae mostly lack the first three pairs of prolegs and progress by a looping motion that gives rise to the family's scientific name. A few species overwinter as adults, but most as eggs, larvae or pupae; the Brimstone Moth as either of the latter two stages.

Archiearis parthenias (Linnaeus, 1761) Orange Underwing

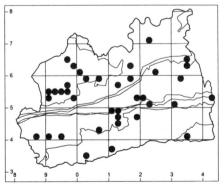

Resident; heathland, wooded commons; widespread and fairly common.

Univoltine; late March to mid-April.

Foodplant – birch.

This species, and the following one, share the habit of flying rather high around the tops of their respective foodplant trees, only rarely coming within reach of the net. This behaviour, together with the relatively early flight period, is likely to result in under-recording and, as close examination is necessary to separate the species, possible confusion between the two. The Orange Underwing is probably genuinely absent from the more urban parts of London, but it occurs fairly freely in most rural areas. The adult has been observed on several occasions feeding on the catkins of tall sallows, and in dull weather may be disturbed from birches by jarring them.

Archiearis notha (Hübner, 1803)   Light Orange Underwing

Notable/Nb

Resident; woodland; extremely local and
     uncommon.

April.

Foodplant – (aspen).

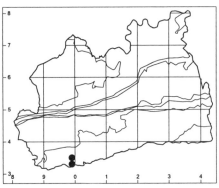

The Light Orange Underwing has only been
recorded from a single woodland complex
during the last 20 years. The close similarity
between this species and *A. parthenias*
necessitates its capture for certain
identification. As previously mentioned, this
is easier said than done and consequently there
is a fair possibility that the current species occurs overlooked in other localities. However,
there is only one site recorded in the north-west Surrey list: Ottershaw, one larva beaten
from aspen 5.6.1948, moths seen 1949 and 1950, but not since or elsewhere (Bretherton,
1957). Other sites from which there are records are Limpsfield (Cockayne in de Worms,
1954-58) and Bookham Common, where larvae were recorded on aspen (Wakely, in Wheeler,
1955); these records are undated but presumably refer to the late forties or early fifties. Also
from: Epsom, reared 1946 (Wakely, *Proc. SLENHS* **1946-47**); Leigh, 31.3.1946 (RF); Kiln
Copse, Wormley, 16.4.1949 (RFB); Oxshott, 24.5.1953 larvae (Thorpe-Young, *Proc.
SLENHS* **1953-54**); and Barnsthorns Wood, 27.5.1961 (Eagles, *Proc. SLENHS* **1961**). At
Fisherlane Wood most of the old aspen was removed in 1977 or 1978 and the species not
seen afterwards (RFB, *pers. com.*).

RECORDS – **Fisherlane Wood**, 12.4.76, several (RFB); **Botany Bay**, 24.4.85 (GAC);
Tugley Wood, 24.4.85 (GAC); **Oaken Wood**, 4.4.97 (DWB).

Alsophila aescularia ([Denis & Schiffermüller], 1775)   March Moth

Resident; woodland, heathland, commons;
     widespread and common.

Univoltine; March and April.

Foodplant – oak, elm, privet.

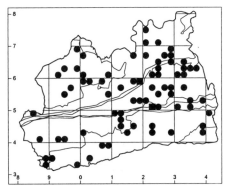

A generally very common early spring moth
found throughout the county. The female,
being wingless, is only rarely noticed but may
be found by searching trunks just after dusk.

Pseudoterpna pruinata (Hufnagel, 1767)   **Grass Emerald**
ssp. *atropunctaria* (Walker, 1863)

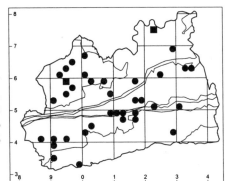

Resident; heathland, grassland; restricted, but fairly common.

Univoltine; July and August.

Foodplant – gorse, broom, (petty whin).

The Grass Emerald is rather generally distributed on the heathland of west Surrey, and also occurs on grassland, both calcareous and acidic. There are, however, only two records from the weald: Horley, 16.7.1986 (JBS); and Oaken Wood, 30.6.95 (GAC).

Geometra papilionaria Linnaeus, 1758   **Large Emerald**

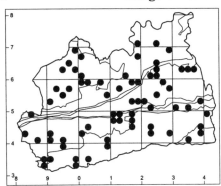

Resident; woodland, heathland, commons; widespread and fairly common.

Univoltine; July.

Foodplant – birch, (alder).

This species, the largest of the true Emeralds, can be found throughout the county but is usually only seen in small numbers. This is possibly the result of a reluctance to come to light or to fly more than a short distance; it is only occasionally recorded from the RES trap at Wisley despite the proximity of large areas of birch-covered heathland, and many other regularly run mv traps only take a few specimens a year, although a trap at Bramley recorded as many as ten individuals in 1986 (RFB).

Comibaena bajularia ([Denis & Schiffermüller], 1775)   **Blotched Emerald**

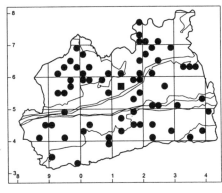

Resident; woodland, wooded commons; widespread and fairly common.

Univoltine; mid-June to mid-July.

Foodplant – oak.

An often fairly common species, the Blotched Emerald shows a preference for older woodland and is thus relatively uncommon in the urban area of south London, being restricted to such sites as Kew, Richmond, and Wimbledon. Elsewhere in the vicinity of woodland it can be quite common with as many as 38 recorded in one season at Bramley (RFB). A specimen lacking the pale markings was taken at Headley, 25.6.1976 (PAM; *Proc. BENHS.* **20**:plate 3).

Hemithea aestivaria (Hübner, 1799)   **Common Emerald**

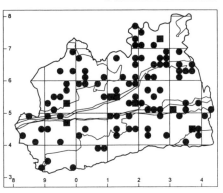

Resident; woodland, commons, heathland; widespread and common.

Univoltine; July.

Foodplant – oak, sloe, field maple, birch, bramble, (hawthorn).

As its popular name suggests this is a common species, indeed the commonest and most wide-ranging of the true Emeralds. The adult is a regular attendee at the light trap, and the larva is frequently found in the spring when beating a number of deciduous tree species.

Chlorissa viridata (Linnaeus, 1758)   **Small Grass Emerald**

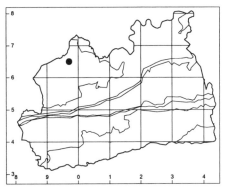

Notable/Na

Resident; heathland; very local and rare.

June to early July.

The Small Grass Emerald is an extremely local species only recorded recently from a single site, where it has been known for some time. Previously recorded from: near Chertsey, common 1863 (Champion, *Week Ent.* **2**:212); Horsell trap once; Chobham Common, "abundant in one small area where it is attached to *Ulex nanus*" [=*minor*] (Bretherton, 1957); Lucas Green, at light 26.6.1959 (Bretherton, 1965). There are also specimens from Dunsfold, June 1950 and 23.5.1953 (Minnion, BENHS coll.). It may well lie undiscovered on unworked heathland, but there is little doubt that this principally western species has only a tenuous foothold in the county.

RECORDS – **Chobham Common**, 2.7.83 (PJB), 3.7.91 (RFMcC), 9.6.93 (3) (DWB), 10.6.93 (GAC), 27.6.93 (DC), 16.6.96 (SWG).

Hemistola chrysoprasaria (Esper, 1794)   **Small Emerald**

Resident; chalk grassland, waste ground; restricted but fairly common.
Univoltine; July to mid-August.
Foodplant – traveller's joy.

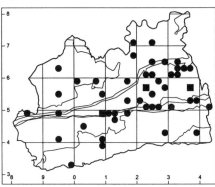

As one would expect of a species that feeds on traveller's joy, the Small Emerald is found most commonly on the chalk. There are also a few scattered records from other geological formations where the foodplant grows on waste ground and railway embankments. A second-brood example was noted at South Croydon, 26.9.1994 (GAC).

Jodis lactearia (Linnaeus, 1758)   **Little Emerald**

Resident; woodland; restricted, but fairly common.
Univoltine; June.
Foodplant – bilberry, birch.

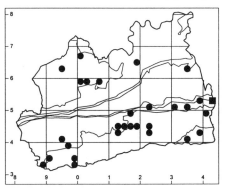

The Little Emerald appears to be restricted to the Bagshot sands and areas south of the chalk. There is only a single record from the London clay, and no records for the last ten years from the chalk. However it can be easily overlooked among other small pale-coloured moths, and seems to prefer to fly at dusk and so is probably under-recorded at light traps.

Cyclophora pendularia (Clerck, 1759)   **Dingy Mocha**

Extinct; not recorded this century.

The Dingy Mocha has probably not occurred in Surrey in this century, and older records are confused by synonymy with the Birch Mocha, both of which have been known as *pendularia*. Barrett considered it to be a Surrey moth though, occurring at Haslemere, and it was also recorded from Redhill in the 19th century (*VCH*).

Cyclophora annulata (Schulze, 1775)   **Mocha**

Notable/Nb

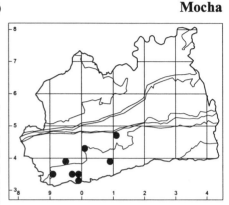

Resident; woodland; very local and uncommon.

Bivoltine; late May and early June, and late July and August.

The Mocha has only been recorded recently from the south-west of the county and indeed only from one restricted area in the last ten years. It was formerly known from north-west Surrey as the records from Bretherton's list testify: New Haw, 20.8.1951, 12.7.1952; Weybridge, 5-13.8.1952 (3); Horsell Common, 4.9.1951 (Bretherton, 1957). Other earlier records are: "not rare in the woods near Charterhouse" (Perrins, 1959); Westhumble 1953-56 (5) (Cole in Evans, 1973), both of which agree with the current distribution. The *VCH* states that it occurs generally amongst maple, but only lists Horsley and Haslemere, again both in the south-west. It was also recorded at Leigh, 25.5.1946, and 30.5.1956 (RF). The general impression is of a species which has been in slow decline for some time but was never very common anyway.

RECORDS – **Haslemere RES**, 23.6.76 (TGW); **Wormley**, 11.8.77 (JLM); **Canterbury Copse**, 29.6.85, 14.9.86, 23.8.89, 8.8.92 (AJ); **Oaken Wood**, 2.6.95 (DC), 10.8.95, 6.6.96 (GAC); **Tugley Wood**, 1994 (3), 23.5.95 (DY); **Chiddingfold**, 6.5.95 (GAC); **Bramley**, 30.5.79, 12.7.84, 23.8.86 (RFB); **Ewhurst**, 31.7.76 (SFI); **Abinger**, 9.7.76 (RFMcC).

Cyclophora albipunctata (Hufnagel, 1767)   **Birch Mocha**

Resident; heathland, commons; fairly widespread and common.

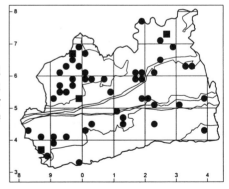

Bivoltine; May, and August.

Foodplant – birch.

Although the Birch Mocha has been recorded throughout the county it is not often seen on the chalk or the weald. Elsewhere it is rather common, especially on the heaths of the Bagshot beds.

Cyclophora puppillaria (Hübner, 1799)   **Blair's Mocha**

Migrant; rare.

Blair's Mocha is a rare migrant that was not known in this country before 1946. 1969 was the moth's best year and six were taken then, but it has not been recorded in recent years. All records are given.

1959 – **Wimbledon**, 16.10 (JVD).
1964 – **Leigh**, 16.6 (RF).
1967 – **Tattenham Corner**, 30.9 (Wallis in Evans, 1973).
1969 – **Nutfield**, 8.10 (PAC); **Bramley**, 13-17.10 (5) (RFB).
1976 – **Addiscombe**, 8.10 (KGWE); **Bramley**, 10.10 (RFB).
1977 – **Bramley**, 22.10 (RFB); **Reigate**, 22.10 (RAC); **Addiscombe**, October (KGWE).

Cyclophora porata (Linnaeus, 1767)   **False Mocha**

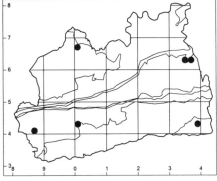

Resident; very local and rare.

Bivoltine; June, and August.

The False Mocha would appear to have declined very seriously in the last 50 years and is currently known from only six sites, with less than a dozen examples noted in the last 20 years. The *VCH* describes it as generally distributed, and as recently as the mid-fifties it was known from all the traps then being run in north-west Surrey and described as "scarce to fairly common; Byfleet; Horsell; Chobham Common" (Bretherton, 1957). Evans, in the north-east Surrey list, could only find one record; South Croydon, 3.5.1971 (PAS), and considered this "most surprising".

RECORDS – **Selsdon**, 1.9.78 (EHW); **Addington**, 9.6.96 (BS); **Thorpe**, 1976 (1), 79, 83 (PJB); **Rushmoor**, 6.6.84 (PAD); **Bramley**, 1976 (2), 3.6.78, 16.8.86 (RFB); **Lingfield**, 13.8.93 (JC).

Cyclophora punctaria (Linnaeus, 1758)   Maiden's Blush

Resident; woodland, wooded commons, heathland; widespread and common.

Bivoltine; May, and August.

Foodplant – oak.

The Maiden's Blush is probably the commonest and most widespread of the genus and occurs throughout the county with one apparent and surprising exception. That is that there are virtually no records from the chalk. In view of the number of records received, it is likely that this absence is real. The larva can often be common on oak in September.

Cyclophora linearia (Hübner, 1799)   Clay Triple-lines

Resident; woodland; restricted, but fairly common.

Univoltine; mid-May to July.

Foodplant – beech.

The Clay Triple-lines seems to be absent from the weald and the urban area of London, otherwise it occurs fairly plentifully wherever its foodplant does, especially in the woods on the crest of the chalk downs.

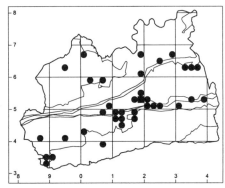

Timandra griseata Petersen, 1902   Blood-vein

Resident; woodland, heathland, commons; widespread and generally common.

Bivoltine; late May and June, and late July and August.

Foodplant – dock.

A very generally distributed species which seems to favour almost every type of habitat, and is as common in the urban areas as in the countryside. The Blood-vein is frequently disturbed by day. Occasional examples recorded in late September and October may

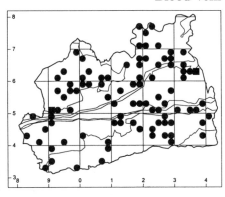

be evidence of a partial third brood. Such examples include: Rushmoor, 1.10.83, 8.10.84 (PAD); Bramley, 14.10.86 (RFB); and Milford, 6.10.92 (DWB).

[*Scopula nigropunctata* (Hufnagel, 1767)   Sub-angled Wave

Status uncertain; one doubtful record.

A specimen of the Sub-angled Wave is recorded from Gatton by Sidney Webb in the *VCH* under the synonym *strigilata* Hübner. The author who applied this name to the moth was actually Haworth, but *strigilata* Hübner is used by Barrett (1902) and from its position in the list it is fairly clear that *nigropunctata* is the species intended. If correct it was probably a migrant.]

Scopula ornata (Scopoli, 1763)   PLATE 14   Lace Border

Notable/Na

Resident; downland; local and scarce.

Bivoltine; June, and August.

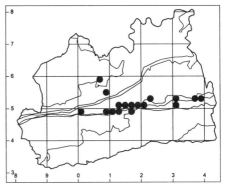

The Lace Border is more or less confined to the scarp slopes of the North Downs, especially those in the vicinity of Dorking but also at Pewley Down and at Oxted Downs. A number of specimens were recorded at the Rothamsted trap at Wisley in 1976, and in decreasing numbers for a few years afterwards; the possibility that they were introduced with downland plants cannot be excluded, although it was also taken at East Horsley that year – on the chalk but away from the scarp. It appears to have declined nationally of late and is now more or less confined to Surrey and Kent. The species is conspicuous and readily flies by day, so is unlikely to have been overlooked.

RECORDS – **Wisley RES**, 1976 (8), 77 (5), 78 (1), 82 (1) (AJH); **East Horsley**, 27.6.76, 20.8.76 (LJDW); **Pewley Down**, 27.8.81 (RFB), 1.6.87, 29.5.84, 7.6.93, 17.8.93, 19.8.94, 24.7.95 (DWB); **Hackhurst Downs**, 25.7.95 (DY); **White Downs**, 4.6.79 (RFMcC), 11.8.85 (RFB), 16.8.91 (GAC), 9.8.92, 14.6.96 (DC); **Westcott Downs**, 16.6.84, 9.8.84, 29.5.85, 3.8.96 (GAC); **Ranmore**, 21.6.76 (PAC), 2.9.77 (RFMcC), 4-9.6.78 (JP), 13.8.83 (RGS), 4.6.84 (GAC); **Dorking**, 13.8.83, 19.8.84, 31.5.85 (PC), 2.6.84 (DAT); **Box Hill**, 12.8.82 (RKAM); **Boxhurst**, 9.8.84 (GAC); **Betchworth**, 2.6.79 (RAC), 16.5.90 (1) (BS); **Buckland Hills**, 16.5.90 (2) (BS), 15.7.96 (PAC); **Nutfield**, 3.8.95 (PAC); **Quarry Hangers**, 31.7.96 (RMP); **Tandridge Hill**, 1-9.6.82, 2.8.82, 13.6.83 (RGS), 2.8.89 (GAC); **Oxted**, 7.96 (TD).

Scopula marginepunctata (Goeze, 1781)   PLATE 16   Mullein Wave

Resident; waste ground, gardens; local but fairly common.

Bivoltine; June and early July, and August to mid-September.

The Mullein Wave is a principally coastal species that occurs not uncommonly in the urban area of north-east Surrey, presumably by following the Thames estuary. In view of its distribution it is not surprising that the majority of records come from garden moth traps; as many as 31 individuals were recorded from South Croydon in 1984 (GAC), but smaller numbers are more normal.

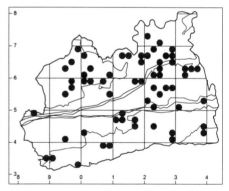

Scopula imitaria (Hübner, 1799)   Small Blood-vein

Resident; commons; widespread and locally fairly common.

Univoltine; July and August.

The Small Blood-vein has been recorded throughout the county but very often as single specimens. Larger numbers have been found at regularly trapped sites, especially Wisley, Ashtead and Banstead, the last site producing 34 specimens in 1990 (SWG).

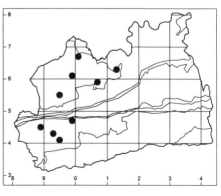

Scopula immutata (Linnaeus, 1758)   Lesser Cream Wave

Resident; marshy areas, water meadows; local and scarce.

Univoltine; July.

The Lesser Cream Wave is certainly a very scarce and local species in Surrey, although its liking for wetter areas may have resulted in it being under-recorded. To the inexperienced observer it superficially resembles several other members of the genera *Scopula* and *Idaea,* and some records have been omitted where voucher specimens do not exist.

RECORDS – **Thundry Meadows**, 26.7.96 (GM); **Elstead**, 22.7.85 (DWB); **Shalford**,

7.8.91 (1) by day (DWB); **Milford**, 22.7.95 (DWB [det. GAC]); **Pirbright RES**, 1980 (5), 81 (5) (ED); **Pirbright**, 16.7.94 (GAC); **Horsell**, 29.6.94 (J.Pontin); **Thorpe**, 1976-78, not since (PJB); **Wisley RES**, 1986 (2), 95 (1) (AJH); **Esher Common**, 21.7.90 (1) by day (JP).

Scopula floslactata (Haworth, 1809)   Cream Wave

ssp. *floslactata* (Haworth, 1809)

Resident; woodland, wooded commons and downs; restricted and generally uncommon.
Univoltine; May and June.
The Cream Wave seems to be absent from the whole of the north-east of the county together with the chalk area and large areas of the western side where heathland predominates. Elsewhere, especially on the weald and greensand, it occurs regularly if in small numbers. The moth can be disturbed by day and flies at dusk, and it is likely that those who rely on light traps have to some extent overlooked this species.

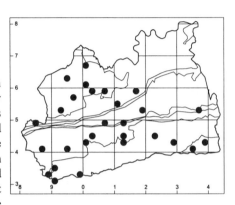

Idaea serpentata (Hufnagel, 1767)   Ochraceous Wave

Status uncertain.
This species has a very uncertain history in Britain as a result of confusion with the Bright Wave (*Idaea ochrata* (Scopoli)). There were two Surrey specimens which Barrett (1902) considered to have a reliable history. He gave the details as: Redhill, 1865, by Mr. Sydney Webb, and another in the same place four years later by the late Mr. Walter Weston. The *VCH*, which was published in the same year, gives the localities as Leigh (Webb), and either on Reigate Heath or in Redstone Wood (Weston). It has not been recorded in the county since, and, as the Bright Wave is not a Surrey species, must be considered to be long extinct.

Idaea muricata (Hufnagel, 1767)   **Purple-bordered Gold**

Notable/Na

Resident; damp heathland; very local and scarce.

Univoltine; July.

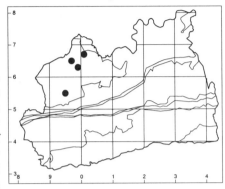

This species is currently known from only two sites with only a handful of dated records. The Purple-bordered Gold occurs on damp heathland, and the Thorpe record probably represents a stray from Chobham. A lot of suitable habitat in north-west Surrey is army land which is necessarily out of bounds, and the moth may well occur more widely than we know, but is certainly on the edge of its range in the county. In the past it used to be found in the Croydon area (Barrett, 1901); this presumably refers to Addington Hills. Also from: Woking, 1912 (Champion, *E.M.M.* **49**:35); Butts Wood; Brookwood, 1.7.1911; North Camp station, 1932; Ash Vale, 28.7.1951 (Bretherton, 1957); Horsell, 1968 (CGMdeW). The larva is said to feed on marsh cinquefoil, but in Surrey the distribution of moth and plant is mutually exclusive (Lousley, 1976).

RECORDS – **Pirbright**, 14.7.96, fertile female at mvl (GAC); **Chobham Common: Gracious Pond**, 10.7.81, by day (GAC), 30.6.95, at mvl (CT), **Albury Bottom**, 13.7.85, by day (GAC), 28.6.92 (RFMcC), 11.7.93 (DWB), 17.7.93 (DC); **Thorpe**, 16.7.90, at mvl (PJB).

Idaea vulpinaria (Herrich-Schäffer, 1851)   PLATE 16   **Least Carpet**
ssp. *atrosignaria* Lempke, 1967

Notable/Nb

Resident; gardens, commons; restricted but common.

Univoltine; July and early August.

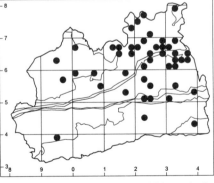

The Least Carpet is an example of a species which has extended its range in recent years, moving westwards from Kent. It was first recorded from Surrey at Dulwich, 4.8.1954 (Edwards, *Ent. Rec.* **66**:253), and by the sixties was found regularly throughout south London. It has greatly increased its numbers within this region and is evidently attempting to establish itself further south and west, mostly without much success. In 1976, no doubt encouraged by the exceptional weather, it was seen at Wormley, but has not occurred so far south-west since. In that year it was also taken at Thorpe and Windlesham, odd specimens still being found in the area, also at Wisley where it has been seen in decreasing numbers up to 1989. Its stronghold, however, is still the gardens of suburban London where it can be very common as the following trap counts show: South Croydon, 1984 (62) (GAC), Mitcham, 1984 (89) (RKAM). A second brood-example was noted at South Croydon, 24.9.1989 (GAC).

Idaea sylvestraria (Hübner, 1799)   Dotted Border Wave

Notable/Nb
Resident; heathland; local and scarce.
Univoltine; July.
Unlike its ubiquitous congeners, with which it may easily be confused, the Dotted Border Wave is a characteristic heathland insect. In Surrey it occurs on all the major heaths, both on the greensand and the Bagshot beds, but rarely seems to be found in any great numbers.

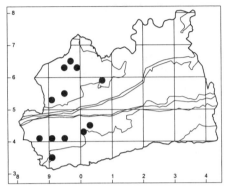

Idaea biselata (Hufnagel, 1767)   Small Fan-footed Wave

Resident; woodland, heathland, commons; widespread and common.
Univoltine; July and August.
The Small Fan-footed Wave is a very generally distributed species which occurs in good numbers everywhere.

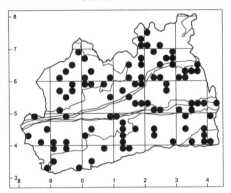

Idaea fuscovenosa (Goeze, 1781)   Dwarf Cream Wave

Resident; woodland, commons; restricted but fairly common.
Univoltine; late June and July.
Although fairly common over much of the county including the London area, the Dwarf Cream Wave does seem to be absent from the weald and from much of the heathland of western Surrey.

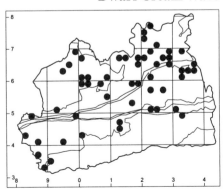

Idaea seriata (Schrank, 1802) Small Dusty Wave

Resident; gardens, commons; fairly widespread and locally common.

Bivoltine; mid-May to July, and August and September.

Foodplant – (hawthorn).

Although occurring thinly throughout the county this species must be regarded as principally an urban moth especially favouring the London area. Indeed most rural trap operators do not consider it as anything more than scarce. One exception to this is the Rothamsted trap at Wisley where annual trap

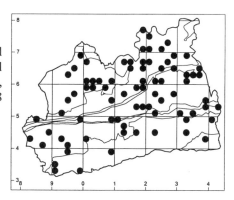

counts regularly exceed 50 individuals. Clearly the site more resembles a domestic garden than a "natural" habitat, but the type of trap also has a bearing. Rothamsted traps use an incandescent bulb rather than an ultra-violet light source, and this seems to attract much greater numbers of moths of the genera *Idaea* and *Scopula*.

Idaea dimidiata (Hufnagel, 1767) Single-dotted Wave

Resident; commons, woodland, gardens; widespread and fairly common.

Univoltine; July to mid-August.

Another common Wave which is found all over the county. Possible examples of a partial second brood are those taken at: Mitcham, 17.9.1982 (RKAM); and Ashtead, 29.9.1988 (GG).

Idaea subsericeata (Haworth, 1809)   Satin Wave

Resident; commons, gardens; widespread
    and fairly common.
Univoltine; June.
The Satin Wave is certainly less common than
many of its congeners amongst which it is
often overlooked. It appears to be fairly
generally distributed, however, and the
paucity of records from the weald probably
represents under-recording rather than lack of
some ecological requirement.

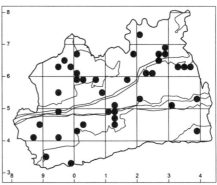

Idaea trigeminata (Haworth, 1809)   Treble Brown Spot

Resident; woodland, commons, gardens;
    widespread and fairly common.
Univoltine; mid-June to mid-July.
The Treble Brown Spot is a rather widely
distributed species which probably reaches its
greatest numbers in the gardens of south
London.

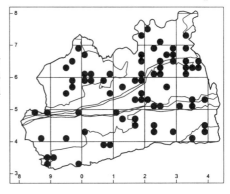

Idaea emarginata (Linnaeus, 1758)   Small Scallop

Resident; commons; widespread but
    usually uncommon.
Univoltine; July and August.
Although found throughout the county, the
Small Scallop is only seen in very small
numbers, at least at light traps. Even regularly
run traps rarely record more than a few
specimens each year. This is another species
which flies strongly at dusk, and searching at
this time of day should reveal it to be more
common than the records suggest.

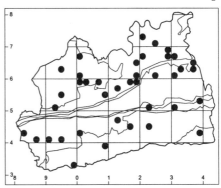

Idaea aversata (Linnaeus, 1758) Riband Wave

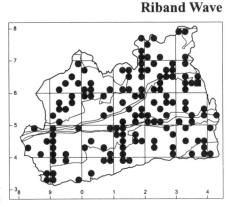

Resident; commons, woodland, heathland; widespread and common.

Univoltine; June to August.

Foodplant – hedge bedstraw.

An ubiquitous species in the county, and the commonest geometer at the light trap. Like most normally univoltine members of this genus it is capable of producing a small second generation; its overall greater numbers mean that this phenomenon is more obvious in this species, although such second-brood examples are still less than one percent of the population. Trap counts at South Croydon show: 1983 – 21.6-21.8 (573), 25-30.9 (4); 1984 – 16.6-2.9 (1055), 15.9 (2); 1985 – 18.6-12.9 (560), 25.9 (2) (GAC).

Idaea straminata (Borkhausen, 1794) Plain Wave

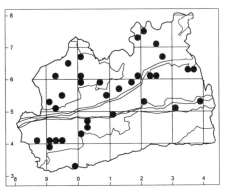

Resident; heathland, commons; restricted and uncommon.

Univoltine; July and early August.

This species has a superficial resemblance to the Riband Wave and may be overlooked among it. There can be little doubt though that it is a much scarcer species with a rather restricted distribution being scarcely recorded from either the chalk or the weald. Elsewhere, even at regularly run traps, the annual counts are only in single figures.

Rhodometra sacraria (Linnaeus, 1767) PLATE 7 Vestal

Migrant; recorded most years.

The Vestal has been an almost annual migrant to Surrey during the survey period, but usually only seen in small numbers. The exception to this was in 1983 when a huge immigration occurred and in excess of 150 examples were noted; in 1996 when record numbers of such migrant species as the Gem and the Bordered Straw appeared in Surrey, not a single Vestal was noted. Occasional examples occur in the spring and early summer but the peak of records is for September.

1976 – **Wormley**, 9.9, 10.10 (JLM); **Bramley**, 30.9 (RFB).

1978 – **Wormley**, 7-14.10 (JLM); **Leigh**, 9.10 (RF); **South Norwood**, 9.10 (RGS); **Purley**, 11.10 (PMS); **Addington**, 15.10 (BS); **Wisley RES**, 15.10 (AJH); **Addiscombe**, 19.10 (KGWE); **Selsdon**, 21.10 (EHW).

1979 – **Leigh**, 1.9 (RF).

1980 – **Mitcham**, 7.8. (RKAM); **Addiscombe**, 13.8 (KGWE); **Selsdon**, 15.8 (EHW).
1981 – **Addiscombe**, 7-26.9 (3) (KGWE); **South Norwood**, 26.9 (RGS); **Tolworth**, 8.10 (JTS).
1982 – **Pirbright RES** (1) (ED); **Wisley**, 7.9 (AJH); **Bramley**, 14.9, 1.10 (RFB); **Rushmoor**, 19.9 (PAD); **Addington**, 20.9 (BS); **Addiscombe**, 25.9 (2) (KGWE); **Buckland**, 28-29.9 (2) (CH); **Leigh**, 29.9 (2) (RF).
1983 – **Thorpe**, April (1), August (5) (PJB); **Rushmoor**, 22.7-2.10 (24) (PAD); **South Croydon**, 1.8-29.9 (9) (GAC); **Bramley**, 21.8-9.10 (21) (RFB); **Wisley RES**, 21.8-30.9 (11) (AJH); **North Cheam**, 23.8-28.9 (6+) (RFMcC); **Leigh**, 13.9-1.10 (19) (RF); **Buckland** 22.9-4.10 (12) (CH); **Featherbed Lane**, 30.8 (RGS); **Addington**, 23-30.9 (12) (BS); **Dorking**, 26-30.9 (12) (DAT); **Worms Heath**, 24.9 (DWB); **Milford**, 24.9- 5.10 (10) (DWB); **Epsom Downs**, 26.9 (DWB); **Virginia Water**, 26.9 (AG); **Surbiton**, 26.9 (2) (JP); **Mitcham**, 26-29.9 (7) (RKAM); **Wimbledon**, 26.9-1.10 (4) (JVD); **Putney**, 1.10 (Sealey per RFB).
1984 – **Leigh**, 8.8, 25.8, 7.10 (RF); **Oxted**, 2.9 (TD); **Wisley RES**, 2.9 (AJH); **Rushmoor**, 8.10 (PAD).
1985 – **Rushmoor**, 25.7 (PAD); **Wisley RES**, 19.9, 2.10 (AJH); **Bramley**, 22.9 (2) (RFB); **Buckland**, 23.9 (CH); **Leigh**, 2.10 (RF).
1987 – **Thorpe** (PJB); **Buckland** (8) (CH); **Leigh**, 21.8-2.10 (9) (RF); **Tolworth**, 24.8 (JTS); **Wimbledon**, 30.8, 17.9 (JVD); **Wisley RES**, 30.8, 29.9 (AJH); **Coulsdon**, 2.9 (PMS); **Bramley**, 1-22.9 (10) (RFB); **Addington**, 2-20.9 (8) (BS); **Oxted**, 18.9 (TD); **Horley**, 19.9 (JBS); **Woking**, 17.10 (SCP).
1988 – **Addington**, 30.8 (BS).
1989 – **Thorpe** (PJB); **Nutfield**, 28.7 (PAC); **Thursley Common**, 4.9 (AJ); **Leigh**, 12.9 (RF); **Bramley**, 14.9, 27.10 (RFB); **Woking**, 22.10 (SCP); **Carshalton**, 25.10 (DC); **Oxted**, 28.10 (TD).
1990 – **Leigh**, 13-19.10 (2) (RF); **Milford**, 15.10 (DWB); **Lingfield**, 18.10 (JC).
1991 – **Buckland**, 4.9 (CH).
1992 – **Wisley RES**, 12.8 (AJH); **Milford**, 23.8 (DWB); **Lingfield**, 21.9 (JC); **Leigh**, 24.9 (RF); **Buckland**, 27-30.9 (2) (CH).
1994 – **Wisley RES** (1) (AJH); **Stroude**, common on allotment (PJB); **East Sheen**, 3.8 (D. Couzens); **Wimbledon**, 4-26.8 (2) (JVD); **Richmond Park**, 6.8 (DC); **Nutfield**, 7-13.8 (2), 29.8 (4) by day (PAC); **Milford**, 18.8 (DWB); **Lingfield**, 21.8 (3) (JC); **Leatherhead**, 26.8 (WJ).
1995 – **Wisley RES** (1) (AJH); **Nutfield**, 24.8 (PAC); **Buckland**, 29.8, 11.9 (CH); **Milford**, 15.9 (DWB); **Lingfield**, 15.9-13.10 (3) (JC); **Wimbledon**, 13.10 (JVD); **Pirbright**, 14.10 (GAC); **Woking**, 16.10 (SCP).

Phibalapteryx virgata (Hufnagel, 1767)   Oblique Striped

Vagrant; one recent record.

Only a very small number of examples of the Oblique Striped have ever been recorded in Surrey. The species occurs on chalk downland in North Hampshire (Goater, 1974), and most likely our specimens are vagrants from there, although it also occurs in coastal localities in Sussex and Kent. There is only one recent record, older records being: Chobham, 18.7.1914 (Champion), specimen in Oxford University Museum collection (Bretherton, 1957); and Bramley, 19.7.69 (1), 22.7.70 (1) (RFB).

RECORDS – **Milford**, 7.8.92 (DWB).

Orthonama vittata (Borkhausen, 1794)   Oblique Carpet

Status uncertain; possible resident

August.

There appear to have only ever been a handful of records of the Oblique Carpet in Surrey, with only two for the survey period and none in the last decade. Whether it is an overlooked resident or merely a vagrant is difficult to say. It is an inhabitant of marshy places, a habitat both scarce and under-worked in Surrey, and searching with a lamp at dusk in such places may reveal new sites for it. A specimen was taken at Dormansland, August 1926 (coll. H. Jeddere-Fisher). The north-west Surrey list gives: Egham, 1929 (2), 1933 (1); Weybridge trap, 2.6.1952, 11.6.1953 (Bretherton, 1957). It was also seen along the River Wey at Charterhouse, 14.6.1952 (RFB). Further records from north-east Surrey are: Westhumble, 3.9.1952; Warlingham [undated] (Evans, 1973).

RECORDS – **Wisley RES**, 15.8.78 (AJH); **Leigh**, last seen 1979 (RF).

Orthonama obstipata (Fabricius, 1794)   Gem

Migrant; uncommon.

The Gem is currently an uncommon migrant, not recorded every year and seldom seen in numbers. In 1996 there was a larger invasion with examples recorded from May to late August, some of the later individuals possibly resulting from local breeding.

1978 – **Reigate**, 4.6 (RAC); **Wormley**, 11.9, 8.10 (JLM); **Croydon**, 12.10 (JC); **Tolworth**, 14.10 (JP); **Bramley**, 2.11 (RFB); **Selsdon**, 2.11 (EHW); **Leigh**, 9.11 (RF).

1979 – **Ashtead Common**, 30.7 (DCL); **Wormley**, 25.9 (JLM).

1981 – **Buckland**, 28.5 (CH).

1982 – **Bramley**, 2.9-4.11 (3) (RFB); **Rushmoor**, 25.10 (PAD); **Leigh**, 7.11 (RF); **Wisley RES**, 9.11 (AJH).

1983 – **Mitcham**, 31.7 (RKAM); **Leigh**, 5.11 (RF); **Bramley**, 6.11 (2) (RFB); **North Cheam**, 6.11 (RFMcC); **Dorking**, 7.11 (DAT).

1985 – **Rushmoor**, 26.7 (PAD).

1988 – **Bramley**, 16.10 (RFB).

1992 – **Wisley RES** (1) (AJH); **Surbiton**, 17.7 (JP).

1994 – **Lingfield**, 7.8 (JC); **Buckland**, 8.11 (CH).

1995 – **Lingfield**, 12.10 (JC).

1996 – **Woking**, May (3) (SCP); **Banstead**, 7.6 (SWG); **Mitcham**, 17.6, 31.7 (DC); **Lingfield**, 23-30.7 (6) (JC); **Woking**, 26.7 (J. Pontin); **South Croydon**, 26.7 (GAC); **Chessington**, 26.7, 8.8 (JP); **Nutfield**, 29.7 (PAC); **Buckland**, 1.8, 6-12.10 (2) (CH); **Tolworth**, 1-14.8 (2) (JTS); **Leigh**, 19.8 (RF).

Xanthorhoe biriviata (Borkhausen, 1794)   PLATE 12   Balsam Carpet

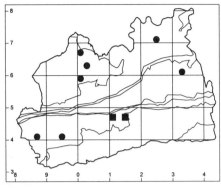

Notable/Na
Resident; damp woodland; local but fairly
   common.
Bivoltine; May and early June, and late
   July to mid-August.
Foodplant – orange balsam, small balsam.
The Balsam Carpet was only announced as a
new British species in 1955 from a site in
Middlesex (Minnion and Goodban, *Ent. Gaz.*
7:3), but had been found at Byfleet in Surrey
by the following year. It was taken at
Ottershaw, 14.8.1959 and 9.5.1960
(Bretherton, 1965). The species is associated with the introduced alien plant, orange balsam,
and occurs at sites along the Wey and its tributaries, especially the Tillingbourne. At its best
known site near Abinger it is often common, and here the larvae have also been recorded
from small balsam. In the last few years a couple of specimens have been taken in north-
east Surrey, away from the normal foodplant but near to areas of the small balsam, and the
discovery of new colonies in this area cannot be ruled out. Interestingly all the records from
static traps, which represent wanderers from breeding areas, have been of the second brood.

RECORDS – **Rushmoor**, 26.7.84 (PAD); **Milford**, 10.8.92, 14.8.96 (DWB); **Abinger**,
6.6.79 (PMS), 3.5.80 ova on orange balsam (BS), 8.6.80, 31.5.81 (RFMcC), 6.82 larvae
on orange balsam (JP), 4.6.84, 29.5.85, 4.5.92 (GAC), 18.5.92 (SWG), 16.7.92 (RFMcC);
Abinger Forest, 7.76 larvae on small balsam, 10.5.79 (PAC); **Thorpe**, scarce, usually
second brood; 1990, 94 (PJB); **Woking**, 14.8.95 (2) (SCP); **Woodham**, 7.5.88 (GAC);
Wimbledon, 8.7.89 (JVD); **Purley**, 16.8.91 (PJS).

Xanthorhoe designata (Hufnagel, 1767)   Flame Carpet

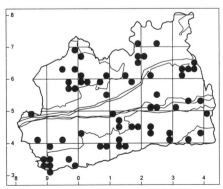

Resident; woodland, commons, gardens;
   widespread and fairly common.
Bivoltine; May and June, and August to
   mid-September.
The Flame Carpet occurs in suitable places
all over the county, preferring woodland.

Xanthorhoe spadicearia ([Denis & Schiffermüller], 1775) **Red Twin-spot Carpet**

Resident; woodland, commons, heathland; widespread and common.

Bivoltine; mid-May to mid-June, and mid-July to August.

This species and the next are subject to a certain amount of confusion, especially as *ferrugata* has a form with the median fascia reddish. Both are fairly common and widespread although there are more records relating to the present species.

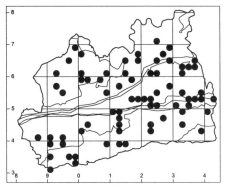

Xanthorhoe ferrugata (Clerck, 1759) **Dark-barred Twin-spot Carpet**

Resident; woodland, commons, heathland; widespread and fairly common.

Bivoltine; mid-May to mid-June, and mid-July to August.

This species would appear to be less common than *spadicearia*, but no distinct differences in habitat preferences can be detected from the records. Where trap counts have been kept the indications are that at Bramley roughly equal numbers were taken, at South Croydon, Ashtead and Banstead many more *spadicearia* than *ferrugata* occur, and at

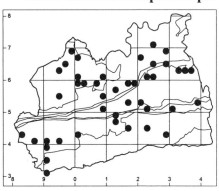

Wisley this species outnumbers *spadicearia* by about three to one.

Xanthorhoe quadrifasiata (Clerck, 1759) **Large Twin-spot Carpet**

Resident; heathland, wooded commons; local and scarce.

Univoltine; July.

In Surrey the Large Twin-spot Carpet occurs only in the west where it is particularly associated with heathland and surrounding commons. It has only been recorded in very small numbers and even at regularly run traps is scarce: for example Bramley, 1985 (2), 86 (2) (RFB). It appears to be quite absent from the east of the county (but see distribution in Plant, 1993).

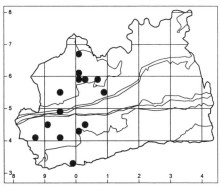

Xanthorhoe montanata ([Denis & Schiffermüller], 1775) **Silver-ground Carpet**

ssp. *montanata* ([Denis & Schiffermüller], 1775)

Resident; woodland, downland, heathland, commons; widespread and common.

Univoltine; late May and June.

A very widespread and common species which is frequently disturbed by day.

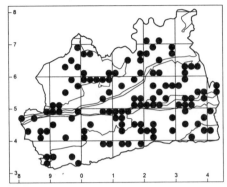

Xanthorhoe fluctuata (Linnaeus, 1758) **Garden Carpet**

Resident; gardens, woodland, commons; widespread and common.

Bivoltine; mid-May to July, and September and October.

Foodplant – garlic mustard, nasturtium.

The Garden Carpet is found throughout the county, though, as its vernacular name suggests, it prefers domestic gardens. It is also much commoner in suburban areas compared to rural ones as the following trap counts show: Bramley (rural), 1985 (15), 86 (31) (RFB); Milford (rural), 1992 (28) (DWB); Wisley (RHS garden), 1986 (56), 87 (54) (AJH); South Croydon (suburban), 1983 (79),

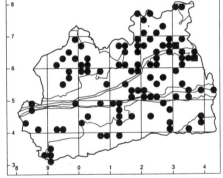

84 (58), 85 (84) (GAC); Selsdon (suburban), 1980 (210) (EHW); and Carshalton (suburban), 1988 (224) (DC) – this last site being the window of a second-floor flat.

Scotopteryx bipunctaria ([Denis & Schiffermüller], 1775)   Chalk Carpet
ssp. *cretata* (Prout, 1937)

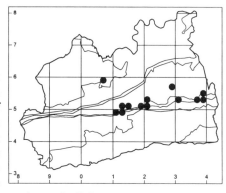

Notable/Nb

Resident; chalk downland; local and uncommon.

Univoltine; July and August.

With the exception of a couple of vagrant examples caught at Wisley this species seems to be currently restricted to the scarp slope of the North Downs where it is usually less than common. It would appear that the Chalk Carpet has declined somewhat as there are no recent records from the dip slope of the downs. Under-recording is unlikely as the species is readily disturbed by day as well as coming to the light trap.

Westcott Downs, 13.7.83 (GAC); **Ranmore**, 2.9.77 (RFMcC); **Dorking**, 28.7.78, 17.7.79 (PC); **Boxhurst**; 15.7.77 (PAM); **Brockham**, 6.9.96 (GAC); **Betchworth**, 7-13.7.79 (RAC); **Dawcombe**, 13.7-3.8.90, 20.7-9.8.91, 31.7.92 (DC); **Hooley**, 3.8.78 (CH); **Quarry Hangers**, 1994-96 (RMP); **Tandridge Hill**, 5.7.82, 2.8.82 (RGS); **Oxted Downs**, 29.7-19.8.78 (3), 18.8-1.9.80 (6) (RGS), 4.8.83 (KNAA), 9.94 (GAC); **Oxted**, 7.94 (TD); **Wisley RES**, 1978 (1), 7.91 (1) (AJH).

Scotopteryx chenopodiata (Linnaeus, 1758)   Shaded Broad-bar

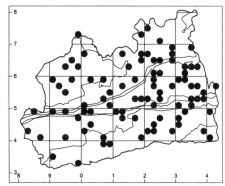

Resident; downland, commons, heathland; widespread and common.

Univoltine; July and August.

The Shaded Broad-bar is another common, widely distributed species that is often observed by day. At Addington several larvae were found by sweeping but the foodplant remains unrecorded.

Scotopteryx luridata (Hufnagel, 1767)   July Belle

ssp. *plumbaria* (Fabricius, 1775)

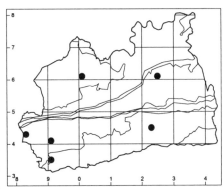

Resident; heathland, grassland; very local and rare.

Univoltine; mid-June to mid-August.

The July Belle is clearly a rare species in Surrey with only eight individuals recorded during the survey period. It would seem to have always been so, as there are only a handful of records in the north-east Surrey list, and the north-west Surrey list states "a characteristic heath insect, curiously scarce" (Bretherton, 1957). Quite why this should be so is something of a mystery as the heathland of west Surrey would appear to be equally as suitable as that of the New Forest where the species is much commoner.

RECORDS – **Boundstone**, 14.8.87 (BH); **Haslemere RES**, 1977 (1) (TGW); **Thursley Common**, 12.7.86 (2) (DWB); **Horsell**, 14.6.76 (CGMdeW); **Leigh**, 1976 (1) (RF); **Banstead Downs**, 25.7.80 (JP), 14.6.89 (DC).

Catarhoe rubidata ([Denis & Schiffermüller], 1775)   Ruddy Carpet

Notable/Nb

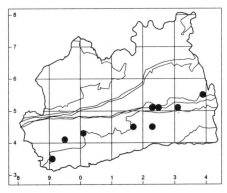

Resident; wooded commons, downland; very local and rare.

Univoltine; July.

The Ruddy Carpet is only known from 14 examples in the last 20 years, and consequently its requirements are difficult to determine. Eight examples come from the scarp of the North Downs, whence it is also recorded in Evans (1973), the rest from the south of the county on or near the weald. It was unrecorded in the north-west Surrey list.

RECORDS – **Haslemere RES**, 25.7.80 (TGW); **Milford**, 5.8 .96 (DWB); **Bramley**, 17.7.85 (RFB); **Holmwood Common**, 19.7.85 (PC); **Leigh**, 1978, 87 (RF); **Buckland**, 29.6.92 (CH); **Reigate**, 8.7.85 (RAC); **Nutfield**, 11.6.77, 21.7.89, 4-5.7.91 (2), 16.7.94 (PAC); **Oxted Downs**, 10.7.78 (RGS).

Catarhoe cuculata (Hufnagel, 1767)   **Royal Mantle**

Resident; chalk grassland, local and rare.
Univoltine; late June and July.
Foodplant – bedstraw, (lady's bedstraw).
The Royal Mantle is a local species, virtually restricted to the chalk with the most recent records coming mostly from the scarp of the North Downs. As with several of the other chalk downland specialities this species may prove to be tolerably common on the more inaccessible areas of the downs.

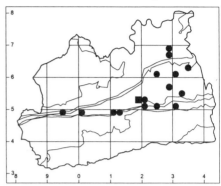

[*Epirrhoe tristata* (Linnaeus, 1758)   **Small Argent and Sable**

Doubtful;
This species is listed as occurring at Croydon in Buckell and Prout (1898-1901); an undoubtedly erroneous record.]

Epirrhoe alternata (Müller, O. F., 1764)   **Common Carpet**

ssp. *alternata* (Müller, O. F., 1764)

Resident; commons, woodland, downland, heathland; widespread and common.
Bivoltine; May to mid-June, and mid-July to August.
The Common Carpet is a very common and widespread species which can occur in numbers at regularly run traps, both rural and suburban, as the following counts show: Bramley, 1985 (60), 86 (89) (RFB); Mitcham, 1981 (60), 82 (47), 83 (32) (RKAM).

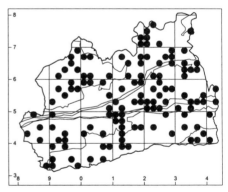

Epirrhoe rivata (Hübner, 1813)   **Wood Carpet**

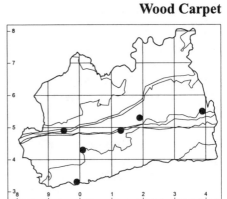

Resident; downland, woodland, very local and rare.

Univoltine; mid-June to early July.

The exact status of the Wood Carpet is difficult to determine as it is liable to be confused with the Common Carpet and, in at least a couple of cases I have come across, with the Sharp-angled Carpet. All the evidence suggests that it is a rare and possibly declining species. Bretherton (1957) lists only three examples, and Evans (1973) describes it as local with most of his records coming from the downs. Only seven examples have been noted during the survey period.

RECORDS – **Tugley Wood**, 6.86, 7.6.87 (SCP); **Bramley**, 16.6.82 (RFB); **Compton**, 7.7.86 (DWB); **Westcott Downs**, 19.6.79 (JP); **Headley Warren**, 5.7.95 (GAC); **Oxted Downs**, 10.7.78 (RGS).

Epirrhoe galiata ([Denis & Schiffermüller], 1775)   **Galium Carpet**

Resident; chalk downland; very local and scarce.

June.

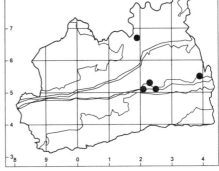

A very local species virtually confined to the scarp of the North Downs and only recorded from a very limited area during the last decade. It can, on occasion, be moderately common where it does occur and may be overlooked at other sites due to superficial resemblance to both the Common Carpet and the Garden Carpet. Only the first brood has been recorded during the survey period.

RECORDS – **Betchworth**, 12.6.89 (RFMcC); **Buckland Quarry**, 1-7.6.83 (CH); **Reigate**, 1.6.79 (RAC); **Oxted Downs**, 8-10.6.78 (4) (RGS); **Surbiton**, 18.6.91 (JP).

Camptogramma bilineata (Linnaeus, 1758)   Yellow Shell

ssp. *bilineata* (Linnaeus, 1758)

Resident; downland, commons, woodland; widespread and common.

Univoltine; mid-June to early September.

Foodplant – (dandelion, horse-chestnut).

A very common and generally distributed species. The moth is reluctant to come to light and can be better obtained by beating scrub and rank herbage during the day. A larva was found in vegetation at the base of an oak tree on 7.12.1988, and the moth reared (GAC), but otherwise the early stages have hardly been noted.

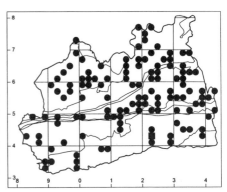

Larentia clavaria (Haworth, 1809)   Mallow

Resident; commons, waste ground; restricted and scarce.

Univoltine; September and October.

Foodplant – common mallow, hollyhock.

The Mallow is rather restricted in its distribution, favouring in particular the commons of south London. Many records are of singletons at mvl, but it is occasionally seen in larger numbers, such as: Bramley, 1986 (21) (RFB); Mitcham, 1984 (11) (RKAM). The adult can be found by searching amongst mallow with a Tilley lamp.

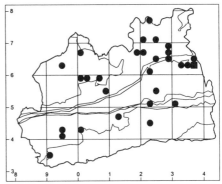

Anticlea badiata ([Denis & Schiffermüller], 1775)   Shoulder Stripe

Resident; commons, downland, woodland; widespread and fairly common.

Univoltine; late March and April.

Foodplant – rose.

The Shoulder Stripe is a fairly common, early spring species found over most of the county with the exception of urban London. This species and its congener, *derivata*, have very similar flight periods and a common foodplant – they are usually both found together.

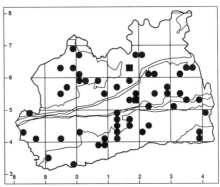

Anticlea derivata ([Denis & Schiffermüller], 1775)   **Streamer**

Resident; commons, downland, woodland; widespread and fairly common.

Univoltine; April to mid-May.

Foodplant – rose.

A species with very similar habits and distribution to its congener *badiata* (*q.v.*), although the Streamer possibly shows a slight preference for the chalk.

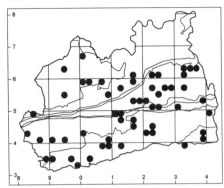

Mesoleuca albicillata (Linnaeus, 1758)   PLATE 4   **Beautiful Carpet**

Resident; woodland; local and generally scarce.

Univoltine; July.

Although distributed across the county with no apparent geological preferences, the Beautiful Carpet is a rarely encountered species. Even regularly run traps have produced no more than two individuals per year, and single records from the most heavily worked sites are more typical. Such scarcity is unlikely to represent the true situation and some aspect of its behaviour or habitat requirement must be being overlooked.

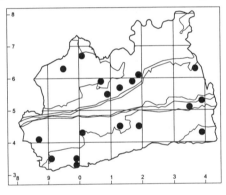

Pelurga comitata (Linnaeus, 1758)   **Dark Spinach**

Resident; commons, waste ground; local and rather scarce.

Univoltine; August.

Foodplant – goosefoot, fat hen, (orache).

The Dark Spinach is very much a species favouring ruderal habitats, and is consequently most often recorded in the London area. In more rural areas it is fairly regular at Windlesham, Thorpe and Milford; elsewhere it is only occasional.

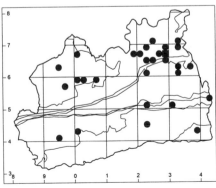

Lampropteryx suffumata ([Denis & Schiffermüller], 1775)   **Water Carpet**

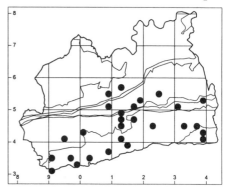

Resident; woodland, wooded commons; restricted and uncommon.

Univoltine; late April and May.

The Water Carpet is an uncommon species, possibly overlooked due to its rather secretive habits, often being found in the denser parts of damp woods, where it is as easily found by torch-light as at the moth trap. Its distribution is principally restricted to southern and central Surrey.

Cosmorhoe ocellata (Linnaeus, 1758)   **Purple Bar**

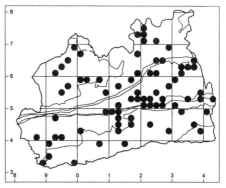

Resident; woodland, wooded commons, downland; widespread and fairly common.

Bivoltine; June, and August.

A generally distributed species that is rarely more than fairly common, it being unusual for annual counts at the static traps to exceed single figures.

Nebula salicata (Hübner, 1799)   **Striped Twin-spot Carpet**
ssp. *latentaria* (Curtis, 1830)

Vagrant; origin uncertain.

Nationally this species is typically a moth of northern and western moorlands, which makes its appearance in Surrey somewhat surprising. Two specimens have been taken, both in the same general area, as follows: Wormley Hill, 22.5.1962 (JLM); and Bramley, 31.5.1982 (RFB); possible sources of origin are discussed in Bretherton (1983).

Eulithis prunata (Linnaeus, 1758)

Phoenix

Resident; gardens, commons; widespread and fairly common.

Univoltine; July and August.

Although recorded from all over the county, the Phoenix is another species which is at its commonest in the gardens of suburban London. Rural traps rarely attract more than two or three a year whereas at South Croydon 16 were taken in 1983 (GAC).

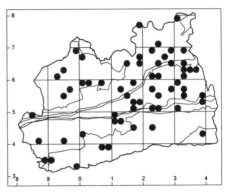

Eulithis testata (Linnaeus, 1761)

Chevron

Resident; heathland, grassland; restricted and scarce.

Univoltine; July and August.

In Surrey the Chevron is mainly a heathland moth and hence is commonest in the west. There are a few records from grassland in central Surrey but only one from the extreme east. Most records are of singletons, often disturbed during the day, and even the most regularly run traps record no more than three examples during a year.

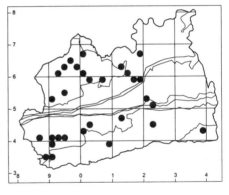

Eulithis mellinata (Fabricius, 1787)

Spinach

Resident; gardens, commons; fairly widespread and common.

Univoltine; late June and July.

Foodplant – (black currant).

The Spinach is found through most of the county but is commonest in the vicinity of domestic gardens and hence the greatest density of records is in the London area. Rural gardens are also capable of producing fair numbers as the following trap counts show: Bramley, 1985 (12), 86 (32) (RFB). It is evidently more attached to cultivated varieties of currant than to plants in the wild.

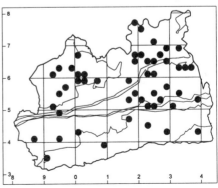

Eulithis pyraliata ([Denis & Schiffermüller], 1775)   **Barred Straw**

Resident; commons, gardens; widespread and common.

Univoltine; July.

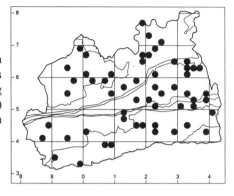

If the preceding species is commonest in suburban areas, then the Barred Straw is commonest in rural ones. The corresponding counts for Bramley are: 1985 (21), 86 (31) (RFB), whereas most of the London traps can only manage two or three specimens a year.

Ecliptopera silaceata ([Denis & Schiffermüller], 1775)   **Small Phoenix**

Resident; woodland, wooded commons; widespread and common.

Bivoltine; May and June, and late July and August.

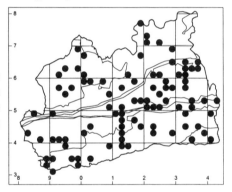

A rather common moth found throughout the county. Large numbers are a feature of urban waste ground as well as more rural areas, the trap at Mitcham producing the following counts: 1981 (57), 82 (14), 83 (53) (RKAM).

Chloroclysta siterata (Hufnagel, 1767)   **Red-green Carpet**

Resident; downland, woodland, heathland; currently widespread and fairly common.

Univoltine; October and November, and after hibernation from March to early May.

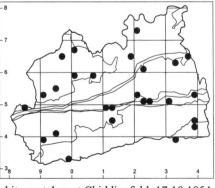

Until the autumn of 1990 this was a very rare moth with only three examples in the previous 20 years. The north-east Surrey list gives only one locality where it was evidently well established: Westhumble 1948-59 (18) (Cole in Evans, 1973), also Givons Grove, 28.9.1965 (JDH, *pers. com.*). At the same period it was taken at Chiddingfold, 17.10.1954, and Wormley, 23.10.1958 (JLM). Bretherton (1957) had no records for the north-west of the county. The impression was of a species established at low density on the downs around Dorking and in the woods of the south-west. However, since the end of 1990 the moth has increased greatly and has now been found in all four quarters of the county; hopefully this increase will continue.

RECORDS – 1976-89: **Reigate,** 5.5.76, 8.10.78 (RAC); **Ranmore,** 4.10.86 (Rfmcc). 1990-96: **Dawcombe,** 10.11.90 (2), 4.11.92 (4) (DC); **Banstead,** 12.11.90, 11.9-24.10.96 (3) (SWG); **Effingham Park,** 10.91 (1) (JC); **Lingfield,** 10.91 (1), 23.11.91 (1), 20.3.92, 21.9-5.11.92 (5), 10.11.94 (4), 14.10-23.11.95 (9), 1-31.10.96 (6) (JC); **Nutfield,** 2.10.91, 17.9.92, 7.10.96 (PAC); **Thursley Common,** 25.10.92 (2) (RFmcc); **Milford,** 30.9-25.10.92 (4), 93 (5), 94 (6), 95 (5), 96 (3) (DWB); **Rowhills,** 4.11.92, 14.10.95, 14.9-6.10.96 (JKH); **White Downs,** 5.11.92 (DC), 4.11.94 (3) (GAC); **Chobham Common,** 7.11.92 (GAC); **Friday Street,** 22.11.92 (DC); **Buckland,** 27.11.92, 4.11.93, 9.10-8.11.95 (4), 25.10.96 (CH); **Wisley RES,** 12-28.10.93, 94 (4), 95 (1), 96 (3) (AJH); **Enton,** 30.10.93 (DWB); **Thorpe,** 1993 (5), 94 (3) (PJB); **South Croydon,** 2.11.94, 21.10.96 (GAC); **Oxted,** 11.94, 10.95 (TD); **Woking,** 1994 on (SCP); **Pirbright,** 2.9.95, 13.10.95 (5) (GAC); **Richmond Park,** 7.10.95 (MP); **Wyke Common,** 14.10.95 (GAC); **Oaken Wood,** 11.11.95 (DC); **Chessington,** 23.10.96 (JP); **Threehalfpenny Wood,** 1996 (BS).

Chloroclysta miata (Linnaeus, 1758)   **Autumn Green Carpet**

Status uncertain; one recent record. November.

The status of this species in Surrey is not easy to determine. There is only one record for the survey period, listed below. It was also taken at Thorpe, 18.9.1972 (PJB), and Juniper Hall, 20.2.1973 (CGMdeW). There are only a few historical records: Worcester Park, 1893 (Kaye), and Redhill (Webb, Hope coll.) (de Worms, 1954-58); Dormansland, October 1912 and May 1919 (coll. H. Jeddere-Fisher); Butts Wood, reared from a larva 24.8.1947, and Egham, 15.9.1932 (Bretherton, 1957).

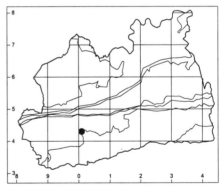

This species and *siterata* are prone to confusion, especially post-hibernation, but in view of the recorders the determinations would seem to be accurate. The wide spacing of the records suggests vagrancy, but whether from other areas of the south-east of England or by continental migration can only be conjecture. [Givons Grove, 28.9.1965 (JDH in Evans, 1973) refers to *siterata*].

RECORDS – **Bramley,** 8.11.83 (RFB).

Chloroclysta citrata (Linnaeus, 1761)   **Dark Marbled Carpet**

ssp. *citrata* (Linnaeus, 1761)

Resident; woodland; restricted and scarce.
Univoltine; late July and August.
Separation of this species and the following
one gives rise to some confusion. The Dark
Marbled Carpet is univoltine and appears
between the two broods of *truncata* although
there is a fair degree of overlap. The characters
for separation given in Skinner (1984) should
dispel any doubt. This species is undoubtedly
the scarcer of the two with most records
coming from woodland south of the chalk.

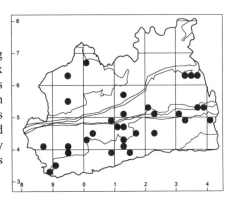

Chloroclysta truncata (Hufnagel, 1767)   **Common Marbled Carpet**

Resident; commons, woodland, downland;
    widespread and very common.
Bivoltine; late May to early July, and
    September and October.
Foodplant – bramble, bilberry.
The Common Marbled Carpet is a common
to abundant species everywhere, although
numbers are subject to a fair degree of annual
variation. The better attended traps give the
following counts: South Croydon, 1983 (204),
84 (107), 85 (178) (GAC); Bramley, 1985
(93), 86 (153) (RFB); Wisley RES, 1986 (73),

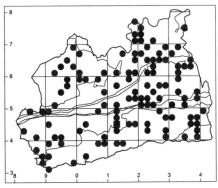

87 (38), 89 (3), 91 (10) (AJH). Melanic forms are common, as is the form with the centre of
the forewing occupied by a fulvous blotch.

Cidaria fulvata (Forster, 1771) — Barred Yellow

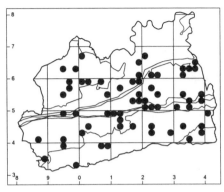

Resident; downland, commons, woodland; widespread and fairly common.

Univoltine; late June to mid-July.

Foodplant – rose.

The Barred Yellow occurs over much of the county but is absent from urban London and perhaps commonest on the chalk. It is usually only found in small numbers, the exception to this being at Banstead Downs where the following totals were noted: 1989 (30), 90 (11), 91 (17) (DC).

Plemyria rubiginata ([Denis & Schiffermüller], 1775) — Blue-bordered Carpet

ssp. *rubiginata* ([Denis & Schiffermüller], 1775)

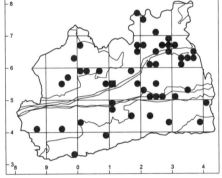

Resident; commons, woodland; fairly widespread but uncommon.

Univoltine; late June and July.

Foodplant – sloe.

Although found through most of the county, there is a distinct bias towards the commons of suburban London, records declining as one goes further westwards or southwards. The moth is absent from much of the heathland of west Surrey where its foodplant is also scarce. The only record of it occurring in reasonable numbers is: Mitcham, 1981 (7), 82 (2), 83 (6) (RKAM). The whitish ova, quite distinct from those of the Brown Hairstreak, can be found by searching sloe branches during the winter.

Thera firmata (Hübner, 1822) — Pine Carpet

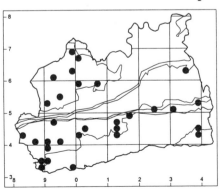

Resident; pine woods, heathland; restricted and scarce.

Univoltine; July to October.

The Pine Carpet is a curiously scarce and localized species in Surrey, although it is possible that it is spreading from the south-west. It occurs mainly amongst mature pine in the west of the county, but only in small numbers whereas the next species usually swarms. There is only one old record in Evans (1973) despite the presence of well established pine about Shirley. Bretherton was only able to find two examples in north-west Surrey: once only, Cobbett Hill, 24.10.1955 (Stroyan in Bretherton, 1957); Ottershaw trap, 15.10.1961; the second district [north-west Surrey] record (Bretherton, 1965). This species and *obeliscata* are often confused and in addition to the characters given in Skinner (1984) it should be noted that the antennae of male *firmata* are weakly but distinctly pectinate whereas those of *obeliscata* are simple.

Thera obeliscata (Hübner, 1787)   Grey Pine Carpet

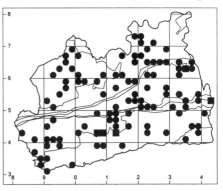

Resident; woodland, heathland, commons; widespread and common.

Bivoltine; May to July, and September and October.

Foodplant – Scots pine, lodgepole pine, Norway spruce, Douglas fir.

A very common species found throughout the county. Although perhaps commonest in pine plantations it also exists in numbers on pines scattered amongst gardens and deciduous woodland. The sort of frequency that it can reach is shown by the following trap counts: Wisley RES, 1986 (47), 87 (35) (AJH); South Croydon, 1983 (21), 84 (50), 85 (130) (GAC); Bramley, 1985 (142), 86 (215) (RFB). The range of forms shown in Skinner (1984) all occur in Surrey with melanic forms predominating in the London area.

Thera britannica (Turner, H. J., 1925)   Spruce Carpet

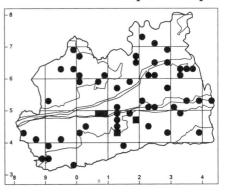

Resident; widespread and fairly common.

Bivoltine; May to early July, and mid-September to October.

Foodplant – Norway spruce, larch, western hemlock, Douglas fir.

The Spruce Carpet has been recorded throughout the county, but usually only in small numbers. Differentiation of this species from grey forms of *obeliscata* can be difficult and there has certainly been much confusion in the past. This may be responsible for the very small numbers of records in both the previous Surrey lists; otherwise the moth has increased considerably in recent years.

Thera juniperata (Linnaeus, 1758) Juniper Carpet
ssp. *juniperata* (Linnaeus, 1758)

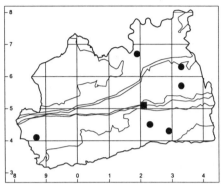

Resident; gardens, downland; very local and scarce.

Univoltine; second half of October.

Foodplant – juniper.

The status of this species has changed considerably since the publication of the north-east Surrey list (Evans, 1973). Then it was a resident on the chalk downs amongst native juniper, and where found often occurred in numbers. Since then the wild juniper has declined drastically; Riddlesdown was a noted locality where dozens of moths could be seen in a night in the early fifties, but the moth has not persisted there into the survey period and there are now only a couple of juniper bushes hidden under trees. Larvae were found at Betchworth as recently as 1983, but recent searching at Hackhurst and other localities on the downs has proved in vain. The small number of recent records have come from domestic gardens where the suggestion is that the moth may be breeding on cultivated juniper (*q.v.* Juniper Pug, and see Waring, 1992a). Ab. *infuscata* Schwingenschuss, probably an industrial melanic, has been recorded from the Riddlesdown population (Kettlewell, 1973).

RECORDS – **Betchworth**, 21.9.80 larva on juniper, 8.8.83 larvae (RFMcC); **Rushmoor**, 2.11.83 (PAD); **Leigh**, 30.10.84 (RF); **Surbiton**, 15.10.85 (JP); **Horley**, 16.10.86 (JBS); **South Croydon**, 18.10.87 (GAC); **Caterham**, 10.91 (RMP).

Thera cupressata (Geyer, [1831]) Cypress Carpet
Migrant; a single record.

The Cypress Carpet has occurred in a number of spots on the south coast in the last few years following an expansion of its range in Europe, and is now breeding at at least one site. A single example has been recorded in Surrey; and it remains to be seen whether the moth can establish itself inland in the manner of Blair's Shoulder-knot, or whether, like the Cypress Pug, it will remain coastal. An illustration of the adult can be found in Costen and Peet (1986).

1990 – **Nutfield**, 12.10 (PAC).

Electrophaes corylata (Thunberg, 1792)　　Broken-barred Carpet

Resident; woodland, commons;
　　widespread and common.
Univoltine; mid-May to June.
Foodplant – birch, (wayfaring-tree).
A rather common species found throughout
the county. Although it occurs as close to
London as Wimbledon and Mitcham,
numbers increase rapidly away from the
metropolis as the following trap counts show:
Mitcham, 1982 (1), 83 (1), 84 (1), 85 (1)
(RKAM); South Croydon, 1983 (12), 84 (10),
85 (8) (GAC); Bramley, 1985 (49), 86 (64)
(RFB).

[*Colostygia olivata* ([Denis & Schiffermüller], 1775)　　Beech-green Carpet
Doubtful.
A report of a SLENHS field meeting at Horsley on 30.6.1957 mentions this species as
being disturbed from herbage. There can be little doubt that *pectinataria* was the intended
species, and there remains no evidence that this moth has ever occurred in Surrey.]

Colostygia multistrigaria (Haworth, 1809)　　Mottled Grey

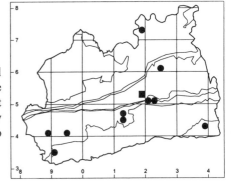

Resident; downland, woodland; local and
　　scarce.
Univoltine; March and April.
Foodplant – bedstraw.
The Mottled Grey would appear to be a local
and generally scarce species, although the
early flight period may have resulted in it
being overlooked. Further search, especially
on the North Downs, can be expected to
provide additional records.

RECORDS – **Hankley Common**, 17.4.76
(DWB); **Haslemere RES**, 1982 (1), 84 (1),
87 (2) (TGW); **Milford**, 4.86, 19-22.4.87 (DWB); **Friday Street**, 29.4.83 (RFMcC),
15.3.93 (5) (DC); **Wotton**, 5.4.76, 5-23.3.77 (JDH); **Headley Warren**, 31.3.95, 16.6.95
larvae, 21.4.96 (GAC); **Betchworth**, 1.4.76 (BS); **Buckland**, 3.90 (2) (ID); **Banstead
Downs**, 15-21.4.89 (3), 20.3.90, 14.3.91 (15), 17.3.93 (DC); **Richmond Park**, 30.3.95
(15) (MP).

Colostygia pectinataria (Knoch, 1781)   Green Carpet

Resident; downland, woodland, commons; widespread and common.

Bivoltine; mid-May to mid-July, and mid-August to mid-September.

The Green Carpet has been recorded over most of the county and often occurs in good numbers as the following trap counts show: Bramley, 1985 (75), 86 (29) (RFB); Dawcombe, 1991 (30) (DC); Banstead Downs, 1989 (31), 90 (15), 91 (4) (DC). There are two distinct broods of roughly equal numbers.

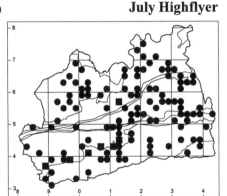

Hydriomena furcata (Thunberg, 1784)   July Highflyer

Resident; woodland, commons, widespread and common.

Univoltine; July and August.

Foodplant – bilberry, sallow, oak, (hazel).

A very common species throughout all of the county. As the following trap counts show it can be found in good numbers even in London: Mitcham, 1981 (46), 82 (63), 83 (72), (RKAM); South Croydon ,1983 (29), 84 (13), 85 (7) (GAC); Bramley, 1985 (67), 86 (260) (RFB). In the south-west of the county the larva feeds on bilberry and the resulting adults are rather smaller than the races that feed on deciduous trees.

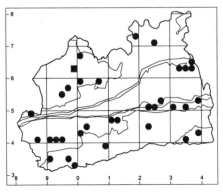

Hydriomena impluviata ([Denis & Schiffermüller], 1775)   May Highflyer

Resident; damp woodland; restricted but fairly common.

Univoltine; late May and June.

Foodplant – alder.

The May Highflyer is associated with alder which prefers damp, low-lying ground, and is therefore absent from the chalk. Where the foodplant does grow the moth is often found in good numbers, i.e.: Bramley, 1985 (15), 86 (28) (RFB); Pirbright RES, 1980 (12), 81 (11) (ED). Specimens from the London area are frequently melanic and are referable to f. *obsoletaria* Schille.

Hydriomena ruberata (Freyer, 1831)   **Ruddy Highflyer**

Extinct; not recorded for 80 years.
Barrett (1902) describes this species as widely distributed throughout the southern and eastern counties, and lists it, along with its two congeners, from Haslemere in the *VCH*. It was given as occurring at Wimbledon Common (Buckell and Prout, 1898-1901), and at Brookwood, in a street lamp, 5.6.1912 (Champion, *E.M.M.* **49**:35). It is easily confused with *impluviata* and Chalmers-Hunt (1968-81) considers it doubtfully Kentish while Goater (1974) gives some mainland Hampshire records but considers them all to require confirmation. There is little doubt that, whatever its previous status, it no longer occurs in Surrey.

Horisme vitalbata ([Denis & Schiffermüller], 1775)   **Small Waved Umber**

Resident; chalk grassland, commons; restricted, but fairly common.
Bivoltine; June, and August.
Foodplant – traveller's joy.

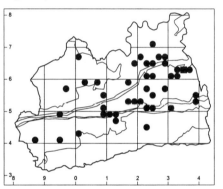

The distribution of the Small Waved Umber is restricted mainly to the chalk, but it is also found in smaller numbers elsewhere, particularly in areas of south London. These records off the chalk, however, only amount to an insignificant proportion of the total. Along the course of the North Downs it can be quite common, both as an adult at light and as a larva.

Horisme tersata ([Denis & Schiffermüller], 1775)   **Fern**

Resident; chalk grassland, commons; restricted, but fairly common.
Univoltine; late June to mid-August.
Foodplant – traveller's joy.

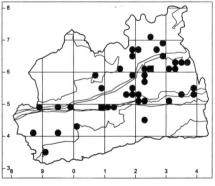

The Fern shares a common larval foodplant with its congener, and has a very similar distribution. Its frequency is also similar to *vitalbata*, although it is univoltine, peaking between the two broods of the other species. A single example taken at Milford, 19.9.1995 (DWB), may have been an example of a second brood, but is perhaps more likely to have been due to delayed emergence as the species is normally still a larva in September.

Melanthia procellata ([Denis & Schiffermüller], 1775)   **Pretty Chalk Carpet**

Resident; chalk grassland; restricted and uncommon.

Univoltine; late June to early August.

Foodplant – (traveller's joy).

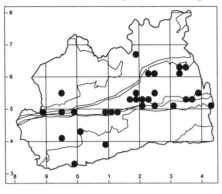

As with the two preceding species, the Pretty Chalk Carpet is more or less restricted to the chalk; it is certainly less common in the London area, and in the south-west may be associated with the Bargate beds which support calcicole plants in an otherwise acidic area. It is usually the scarcest of the three species, although 27 individuals were recorded at Banstead Downs in 1989 (DC).

Spargania luctuata ([Denis & Schiffermüller], 1775)   **White-banded Carpet**

Vagrant; two specimens only.

This species, only established in this country in the last 40 years and resident in Kent, Sussex and East Anglia, has only been recorded twice in Surrey: Wormley, 21.8.1970 (JLM); and Reigate, 28.6.1986 (RAC). These are undoubtedly vagrant specimens, possibly trying to establish new colonies. There is no reason why this species should not become resident in the county.

Rheumaptera hastata (Linnaeus, 1758)   **Argent and Sable**

ssp. *hastata* (Linnaeus, 1758)

Notable/Nb

Resident; woodland, wooded commons; very local and scarce.

Univoltine; late May to mid-June.

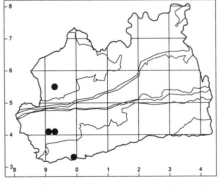

During the survey period the Argent and Sable has only been recorded from three areas, all in the south and west of the county, where it is certainly resident. It would appear always to have been rather local. The *VCH* gives near Croydon, and Haslemere; and it was taken at Oxshott, 26-29.5.1928 (JVD). The north-west list has: Sheerwater, 4.6.1940; Longcross, 1945; "should be commoner here" (Bretherton, 1957); and the supplement: Pirbright, 30.5.1959 (Bretherton, 1965). The north-east list gives: Ashtead Woods, 1947 fairly common (Wild in Evans, 1973). It was also seen at Leigh, 17.5.1941 (RF), at Oxshott again in 1950 (CGMdeW), and one at Canfold Wood in 1954 (Perrins, 1959). Thus there is some evidence of a decline since the 1940s, a situation reflected nationally.

RECORDS – **Ash Ranges**, 31.5.93 (J. Pontin); **Thursley Common**, 29.5.82 (DWB); **Witley Common**, 4.6.83, 4.6.85, 30.5.87 (DWB); **Borough Farm**, 29.5.82 (DWB); **Fisherlane Wood**, 26.6.76 (RFB); **Tugley Wood**, 2.6.85, 6.86 (15), 4-16.6.87, 14.6.96 (SCP), 21.6.87 (SWG), 10.6.89 (GAC).

Rheumaptera cervinalis (Scopoli, 1763)   Scarce Tissue

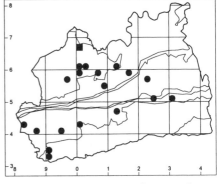

Resident; gardens; local and scarce.
Univoltine; late April to early June.
Foodplant – Oregon grape, (barberry).
The Scarce Tissue is a local species found recently in a band from the south-west to the north of the county, apparently avoiding the weald and the chalk although this may be an artefact of the relatively low number of records received. It is evidently attached to domestic gardens where the larva has been found on Oregon grape (PJB), and it probably also utilizes cultivated *Berberis* spp.. The former plant occurs quite widely as an established alien in the extreme south-west, whence the moth is also recorded, and on the chalk where the moth has only been recorded once. Wild *Berberis* is virtually absent in Surrey (Lousley, 1976). A second-brood example was noted at Woking, 26.9.94 (SCP).

Rheumaptera undulata (Linnaeus, 1758)   Scallop Shell

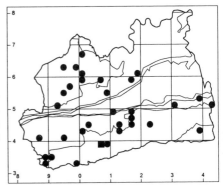

Resident; woodland, wooded commons; fairly widespread but uncommon.
Univoltine; mid-June to mid-August.
Foodplant – sallow, bilberry.
An uncommon species which is absent from the chalk and from the London area; elsewhere it is fairly widespread but seldom seen in numbers. It has possibly increased its range slightly in recent years.

Triphosa dubitata (Linnaeus, 1758)   Tissue

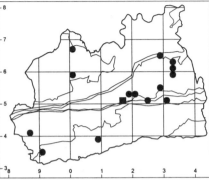

Resident; chalk downland, woodland; local and scarce.

Univoltine; September and October, and after hibernation in April and early May.

Foodplant – buckthorn.

If light trap records were anything to go by, this species would be considered rare, but in view of the numbers that can be found hibernating it is evident that light holds little attraction for the Tissue. During the winter of 1985/86 hibernating Tissues were studied at Box Hill where as many as 42 individuals were found together at one time (Morris and Collins, 1991). Mating was observed in October and November but there was no noticeable decline in the proportion of males towards spring. Larvae have been found on buckthorn in the vicinity of the hibernation site, but it is possible that the moths originate from further afield. More recently, similar numbers have been found hibernating at Kenley Common (ME).

RECORDS – **Rushmoor**, 5.5.83 (PAD); **Haslemere RES**, 1976 (1), 87 (1) (TGW); **Thorpe**, 1992, 93 (PJB); **Woking**, 23.5.86 (SCP); **Ewhurst**, 20.10.78 (SFI); **Box Hill**, 6.82 larva on buckthorn (JP), hibernating: 7.11.81, 30.10.82, 4.2.85, 23.3.85 (GAC); **Headley Warren**, 5.5.95 (GAC); **Dawcombe**, 31.7.92 (DC); **Reigate**, 8.10.78 (RAC); **Nutfield**, 12-14.10.79 (3) (PAC); **Alderstead Heath**, 11.8.76 (JC); **Purley**, 14.9.84, 8.10.86 (PJS); **Kenley Common**, 1.10.94 (19), 2.9.96 (47) (ME); **South Croydon**, 27.8.88 (GAC); **Carshalton**, 7.8.94 (DC).

Philereme vetulata ([Denis & Schiffermüller], 1775)   Brown Scallop

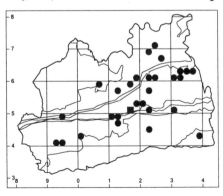

Resident; chalk grassland, woodland; restricted and scarce.

Univoltine; July.

Foodplant – buckthorn.

This species, and the next, are more or less restricted to the vicinity of the chalk, but, from light trap records at least, the Brown Scallop is much the less common species. At Banstead Downs *vetulata* was only noted on one occasion while *transversata* was seen as follows: 1989 (82), 90 (68), 91 (12) (DC). The larvae live in a purse of spun leaves and can be found by searching in May.

Philereme transversata (Hufnagel, 1767)   **Dark Umber**
ssp. *britannica* Lempke, 1968

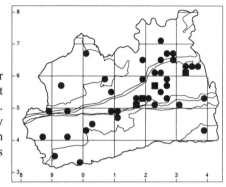

Resident; chalk grassland, woodland; restricted and uncommon.

Univoltine; July.

Foodplant – buckthorn.

The Dark Umber has a rather similar distribution to the Brown Scallop (*q.v.*), but is perhaps observed more widely off the chalk. Whether these examples are merely wanderers, or are evidence that the moth can use alder buckthorn as a foodplant, is unknown.

Euphyia biangulata (Haworth, 1809)   **Cloaked Carpet**
Notable/Nb

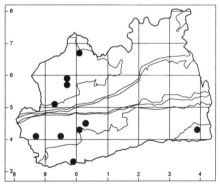

Resident; woodland; very local and uncommon.

Univoltine; July.

The Cloaked Carpet is a very local species, which is perhaps increasing. The main population is associated with the woodlands of south-west Surrey and a couple of the permanent traps have shown quite good catches, especially in recent years. In addition, five specimens have been recorded in the north-west, from where it was recorded on several occasions in Bretherton (1957) although he regarded it as rare, and, in 1996, it was first noted from the south-east of the county.

RECORDS – **Rushmoor**, 19.7.82, 8.7.84, 12.7.85 (PAD); **Milford**, 3.8.80, 16.7.82, 20.8.83, 85 (5), 86 (4), 87 (7), 30.7.89, 90, 91, 92 (9), 93 (5), 94 (12), 95 (10), 96 (7) (DWB); **Tugley Wood**, 14.7.90 (EE), 19.7.91 (SCP), 14-26.7.94 (DY); **Oaken Wood**, 30.6.95, 20.7.96 (GAC); **Bramley**, 1985 (6), 86 (5) (RFB); **Blackheath**, 20.8.87 (BS); **Normandy**, 27.7.96 (2) (GAC); **Knaphill**, 15.7.92 (AJH); **Woking**, 27.7.96 (J. Pontin); **Thorpe**, 1.8.85 (PJB); **Lingfield**, 5.9.96 (JC).

Euphyia unangulata (Haworth, 1809)   Sharp-angled Carpet

Resident; commons, woodland; restricted, but fairly common.

Partially **bivoltine**; June and July, and mid-August.

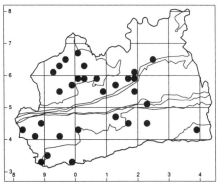

The Sharp-angled Carpet is certainly not to be found everywhere in the county, being virtually absent from the heathland of west Surrey, the chalk, and the London area. Elsewhere, in south Surrey and parts of the north-west, it is quite a regularly seen species and sometimes common as the following trap counts show: Bramley, 1985 (18), 86 (67) (RFB); Wisley RES, 1986 (9), 87 (8), 90 (3), 91 (2) (AJH). The moth is generally considered to be single-brooded, but there is a distinct peak in records for the middle of August, and these probably represent a partial second brood.

Genus *Epirrita* – November Moths

The genus *Epirrita* comprises, in Surrey, three species, all of which are very similar and show a similar range of variation. Certain identification can only be achieved by structural examination of the genitalia and, as a consequence of most entomologists' reluctance to carry out what is really a very simple procedure, the full range of the three species is not as well known as it should be. Nevertheless, certain patterns do emerge and these are discussed under the individual species.

Epirrita dilutata ([Denis & Schiffermüller], 1775)   November Moth

Resident; woodland, commons, heathland, downland, widespread and common.

Univoltine; October and November.

Foodplant – oak, ash, birch, wych elm, field maple, sycamore, sloe, (hawthorn, lime, bilberry).

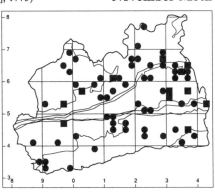

The November Moth is certainly the most widespread and commonest of the genus, and is found almost everywhere, often in abundance. The larva is clearly polyphagous on deciduous trees and is a common sight in the beating tray in spring.

Epirrita christyi (Allen, 1906)   Pale November Moth

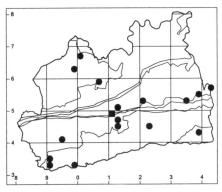

Resident; woodland; local.
Univoltine; October to mid-November.
Foodplant – beech.
The Pale November Moth appears, from the limited number of records available, to be restricted to woodland. It is certainly of regular occurrence in the woods along the crest of the North Downs and will probably be found to be more widespread when specifically looked for.

Epirrita autumnata (Borkhausen, 1794)   Autumnal Moth

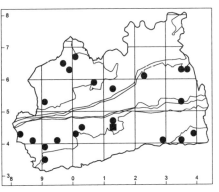

Resident; heathland, commons; restricted.
Univoltine; October to mid-November.
Foodplant – birch.
The Autumnal Moth is the typical *Epirrita* of the heathland in the west of Surrey, but is also found on commons where there is birch invasion. It would appear to be absent from both the weald and the chalk, although further work is needed to establish fully the distribution of this species.

Operophtera brumata (Linnaeus, 1758)   Winter Moth

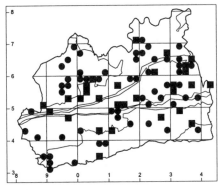

Resident; woodland, commons;
     widespread and common.
Univoltine; November and December.
Foodplant – oak, sallow, sloe, hawthorn,
     field maple, lime, bramble,
     hazel, sycamore, wych elm,
     bilberry, (apple, poplar, sweet
     chestnut, aspen, ash,
     honeysuckle, alder, rose).
A very common moth which is, at least in the larval stage, abundant everywhere. The comparatively smaller number of records of the adult can be explained by the late flight period.

Operophtera fagata (Scharfenberg, 1805)   **Northern Winter Moth**

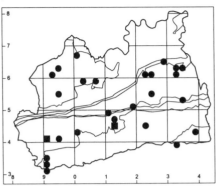

Resident; woodland, wooded commons; fairly widespread but uncommon.

Univoltine; November.

Foodplant – birch, beech.

The Northern Winter moth is certainly much less widespread than its congener, and usually only recorded in small numbers. It is probably overlooked to some extent on account of its flight period which is not only late in the year but rather shorter than that of *brumata*.

Perizoma affinitata (Stephens, 1831)   **Rivulet**

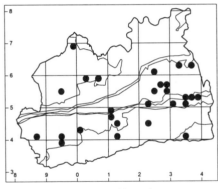

Resident; downland, commons; fairly widespread, but scarce.

Univoltine; May and June.

Foodplant – red campion.

The Rivulet has been reported widely across the county with the exception of the London area. It is, however, rarely recorded in any numbers; even most regularly run traps have only noted singletons, a few exceptions being: Bramley, 1985 (4), 86 (6) (RFB); Pirbright RES, 1980 (9), 81 (17) (ED). The main emergence is in late May and early June, and the few individuals recorded in August may represent a partial second brood.

Perizoma alchemillata (Linnaeus, 1758)   **Small Rivulet**

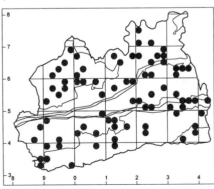

Resident; woodland, commons, downland; widespread and common.

Univoltine; early July to mid-August.

Foodplant – common hemp-nettle.

This species, which rather resembles the preceding one, is more widespread and very much more common. Trap counts show: Bramley, 1985 (3), 86 (70) (RFB); Wisley RES, 1986 (53), 87 (92), 90 (12), 91 (8) (AJH); Ashtead, 1987 (15), 88 (4) (GG).

Perizoma bifaciata (Haworth, 1809) **Barred Rivulet**

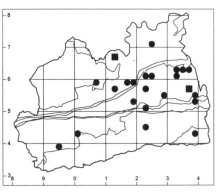

Resident; commons, waste ground; local and uncommon.

Univoltine; August.

Foodplant – red bartsia.

A rather uncommon species which is found mainly on the outskirts of London and on the chalk. It is probably overlooked to some extent, especially in the south-east where the foodplant is widespread, but may be genuinely only casual in the west. The distinctive larva can be swept from the foodplant in September.

Perizoma albulata ([Denis & Schiffermüller], 1775) **Grass Rivulet**

ssp. *albulata* ([Denis & Schiffermüller], 1775)

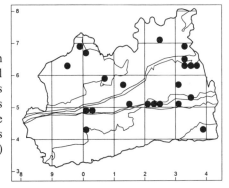

Resident; chalk downs, grassland; restricted and usually scarce.

Univoltine; late May and June.

The Grass Rivulet is certainly most common on the chalk but has been recorded in small numbers off it. These may be wanderers as the normal foodplant, yellow rattle, favours undisturbed downland. On such grassland the moth may be disturbed in numbers by day, as has been observed at Farthing Downs (GAC) and Merrow Downs (DWB).

Perizoma flavofasciata (Thunberg, 1792) **Sandy Carpet**

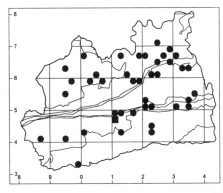

Resident; woodland, downland, commons; fairly widespread and fairly common.

Univoltine; June and July.

Foodplant – red campion.

The Sandy Carpet occurs throughout much of the county and, as the results of static trapping show, can be quite common: Bramley, 1985 (8), 86 (6) (RFB); Wisley RES, 1986 (5), 87 (11), 90 (7), 91 (5) (AJH); Mitcham, 1981 (7), 82 (7), 83 (4) (RKAM).

Perizoma didymata (Linnaeus, 1758)   **Twin-spot Carpet**
ssp. *didymata* (Linnaeus, 1758)

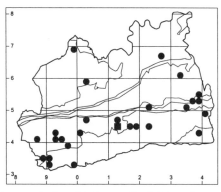

Resident; woodland, commons; restricted and uncommon.

Univoltine; June to early August.

Foodplant – bilberry.

The Twin-spot Carpet is a fairly regular species in the south-west of the county but rather more sporadic elsewhere. It is seldom reported in numbers, especially where there is a reliance on recording by light trap, to which it is only weakly attracted. Dusking along lanes and in woodland rides is more likely to reveal the moth. In Surrey the normal form is particularly large and brown, contrasting markedly with the smaller brighter forms from the north and west of the country.

Genus *Eupithecia* – Pugs

A genus of some 45 species which, together with *Chloroclystis* and *Gymnoscelis*, are collectively known as the Pugs. Some species are amongst the most difficult of the macrolepidoptera to identify and consequently are overlooked by some entomologists; thus there are some species that are certainly under-recorded in Surrey. Often the easiest method of finding a particular species is to rear it through the larva, and many records have been thus obtained. Records where the identity of the species is in doubt have been excluded. Wherever possible, genitalic examination of difficult specimens has been carried out. There is a need for further work on this group.

Eupithecia tenuiata (Hübner, 1813)   **Slender Pug**

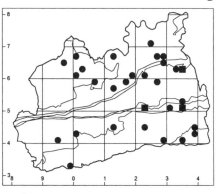

Resident; commons, woodland; fairly widespread and common.

Univoltine; July.

Foodplant – sallow catkins.

The Slender Pug is often common, at least as a larva, and is probably to be found everywhere that sallows grow. The adult, where not overlooked, is also fairly common, for example: Bramley, 1985 (3), 86 (8) (RFB). Although the larvae can be reared from collected catkins, it is just as easy to beat the sallows before the catkins are ready to fall when the larvae will appear on the tray in the usual manner.

Eupithecia inturbata (Hübner, 1817) — Maple Pug

Resident; woodland, hedgerows; fairly widespread and not uncommon.

Univoltine; August.

Foodplant – field maple.

The Maple Pug, like the previous species, is often common as a larva, but the adult, which is fairly distinctive amongst the smaller Pugs, must be somewhat overlooked. The moth is apparently absent from much of the London area and possibly also from parts of the north-west.

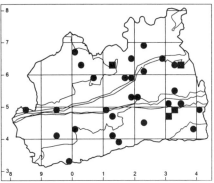

Eupithecia haworthiata Doubleday, 1856 — Haworth's Pug

Resident; chalk grassland, commons; restricted but common.

Univoltine; late June to early August.

Foodplant – traveller's joy.

Like the other species feeding on traveller's joy (*H. chrysoprasaria, H. vitalbata, H. tersata,* and *M. procellata*; *q.v.*) Haworth's Pug is found mainly on or near the chalk where it is often common. The larvae can be found by searching or, more easily, by beating the foodplant over a tray.

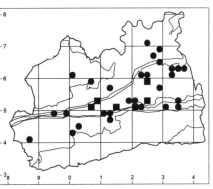

Eupithecia plumbeolata (Haworth, 1809) — Lead-coloured Pug

Notable/Nb

Resident; woodland; very local and rare.

Univoltine; June.

There are only a handful of Surrey records of the Lead-coloured Pug, and only three confirmed individuals from one small area in the last decade. Bretherton (1957) listed two examples but considered the foodplant, cow-wheat, to be very scarce in north-west Surrey. He later (Bretherton, 1965) reports on a colony: "Brookwood, several at light among *Melampyrum* by the canal, 23.vi.[19]57", and

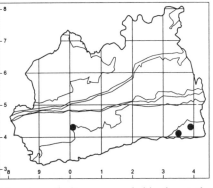

in the same year he took it at Durfold Wood. More recently it was recorded in the south-west from Wormley, 21.7.1972 (JLM). The moth favours open woodland with a good growth

of cow-wheat and might be expected to occur in some of the woods in the south-west of the county.
RECORDS – **Bramley**, 1976 (2) (RFB); **Hedgecourt**, 30.6.87 (GAC); **Lingfield**, 6-30.6.95 (2) (JC).

Eupithecia abietaria (Goeze, 1781)   Cloaked Pug

Status uncertain; probably vagrant.
Only four examples of this elusive species have ever been recorded in Surrey: one near Buckland Hill (Webb, *VCH*); Dorking, July 1951 (R.F. Haynes); Weybridge trap, 8.7.1952 (Bretherton, 1957); Streatham, 15.6.1957, a female on a fence (PAC in Evans, 1973). The origins of these specimens are uncertain, although it was considered to be resident in the New Forest in the nineteenth century; Bretherton's suggestion (*loc. cit.*), that it possibly breeds in the cones of ornamental spruces in gardens, is unlikely in view of the small number of records. It would seem more likely that the records are a result of larvae being brought home in cones by day-trippers. As in other counties, further investigations of mature spruce plantations may reveal the moth to be resident.

Eupithecia linariata ([Denis & Schiffermüller], 1775)   Toadflax Pug

Resident; commons, restricted and uncommon.

Univoltine; July and August.

Foodplant – common toadflax.

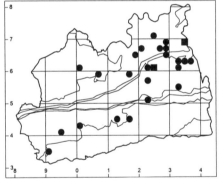

As reference to the distribution map shows, the Toadflax Pug is not recorded from the south-east or the north-west of the county. There are a few scattered records from the south-west, but the moth is found most regularly on the commons of south London. Here it is occasionally fairly common; 11 examples were recorded from a garden at Banstead in 1990 (SWG), and larvae can be fairly easily obtained by collecting seed-heads of toadflax in the autumn.

Eupithecia pulchellata Stephens, 1831

Foxglove Pug

ssp. *pulchellata* Stephens, 1831

Resident; woodland; widespread and common.

Univoltine; June to mid-July.

Foodplant – foxglove.

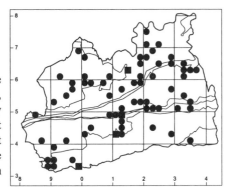

The Foxglove Pug is considerably more widespread, and found in greater numbers, than the Toadflax Pug which it rather closely resembles, this species having an earlier flight period. The adult appears regularly at most static traps, and the larvae can usually be found in the flowers of foxgloves growing in woodland.

Eupithecia irriguata (Hübner, 1813)   PLATE 1

Marbled Pug

Extinct; not seen since 1972.

There are no records of this oak woodland frequenting species from the survey period, and it must now be feared extinct. The most recent record is of one at Bramley, 4.6.1972 (RFB). During the 1960s it was not uncommon in the woods of the extreme south-west of the county, being taken as follows: Chiddingfold, 14-20.5.1960, 8.4.1961 (2), 24.4.1965 (2) (RFB), 21.4.1961 (14), 4.5.1962 (16) (RF); Dunsfold, 25.4.1964 (Cole, BENHS coll.); Wormley, 23.4.1965 (JLM). Entomologists working the same area in spring for the White-marked have failed to relocate the species.

Eupithecia exiguata (Hübner, 1813)

Mottled Pug

ssp. *exiguata* (Hübner, 1813)

Resident; woodland, commons; widespread and common.

Univoltine; late May and June.

Foodplant – hawthorn, ash.

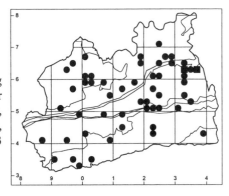

A rather widespread and common late spring pug. Trap counts show good numbers occur in the vicinity of well wooded areas: Bramley, 1985 (61), 86 (12) (RFB); Ashtead, 1987 (2), 88 (10), 89 (10) (GG); South Croydon, 1983 (75), 84 (60), 85 (41) (GAC).

Eupithecia insigniata (Hübner, 1790)   Pinion-spotted Pug

Status uncertain; probably vagrant.

The only recorded occurrence of this species in Surrey is of one at Burford Bridge, Box Hill, 25.5.1881 (Jones, *E.M.M.* **18**:39). This is presumably the specimen referred to in both Barrett (1904) and the *VCH*.

Eupithecia valerianata (Hübner, 1813)   Valerian Pug

Notable/Nb

Resident; very local and uncommon.

The Valerian Pug is apparently very local, only being recorded from two sites. It is almost certainly overlooked and should be searched for amongst valerian in damp woods and along canal and river banks in the west of the county.

RECORDS – **Thorpe**, regular until 1988 when locality destroyed (PJB); **Bramley**, scarce, 1975-84 (11) (RFB).

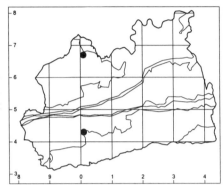

Eupithecia venosata (Fabricius, 1787)   Netted Pug

ssp. *venosata* (Fabricius, 1787)

Resident; chalk grassland, commons; restricted and uncommon.

Univoltine; June.

Foodplant – bladder campion, {sea campion}, (white campion).

The Netted Pug is restricted to the chalk downs and to commons, principally those in the south London area, and seems to be completely absent from the weald. Even here it is only recorded with any regularity at sites in the Addington area, including in a garden on introduced sea campion, and appears to be scarce on the North Downs.

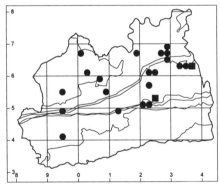

Eupithecia egenaria Herrich-Schäffer, 1848   Pauper Pug

RDB3

Status uncertain; new to Surrey.

June.

The Pauper Pug is known in Britain from the Wye Valley of Gloucestershire and Monmouthshire, from south-west Norfolk and from Lincolnshire, and it was with some surprise that a specimen of the moth was discovered amongst a selection of Pugs retained for identification from a Surrey site, taken on 2.6.1994. A further two examples were taken there on 7.6.1996 suggesting the presence of a breeding colony. At its other known sites the moth is associated with native limes (*Tilia cordata* and *T. platyphyllos*), and both species are believed to occur at the Surrey site although identification is not always straightforward; several saplings of *cordata* were also planted there a number of years earlier. At this stage it is not possible to say whether the moth is a previously undiscovered resident or a temporary resident accidentally introduced. The name of the locality is withheld at present, pending further investigation.

Eupithecia centaureata ([Denis & Schiffermüller], 1775)   Lime-speck Pug

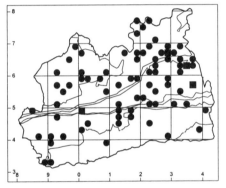

Resident; commons, downland; widespread and common.

May to September, peaks early June and August.

Foodplant – ragwort, mugwort, yarrow, burnet-saxifrage, (golden-rod, knapweed).

The Lime-speck Pug is one of the most distinctive of the genus and is also one of the most frequently recorded. It is widely distributed and probably reaches its greatest numbers in the south London area, for example: Mitcham, 1981 (34), 82 (26), 83 (10) (RKAM). The species is possibly bivoltine, although it can be found throughout most of the summer. The larva is polyphagous and occurs on a number of plant species which are also host to monophagous species, and some care should be exercised when recording these species.

Eupithecia trisignaria Herrich-Schäffer, 1848   Triple-spotted Pug

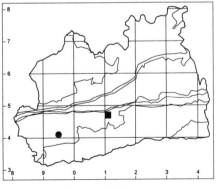

Resident; damp woodland; very local and rare.

Foodplant – wild angelica.

The Triple-spotted Pug would appear to be a rare species as there are records from only two sites. It is however a rather nondescript species and may well lie undetected amongst other Pugs. If more effort were made to examine the genitalia of doubtful specimens then this species might well be found to be more common.

RECORDS – **Milford**, 22-26.7.86 (DWB) [det. RFB]; **Abinger**, 15.9.78 a larva on wild angelica, moth reared (BS).

Eupithecia intricata (Zetterstedt, 1839)   PLATE 15   Freyer's Pug
ssp. *arceuthata* (Freyer, 1842)

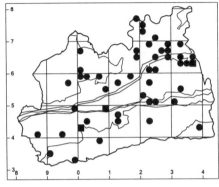

Resident; gardens; fairly widespread and common.

Univoltine; June and early July.

Foodplant – Leyland cypress, Lawson's cypress, juniper.

Freyer's Pug is a species associated with garden conifers and consequently is recorded most often in the gardens of south London and other built-up areas. In the vicinity of the foodplant it can be a common species: South Croydon, 1983 (11), 84 (5), 85 (15) (GAC); Selsdon, 1980 (16) (EHW); Wisley RES, 1986 (22), 87 (18), 89 (5), 90 (2), 91 (4) (AJH). In addition to cultivated conifers the larva has also been found on wild juniper, but only rarely.

Eupithecia satyrata (Hübner, 1813)   Satyr Pug
ssp. *satyrata* (Hübner, 1813)

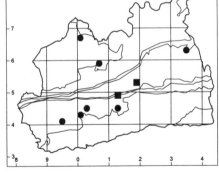

Resident; downland, heathland; very local and uncommon.

Univoltine; June.

Foodplant – scabious, hawkweed.

The Satyr Pug is an apparently local species; the concentration of records from the last decade in one relatively small area suggests that this localization may be genuine, although critical examination of specimens may reveal it to be more widespread.

RECORDS – **Thorpe**, 1976 (1), not since (PJB); **Wisley RES**, 20.6.86 (1), 88 (3) (AJH) [det. A. Riley]; **Milford**, 7.6.82, 2.6.85 (DWB) [det. RFB]; **Bramley**, 1985 (18) (RFB); **Blackheath**, 30.6.86 (BS); **Friday Street**, 15.4.77 (BS); **White Downs**, 5-17.6.85 (BS); **Westcott Downs**, 5.8.80 larvae on scabious and hawkweed (PAC), 8.6.85 (GAC/JP); **Headley Warren**, 16.6.95, 3.8.95 larva (GAC); **Selsdon**, 8.6.79 (EHW).

Eupithecia absinthiata (Clerck, 1759)   **Wormwood Pug**

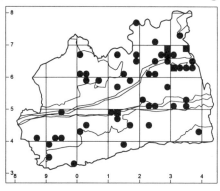

Resident; commons, waste ground; fairly widespread and common.

Univoltine; mid-July to August.

Foodplant – mugwort, ragwort, goosefoot, (golden-rod, knapweed).

This species and the Ling Pug are considered by some authors to be forms of the same species (e.g. Riley, 1986). The habitats and appearance of both the larvae and adults of *goossensiata* are, however, sufficiently different from this species that its records can be treated separately. The Wormwood Pug is a fairly widespread species found throughout most of the county, and, like several other Pugs, is at its commonest in the south London area.

Eupithecia goossensiata Mabille, 1869   **Ling Pug**

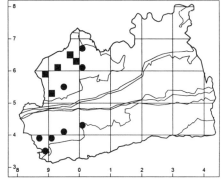

Resident; heathland; local but fairly common.

Univoltine; July and early August.

Foodplant – heather.

The Ling Pug is considered by some to be merely a form of *absinthiata* (*q.v.*); it is not the place of this work to argue for or against this suggestion, but as the two taxa are distinguishable they are here treated separately. It is certainly a local species in Surrey but is probably to be found on all the major heaths.

RECORDS – **Devil's Jumps**, 5.8.89 (GAC); **Hindhead**, 3-5.8.85 (DWB); **Thursley Common**, 14.8.93 (RFMcC); **Milford**, 1.7.87, 18.7.92, 93, 94 (2), 95 (2), 96 (2) (DWB); **Bramley**, 1981 (1), 83 (2) (RFB); **Wyke Common**, 14.10.95 larvae (GAC); **Pirbright**, 16.7.94 (GAC); **Frimley**, 2.10.88 larvae (GAC); **Lucas Green**, 2.10.88 larvae (GAC); **Chobham Common**, 20.9.78 larvae, 7.10.78 larvae (JP), 17.10.85 larvae, 25.7.89, 24.9.93 larvae (GAC); **Horsell**, 1.7.76 (CGMdeW); **Thorpe**, 1992, 93, 94 (PJB).

Eupithecia assimilata Doubleday, 1856   Currant Pug

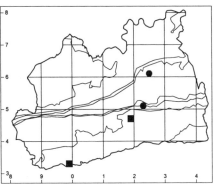

Resident; gardens, woodland; local and uncommon.

Bivoltine; May and June, and August.

Foodplant – hop.

The Currant Pug is a rather local species, possibly overlooked due to its similarity to other species of Pug. However, even in areas such as suburban gardens where it might be expected to occur in reasonable numbers, it seems to be uncommon, and this may reflect a decline in the popularity of currant growing – at South Croydon, based on genitalic examination, I have only recognized two individuals in 15 years' trapping.

Eupithecia expallidata Doubleday, 1856   Bleached Pug

Notable/Nb

Resident; woodland; very local and rare.

Univoltine; July.

Foodplant – golden-rod.

There are very few reliable records of the Bleached Pug, which seems to be confined to central and south-western Surrey. The record from Banstead is not confirmed as the voucher specimen has been destroyed by pests, but as the moth has been recorded from Dartford, Bexley and Orpington in north-west Kent (Plant, 1993), it probably represents a wanderer from that area.

RECORDS – **Fisherlane Wood**, 1977 larvae on golden-rod (RFB); **Bushbury**, 25.10.77 larvae on golden-rod (BS); **Buckland**, 15.7.87 (CH); [**Banstead**, 28.6.79 (RFMcC)].

Eupithecia vulgata (Haworth, 1809) **Common Pug**
ssp. *vulgata* (Haworth, 1809)

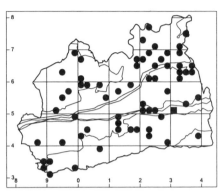

Resident; commons, woodland, downland; widespread and common.

May and June

Foodplant – hawthorn (flowers).

One of the commonest of the Pugs, and found throughout the county. Most of the static traps record it in good numbers: Bramley, 1985 (13), 86 (21) (RFB); Wisley RES, 1986 (64), 87 (34), 89 (67), 90 (20), 91 (10) (AJH); Ashtead, 1987 (22), 88 (13), 89 (19) (GG); Banstead, 1988 (15), 89 (7), 90 (32) (SWG). The Common Pug is stated to be bivoltine (i.e. Barrett, 1904; Skinner, 1984; Emmet, 1991); however I have no records of a second brood, even amongst those critically examined from the Rothamsted traps.

Eupithecia tripunctaria Herrich-Schäffer, 1852 **White-spotted Pug**

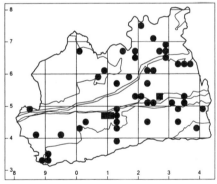

Resident; woodland, commons; fairly widespread and common.

Bivoltine; May, and mid-July to August.

Foodplant – wild angelica, hogweed, (wild parsnip).

The White-spotted Pug is a fairly generally distributed species, which does however appear to be absent from areas of the northwest. Bretherton (1957) described it as scarce in that area. Elsewhere it is a fairly frequently encountered species; as many as 21 individuals were recorded at Bramley in 1986 (RFB).

Eupithecia denotata (Hübner, 1813)

Campanula Pug

ssp. *denotata* (Hübner, 1813)

Notable/Na

Resident; chalk grassland; very local and scarce.

Foodplant – nettle-leaved bellflower.

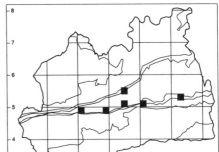

There are very few records of the Campanula Pug, but those which we have suggest that it may well be more common than indicated, at least as a larva. All the records come from the chalk, which is favoured by the only recorded foodplant. I have been unable to find the larva on clustered bellflower (also a chalk species), but search on cultivated *Campanula* may be worthwhile. There are no dated records of adults and so the voltinism cannot be commented upon, although a univoltine pattern is suggested by the larval records.

RECORDS – **Pewley Down**, 1980 (RFB), 7.9.93 larvae (DWB); **Hackhurst Downs**, 18.8.76 larvae (G. Prior per RFB); **Dorking**, 1983 larvae in nettle-leaved bellflower (PC); **Betchworth**, 1978 larvae (PAC); **Hawks Hill**, 1.9.86 larvae (CH), 23.9.86 larvae (RFMcC); **White Hill**, August 1979, larvae (PAC).

Eupithecia subfuscata (Haworth, 1809)

Grey Pug

Resident; woodland, commons, widespread and fairly common.

Univoltine; June.

Foodplant – ragwort, mugwort, (goldenrod, knapweed).

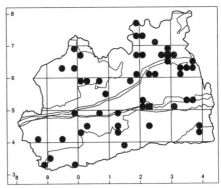

The Grey Pug is a fairly common late spring Pug which is found in most habitats throughout Surrey.

Eupithecia icterata (Villers, 1789)   **Tawny Speckled Pug**
ssp. *subfulvata* (Haworth, 1809)

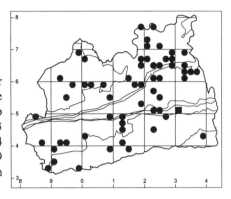

Resident; commons, waste ground;
   widespread and fairly common.
Univoltine; late July and August.
Foodplant – yarrow.
The Tawny Speckled Pug is a rather
widespread species that is commonest in the
south London area as the following trap
counts show: Mitcham, 1981 (36), 82 (8), 83
(10) (RKAM); South Croydon, 1983 (14), 84
(11), 85 (3) (GAC); Banstead, 1988 (18), 89
(6), 90 (17) (SWG). The adult has been taken
at buddleia flowers.

Eupithecia succenturiata (Linnaeus, 1758)   **Bordered Pug**

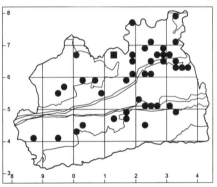

Resident; commons, waste ground; fairly
   widespread and fairly common.
Univoltine; June to August.
Foodplant – mugwort.
The comments about the last species apply
equally well to the Bordered Pug. Common
in London, it becomes progressively scarcer
further south. Waste ground, with a good
growth of mugwort from which larvae may
be had in late summer, is the typical habitat.

Eupithecia subumbrata ([Denis & Schiffermüller], 1775)   **Shaded Pug**

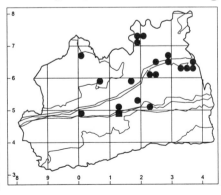

Resident; chalk grassland, commons;
   restricted and uncommon.
Univoltine; June to mid-July.
Foodplant – small scabious.
The Shaded Pug would appear to be restricted
to the chalk downs and to commons,
especially those in the London area. At some
sites on the downs it can be one of the
commoner species at light in June, but
generally it can be regarded as little more than
uncommon. There are no records from south
of the chalk or in the extreme west of the
county.

Eupithecia millefoliata Rössler, 1866   PLATE 16   Yarrow Pug

Notable/Nb

Resident; commons, waste ground; local and scarce.

Univoltine; mid-July to mid-August.

Foodplant – yarrow.

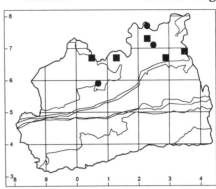

The Yarrow Pug is normally a coastal species which is found along the eastern coast and up the Thames estuary. Prior to 1994 it was known from three sites in Surrey, all of which are near the Thames. The first Surrey record was from Wimbledon on 16.7.1961 (JVD), and it was seen there again on 24.7.1967. A further specimen was taken at Horsell on 7.8.1968, and determined by D.S. Fletcher (CGMdeW); later specimens from Wisley were determined by dissection. As a result of these records the larva was searched for, unsuccessfully, on Wimbledon and Mitcham commons (Evans, 1973), and more recently at Ballards Plantation, also without success. Following the discovery of several specimens at light in 1994, search for the larvae revealed it to be breeding at a number of sites, including some of those previously searched, and it is now clearly resident in the county.

RECORDS – **Wimbledon**, 17.8.77 (JVD); **Wisley RES**, 31.7.86 (1), 16-30.7.91 (2), 23.7-7.8.92 (2), 3.7.93, 1995 (AJH) [det. A. Riley]; **Field Common**, 14.7.94, 16.9.94 larvae, 22.9.95 larvae (GAC); **South Norwood**, 23.9.94 larvae (GAC); **Mitcham Common**, 30.9.94 larvae (GAC); **Beddington**, 9.10.94 larvae (DC); **Chertsey Meads**, 22.9.95 larvae (GAC); **Wimbledon Common**, 29.9.95 larvae (GAC); **Barn Elms**, 19.7.96 (MRH).

Eupithecia simpliciata (Haworth, 1809)   Plain Pug

Resident; commons, waste ground; restricted and uncommon.

Univoltine; late July to mid-August.

Foodplant – goosefoot.

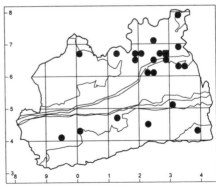

The Plain Pug is widely distributed in the London area, but rarely seen in any numbers. Elsewhere in Surrey, apart from being recorded regularly from Thorpe (PJB), it is only occasionally noted, these specimens probably being just vagrants; it may be expected to move around as the larval foodplants are commonest on disturbed ground.

[*Eupithecia distinctaria* Herrich-Schäffer, 1848   Thyme Pug
ssp. *constrictata* Guenée, 1857
Doubtful.

A specimen of this species was recorded from East Sheen, 6.8.1931 (de Worms, *L.N.* **37**). As it is not normally regarded as a south-eastern species, it cannot be accepted on the Surrey list until further evidence is forthcoming.]

Eupithecia indigata (Hübner, 1813)   Ochreous Pug

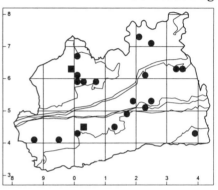

Resident; woodland, heathland; fairly widespread but uncommon.

Univoltine; May to mid-June.

Foodplant – Scots pine.

Although the number of records is rather small the Ochreous Pug would appear to occur in many parts of the county, although possibly avoiding the heavier clay soils especially on the weald. It is usually only seen in small numbers, but could probably be found commonly in areas of open pine.

Eupithecia pimpinellata (Hübner, 1813)   Pimpinel Pug

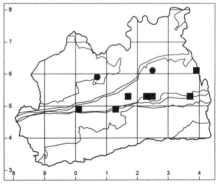

Notable/Nb

Resident; chalk grassland; local.

July.

Foodplant – burnet-saxifrage, (greater burnet-saxifrage).

The Pimpinel Pug has mainly been recorded during the last 20 years as a larva, which can at times be quite common, the adult only being recognized twice. There is a high percentage of parasitism of these larvae, and it is possible that the adult is genuinely scarce. When searched for specifically the species will probably prove to occur widely on the chalk.

RECORDS – **Pewley Down**, 7.9.93 larvae (DWB); **Wisley RES**, 28.6.92 (AJH [det. A. Riley]); **Westcott Downs**, 3.9.89 larvae (GAC); **Juniper Bottom**, 10.10.78 (22) larvae (JP), 1.10.93 larvae (GAC); **Colley Hill/Juniper Hill**, 9.77 larvae (PAC); **South Hawke**, 5.9.92 larvae (GAC); **Banstead Downs**, 22.7.93 (GAC); **Addington**, 12.9.92 larvae (GAC).

Eupithecia nanata (Hübner, 1813)   Narrow-winged Pug

ssp. *angusta* Prout, 1938

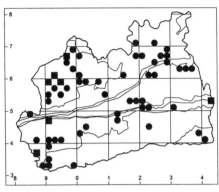

Resident; heathland, gardens; restricted but common.

Probably **bivoltine**; April to August.

Foodplant – heather.

The Narrow-winged Pug, whose larva feeds on heather, is not surprisingly a common species on the heaths of the Bagshot beds and on the greensand. It also occurs in central Surrey where there is heathland at Reigate and Headley, and not uncommonly in the London area. Although there is a fair bit of heather in this area, for example at Wimbledon and Shirley, the scope of the records would suggest that the larva also feeds on ornamental heathers in gardens. The adult is probably bivoltine, but is recorded regularly from April to August; larval records are all for September.

Eupithecia fraxinata Crewe, 1863   Ash Pug

Resident; very local and rare.

Foodplant – ash.

The Ash Pug has only been reliably recorded from three areas. Although a rather distinctively shaped species of Pug, it has probably been overlooked; voucher specimens of possible candidates should be retained. The foodplant is common everywhere but the moth may only occur at a low density.

RECORDS – **Milford**, 27.6.87 (DWB) [det. RFB]; **Wormley**, 18.7.78 (JLM); **Bramley**, 1972-84 (19), 86 (3) (RFB); **Nutfield**, 4.7.79, 2.7.81 (PAC); **Selsdon**, 1980 (1), and larva on ash (EHW).

[*Eupithecia virgaureata* Doubleday, 1861   Golden-rod Pug

Doubtful.

Barrett (1904) listed Surrey as one of the counties from which the Golden-rod Pug had been recorded, but gave no further details. There are no recent confirmed records.]

Eupithecia abbreviata Stephens, 1831 — Brindled Pug

Resident; woodland, wooded commons; widespread and common.

Univoltine; April to mid-May.

Foodplant – oak.

A rather widespread and common spring species which should occur everywhere. The apparent gap in recording in west Surrey is more likely due to insufficient recording in this area during the relatively early flight period than an actual absence. The melanic form, ab. *hirschkei* Bastelberger, occurs frequently, especially in the London area.

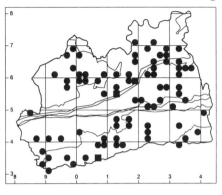

Eupithecia dodoneata Guenée, 1857 — Oak-tree Pug

Resident; woodland, commons; local and uncommon.

Univoltine; May.

Foodplant – hawthorn.

The Oak-tree Pug is a rather local species, but is undoubtedly overlooked in our area. The preferred habitat seems to be open woodland in which there exists an understorey of hawthorn on which the larva is stated to feed. Recent records suggest that the moth may be on the increase.

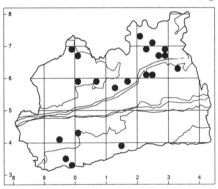

Eupithecia pusillata ([Denis & Schiffermüller], 1775) — Juniper Pug

ssp. *pusillata* ([Denis & Schiffermüller], 1775)

Resident; chalk downland, gardens; local but rather common.

Univoltine; late July to mid-August.

Foodplant – juniper.

Although associated with the juniper on chalk downs, the larva of this species has also been recorded from cultivated juniper in gardens, a situation which may be reflected in *Thera juniperata* (*q.v.*). Where the species occurs, the larvae may usually be beaten in numbers from even isolated bushes. The adult is less often recorded.

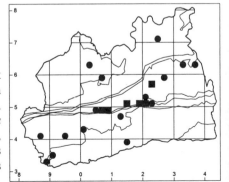

Eupithecia phoeniceata (Rambur, 1834)   **Cypress Pug**

Vagrant; probably not established.

August.

The Cypress Pug was not recorded as British until 1959 when it was found in Cornwall. Since then it has spread along the south coast and the 15 specimens recorded in Surrey probably represent an attempted expansion of the range inland. There is only one site where records suggest possible breeding, and as the larva feeds through the winter, climatic factors are likely to prevent the species' establishment.

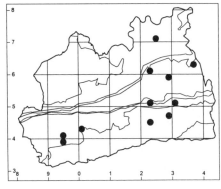

RECORDS – **Bramley**, 16.8.75 (RFB); **Salfords**, 28.8.75 (A. Allen); **Wimbledon**, 15.9.77 (JVD); **Addington**, 2.9.78 (BS); **Wormley**, 30.8.78 (JLM); **Coulsdon**, 19.8.84 (PMS); **Nutfield**, 15.8.89, 15.8.96 (PAC); **Milford**, 22.8.89 (DWB); **Banstead**, 31.7.95 (SWG), 5-12.8.96 (3) (SWG); **Leigh**, 19.8.96 (RF); **Buckland**, 26.8.96 (CH).

Eupithecia lariciata (Freyer, 1842)   **Larch Pug**

Resident; woodland; local and scarce.

Univoltine; June to mid-July.

Foodplant – larch.

There are surprisingly few records of this species which must surely be under-recorded. It probably occurs everywhere that there is larch. The melanic form, f. *nigra* Prout, has not been recorded in the wild, but a number were bred from a typical female taken at South Croydon (GAC).

RECORDS – **Thorpe**, 1986, 92 (PJB); **Horsell**, 2.6.76 (CGMdeW); **Wisley RES**, 1988 (1) (AJH) [det. A. Riley]; **Bramley**, 1986 (6) (RFB); **Blackheath**, 30.6.86, 20-30.8.87 (BS); **Friday Street**, 23.6.81 (RKAM); **Wotton**, 6.76 (JDH); **Headley Warren**, 16.6.95 (GAC); **Leatherhead**, 7.94 larvae (JP); **South Croydon**, 16-21.7.86, 12.6.87, 19.7.93, 20.6.95 (GAC); **Selsdon**, 1975 (2), 76 (1), 77 (2), 80 (1) (EHW); **Threehalfpenny Wood**, 1995 (BS); **Dulwich Upper Wood**, 19.7.85 (CWP).

Eupithecia tantillaria Boisduval, 1840 — Dwarf Pug

Resident; woodland; fairly widespread but uncommon.

Univoltine; late May and June.

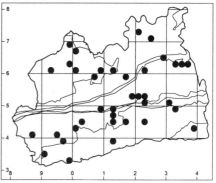

The Dwarf Pug has been recorded through most of Surrey with the exception of the north-west. This may reflect its true distribution as Bretherton (1957) also had very few records for that area. Similarly it appears to be absent from much of the chalk. Elsewhere it occurs in small numbers.

Chloroclystis v-ata (Haworth, 1809) — V-Pug

Resident; commons, woodland, downland; restricted and uncommon.

Bivoltine; May to mid-June, and July.

Foodplant – bramble (flowers).

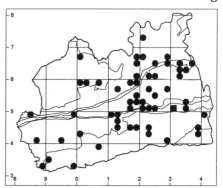

The V-Pug is apparently absent from urban London and from the heaths of west Surrey. With these exceptions it occurs over the rest of the county, with a possible preference for the chalk, but only in small numbers. The only sites where it is at all common are: Ashtead, 1987 (13), 88 (3), 89 (1) (GG); and Dawcombe, 1991 (16) (DC).

Chloroclystis chloerata (Mabille, 1870) PLATE 4 — Sloe Pug

Resident; commons, woodland; fairly widespread and fairly common.

Univoltine; June.

Foodplant – sloe blossom.

The Sloe Pug was first recognized as British when larvae were found at Effingham in April, 1971 (Pelham-Clinton, 1972), but examination of specimens in collections revealed that it had been with us for rather longer and had been overlooked. The larva feeds on the flowers of sloe, preferring mature thickets, and in such situations is fairly common in much of Surrey, especially on areas of clay. It has not yet been recorded from the Bagshot beds of north-west Surrey where the foodplant is scarce. The adult is occasionally recorded at light but is usually overlooked being very dissimilar to reared specimens.

Chloroclystis rectangulata (Linnaeus, 1758)   Green Pug

Resident; gardens, commons; widespread and common.

Univoltine; mid-June to July.

Foodplant – apple blossom, sloe blossom, hawthorn blossom.

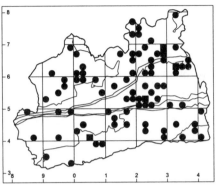

This is the commonest of the "green" Pugs, found everywhere in good numbers; at some traps it is abundant: Bramley, 1985 (128), 86 (199) (RFB); South Croydon, 1983 (50), 84 (60), 85 (72) (GAC). Most specimens are referable to ab. *anthrax* Dietze, and the typical green form is rare.

Chloroclystis debiliata (Hübner, 1817)   Bilberry Pug

Notable/Nb

Resident; woodland; very local but fairly common.

Univoltine; mid-June to July.

Foodplant – bilberry.

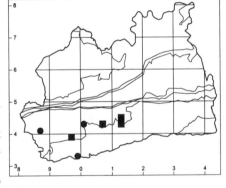

The Bilberry Pug is a typical species of open woods with a ground cover of bilberry such as are found on the greensand in the south-west of Surrey. The adult will come to light and the larvae can be swept in May, often commonly.

RECORDS – **Fisherlane Wood**, 14.7.79 (PC); **Rushmoor**, 9-22.7.84 (PAD); **Hydon Heath**, 13.5.83 larvae on bilberry (DWB), 25.5.86 larvae (GAC); **Bramley**, 25.7.86 (RFB); **Winterfold**, 14.5.76 larvae (RFB), 14.5.95 larvae (GAC); **Friday Street**, 23.6.81 (RKAM), 2.5.82 larvae on bilberry (PMS), 15.5.92 larvae, 27.4.93 larvae (GAC), 12.6.93, 19.6.94 (DC); **Leith Hill**, 2.6.84 larvae, 18.5.85 larvae (PC).

Gymnoscelis rufifasciata (Haworth, 1809) Double-striped Pug

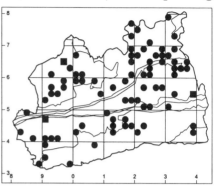

Resident; commons, heathland, downland; widespread and common.

Bivoltine; April and May, and July to early September.

Foodplant – flowers of marjoram, heather, gorse, buddleia.

A rather common species found throughout the county. The Rothamsted trap at Wisley records much higher numbers than elsewhere: 1986 (73), 87 (87), 89 (22), 90 (46), 91 (46) (AJH); possibly the lower power of this type of trap may be more attractive to smaller moths. The distribution on the Weald is perhaps rather more patchy; for example, at Leigh it is only occasionally recorded (in 1988, but not 1989-91). The Double-striped Pug is one of the earliest Pugs to appear in the year.

Anticollix sparsata (Treitschke, 1828) Dentated Pug

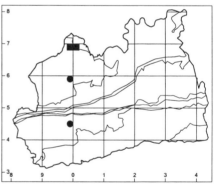

Notable/Na

Resident; damp woodland, canal banks; very local and rare.

July.

Foodplant – yellow loosestrife.

During the survey period there have been reports of this species from only four sites in Surrey. The north-west list suggests that it was rather less restricted in the 1950s: Weybridge, 13.7.1954; Byfleet, Sheerwater, Woking, by canal, moths 1910 and 1911, and larvae in recent years; Butts Wood, 30.6.1953; Longcross, one in 1954 (Bretherton, 1957); Ottershaw trap, 4.7.1957; Horsell trap, 25.7.1956; both some distance from the foodplant (Bretherton, 1965). In the south-west it was taken at Godalming, 14.6.1952 (JLM) and Shalford, 1.7.1972 (PAC). There are also records in the north-east list which want confirmation: Tadworth 25.5.1952 and 11.6.1952 (ASW in Evans, 1973); Upper Warlingham (Welti in de Worms, *L.N.* **37**:149). The foodplant is still quite common along the banks of the Wey Navigation and also occurs in some damp woods in the extreme south-east of the county. Limited search in these areas has failed to reveal its presence. Kettlewell (1973) says of the melanic f. *obscura* Lempke, "common in many places around London, e.g. Byfleet".

RECORDS – **Egham Wick**, 30.8.88, a larva on yellow loosestrife (GAC), **Stroude**, 15.9.87 larvae on yellow loosestrife, also in 1989, 90 (PJB); **Woking**, 10.7.84 (PAC); **Godalming**, 10.7.76 (PAC).

Chesias legatella ([Denis & Schiffermüller], 1775) **Streak**

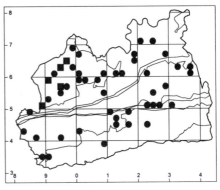

Resident; heathland, commons; restricted but common.
Univoltine; October and early November.
Foodplant – broom.

The Streak is a common species on the heathland of west Surrey, and is also found on heathland remnants in central and north-eastern Surrey. There are no very recent records from the heart of the chalk and only one from the weald: Leigh, 1987 (RF). The larvae are usually very common on broom in May.

Chesias rufata (Fabricius, 1775) **Broom-tip**

ssp. *rufata* (Fabricius, 1775)

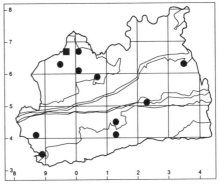

Notable/Nb
Resident; heathland, woodland; very local and scarce.
Univoltine; late April to mid-July.
Foodplant – broom.

A very local species of erratic appearance which has possibly declined since the publication of the north-west Surrey list. In the last decade it has only been recorded from four sites and is currently a very difficult moth to find. Larvae were found in hundreds at Barnes Common on 20.8.1967 (Wall, 1975), but it was noted that the adults were reluctant to fly during the day despite disturbance of the broom bushes.

RECORDS – **Rushmoor**, 18.4.84, 7.5.85 (PAD); **Hindhead**, 12.5.82 (JTS); **Windlesham RES**, 1977 (1) (JAB); **Chobham Common**, 9.82 (2) larvae on broom (JP); **Horsell**, 15.5.76 (CGMdeW); **Thorpe**, 1982, 87 (PJB); **Wisley RES**, 1976 (2), 89 (1) (AJH); **Leith Hill Wood**, 5.5.89 (GAC); **Friday Street**, 7.5.76 (D. O'Keefe); **Buckland**, 24.4.93 (CH); **Selsdon**, 26.6.76 (EHW).

Aplocera plagiata (Linnaeus, 1758)   Treble-bar
ssp. *plagiata* (Linnaeus, 1758)

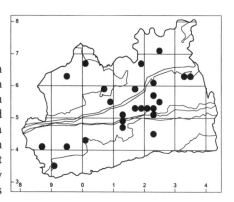

Resident; chalk downland, commons; restricted but fairly common.
Bivoltine; June, and August.
The two species of Treble-bar are often confused and thus there is probably a margin of error in the records. The Treble-bar is much more restricted than the next species and generally less common. Indeed the only area where it could be described as common is on the scarp of the North Downs. The statement in Bretherton (1957) that in north-west Surrey *plagiata* is more common than *efformata* is certainly not the case today.

Aplocera efformata (Guenée, 1857)   Lesser Treble-bar

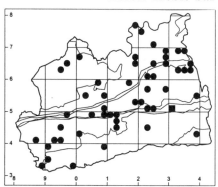

Resident; commons, downland, woodland; fairly widespread and common.
Bivoltine; mid-May to June, and August to mid-September.
Foodplant – perforate St. John's-wort.
The Lesser Treble-bar is rather more widespread than the preceding species and very much more common as these trap results show:

	efformata	*plagiata*	
Bramley	common; 1985 (1), 86 (7)	1 only; 1976	(RFB)
Thorpe	regular	scarce; 1981, 92	(PJB)
South Croydon	1983 (19), 84 (23), 85 (3)	1983 (1), 85 (1), 89 (2)	(GAC)
Mitcham	1982 (1), 83 (1)	not recorded	(RKAM)

The males can be most easily separated by external examination of the claspers which are long and slender in *plagiata* and much shorter and stouter in *efformata*.

Odezia atrata (Linnaeus, 1758)   Chimney Sweeper

Status uncertain.

There are two records, not wholly satisfactory, for this normally day-flying species: Banstead, a specimen at mvl [no date] (Gardner in Evans, 1973) – there is no voucher specimen in the Gardner collection; Wimbledon Common, 1980s (Jenkins in Plant, 1993). Further evidence of the Chimney Sweeper in Surrey is desirable. [The *VCH* says of this species (as *Tanagra chaerophyllata*) "not uncommon amongst bracken . . . reported from Haslemere by Mr Barrett and from Dorking by Mr Webb. I have found it in many places in the county." This is an unlikely habitat and, as Barrett (1904) does not include Surrey in its distribution, I am in little doubt that another species was intended.]

Discoloxia blomeri (Curtis, 1832)   Blomer's Rivulet

Vagrant; one specimen only.

There is but a single record of this species: Hook Heath, in a trap 27.7.1956 (Trundell in Bretherton, 1965), presumably a vagrant from the Chilterns.

Euchoeca nebulata (Scopoli, 1763)   Dingy Shell

Resident; alder carr; fairly widespread but uncommon.

Univoltine; late May and June.

Foodplant – alder.

The Dingy Shell is a species frequenting alder carr and is consequently somewhat localized. As one would expect it is absent from the chalk, but is also only occasional in the London area. There is evidence of a partial second brood, but it is decidedly rare: Wallis Wood, 16.8.1988 (GAC); Thursley Common, 21.8.1991 (RFMcC).

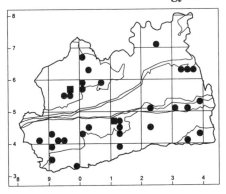

Asthena albulata (Hufnagel, 1767)   Small White Wave

Resident; woodland; fairly widespread but uncommon.

Univoltine; mid-May to June.

A fairly widespread species that is probably commonest in the woods of the south of the county. The adult comes but rarely to light and is more easily found at dusk or by disturbing specimens during the day.

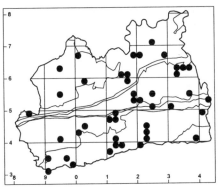

119

Hydrelia flammeolaria (Hufnagel, 1767) Small Yellow Wave

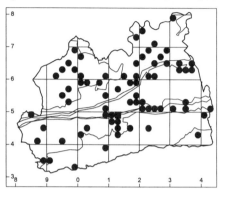

Resident; woodland, commons; widespread but uncommon.
Univoltine; mid-June to mid-July.
Foodplant – field maple.

The Small Yellow Wave is found throughout Surrey including the London area, although it is scarce there. Rather strangely, for a species associated with field maple, there is a dearth of records from the chalk. Normally it is a rather uncommon species seen only in small numbers, but occasionally the static traps record larger catches: Windlesham RES, 1976 (19) (JAB); Bramley, 1986 (17) (RFB).

Hydrelia sylvata ([Denis & Schiffermüller], 1775) Waved Carpet

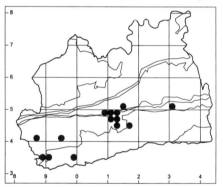

Notable/Nb
Resident; woodland; local and uncommon.
Univoltine; late June and July.

The Waved Carpet is a local species with two centres of distribution: central Surrey, and the extreme south-west of the county. Usually only recorded in ones and twos, the Rothamsted trap at Haslemere produced no less than 22 individuals in 1976.

RECORDS – **Rushmoor**, 22.7.83, 14.8.84 (PAD); **Hindhead**, 14-15.7.83 (4), 18.7.84, 24.6.85 (JTS); **Haslemere RES**, 1976 (22),1981-84 (9), 85 (2), 87 (3) (TGW); **Canterbury Copse**, 4.7.85 (AJ); **Milford**, 29.7.85 (DWB); **Netley Heath**, 21.6.88 (GAC); **Abinger**, 3.7.76 (EHW), 19.7.78 (BS); **Friday Street**, 8.7.81 (JP); **Wotton**, 12.7.77 (JDH); **White Downs**, 10.7.95 (6) (DC); **Westcott Downs**, 13.7.83 (GAC); **Dorking**, 13.7.84 (PC); **Holmwood Common**, 14.7.84 (PC); **Nutfield**, 25.6.90 (2) (PAC).

Minoa murinata (Scopoli, 1763)   **Drab Looper**

Notable/Nb

Resident; woodland; very local but fairly common.

Univoltine; late May and early June.

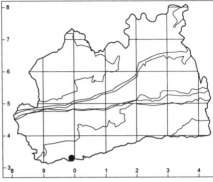

The Drab Looper is confined in Surrey to the woodland about Chiddingfold but here it can be fairly common in clearings, flying by day. The species is not mentioned in either the north-west or the north-east Surrey lists but the *VCH* describes it as generally distributed in woods, recorded from Wimbledon Common and Crohamhurst (sic.), South (1907) says "has been taken at lamps, at Dorking among other places", and examples taken at Selsdon were exhibited by S. Wakely at the 1934 annual exhibition of the SLENHS.

RECORDS – **Fisherlane Wood**, 2.6.85 (3), 15.6.93 (DWB); **Tugley Wood**, 6.86 common, 4.6.87 (10+) (SCP), 10.6.89 (1), 8.6.92 (6+) (GAC), 5.6.93 (SWG).

Lobophora halterata (Hufnagel, 1767)   **Seraphim**

Resident; woodland, commons; restricted and uncommon.

Univoltine; mid-May to mid-June.

Foodplant – aspen.

The Seraphim would appear from the records to be absent from the chalk and from areas of heathland. Elsewhere it occurs widely, even quite far into London, but it is nowhere common, the static traps recording no more than two or three individuals a year. A specimen of f. *zonata* Thunberg was taken at Horsell on 9.5.1975 – a form more normally associated with Scottish specimens (CGMdeW, *Ent. Rec.* **87**:255).

Trichopteryx polycommata ([Denis & Schiffermüller], 1775)   PLATE 1 **Barred Tooth-striped**

Extinct; not recorded since 1960.

This species does not seem to have been noticed in Surrey since 1960 when it was recorded from Headley, 2.4.1960 (HM-P). In the 1940s and 50s it was noted from the following localities, mostly on the downs around Dorking: a series from the Headley Lane district (Wakely, *Proc. SLENHS* **1940-41**:16.); Leigh, 1946 and 1952 (RF); and Cockshot Wood; Dorking 1953, bred series; Mickleham Downs, 7-15.4.1956 (2), 22.3.1957 (1) (Evans, 1973) – due to lack of any recent records it may therefore be assumed to be extinct. The moth is not easy to find as access to its habitats with light traps is difficult and the weather during the flight period (early April) means that suitable nights are few and far between. The larva is apparently very difficult to find even in localities where the adult is known to occur (BS, *pers. com.*). Systematic search of its former localities is needed to establish its true status.

Trichopteryx carpinata (Borkhausen, 1794)   Early Tooth-striped

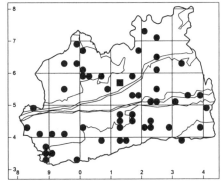

Resident; woodland, heathland; widespread and fairly common.
Univoltine; April and early May.
Foodplant – birch.
The Early Tooth-striped is a fairly regular spring species found throughout much of the county. At some rural sites it can be quite common, as the following trap counts show: Bramley, 1985 (11), 86 (13) (RFB); Windlesham RES, 1980 (26), 81 (20) (JAB).

Pterapherapteryx sexalata (Retzius, 1783)   Small Seraphim

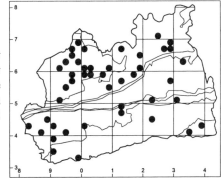

Resident; commons, woodland; fairly widespread and common.
Bivoltine; June, and July and early August.
A fairly common species of scrubby commons. It is only very occasionally recorded on the chalk as its foodplant is scarce here. In suitable areas amongst sallow it can be quite plentiful: Mitcham, 1981 (16), 82 (11), 83 (14) (RKAM).

Acasis viretata (Hübner, 1799)   **Yellow-barred Brindle**

Resident; gardens, commons, woodland; widespread but uncommon.

Bivoltine; May, and August.

Foodplant – ivy, (dogwood).

The Yellow-barred Brindle is a widely distributed species, possibly favouring suburban areas, and somewhat resembling the Holly Blue in its habits and foodplants. The moth is usually only seen in small numbers; the only records of it being common are: Bramley, 1986 (14) (RFB); South Croydon, 1984 (19) (GAC); Banstead, 1992 (16) (SWG). The larva has been found on ivy in the autumn.

Abraxas grossulariata (Linnaeus, 1758)   **Magpie**

Resident; commons, gardens; fairly widespread but uncommon.

Univoltine; July and August.

Foodplant – sloe, currant, (plum, buckthorn, gooseberry, evergreen spindle)

The Magpie Moth has been found throughout Surrey, but is often very uncertain in its appearance. At Bramley and Thorpe it was not recorded at all during the survey period, at South Croydon but once, 12.8.1984 (GAC), and even at the RHS gardens at Wisley only twice. At Leigh it is described as common and recorded every year, and at a few other sites it appears to occur regularly: Mitcham 1981 (3), 82 (2), 83 (5) (RKAM); Selsdon 1980 (14) (EHW). The evidence does however suggest that the moth is very much less common than it was at the beginning of this century.

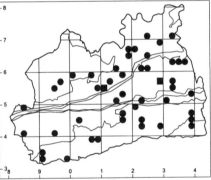

Abraxas sylvata (Scopoli, 1763)   Clouded Magpie

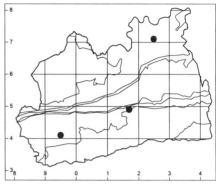

Status uncertain; resident and possible migrant.

Foodplant – (wych elm).

There have only ever been a few records of this species from Surrey, and during the survey period but three examples were noted. There are only three records in Bretherton (1957): New Haw, 30.6.1952; Weybridge, 30.6.1952; and Horsell, 11.7.1955. Migration was considered a possible source of these records, and indeed could explain the current ones. The supplement produced a further record: Horsell trap, 18.6.1957 (Bretherton, 1965). In north-east Surrey it was recorded from Norbury Park, 8.7.1951 and 5.7.1953, and Westhumble, 1951 (Evans, 1973), and Headley 10.7.1952 (HM-P); larvae were found at the former site on 7.9.1958 (Wakely, *Proc. SLENHS* **1958**;15). It has also been recorded from: Leigh, 1.7.1957 (RF); Reigate, July 1969 (DAT in de Worms *L.N.* **49**:69); Thorpe, 1970 (PJB); Purley, June 1972 (DCL); and Wotton, 21.6.1970, 26.9.1970, 20-25.7.1974, and 12.10.1975 (JDH). It is therefore probable that it was resident in central Surrey prior to the survey period, but the dearth of recent records together with the loss of elm does not bode well for its continued existence.

RECORDS – **Milford**, 3.8.82 (DWB); **Dorking**, 28.6.84 (DAT); **Wimbledon**, 20.7.96 (JVD).

Lomaspilis marginata (Linnaeus, 1758)   Clouded Border

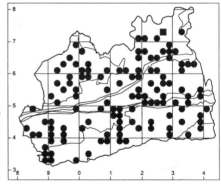

Resident; commons, woodland; widespread and common.

Univoltine; June and July.

Foodplant – sallow, aspen.

A very widespread and common species, the Clouded Border can occur in some abundance, for example: Bramley, 1985 (75), 86 (133) (RFB). Even in the environs of London it can be numerous; at Mitcham the following counts apply: 1981 (31), 82 (23), 83 (30) (RKAM). On the chalk it is perhaps scarcer but still occurs annually at the static traps.

Ligdia adustata ([Denis & Schiffermüller], 1775)   Scorched Carpet

Resident; chalk grassland, woodland, commons; fairly widespread and fairly common.
Bivoltine; May and June, and August.
Foodplant – spindle.

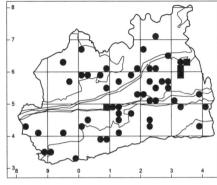

The Scorched Carpet occurs fairly widely in Surrey but does seem to be absent from the heathland areas of the west. Elsewhere it is pretty general but probably commonest on the chalk; 17 were recorded from Dawcombe in 1991 (DC). An example of the melanic ab. *plumbosa* Cockayne was recorded from this site on 25.5.1991 (DC), apparently only the third known occurrence of this form (see Cockayne, *Ent.* **83**:53; West, *Ent. Rec.* **100**:236).

Semiothisa notata (Linnaeus, 1758)   Peacock Moth

Resident; woodland, wooded commons; fairly widespread but uncommon.
Bivoltine; May to June, and July to August.

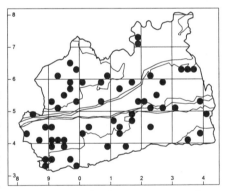

The Peacock Moth is fairly widespread but does not appear to occur any closer to London than the woods around Selsdon. Elsewhere it is of regular occurrence in woodland but rarely seen in any numbers, although there has been a noticeable increase in this species in recent years, especially in west Surrey. A card index of notable species, written by Bretherton in the 1960s, stated that he was unaware of any reliable records from the west of the county; it was not until the 1980s that he took it fairly regularly at Bramley.

Semiothisa alternaria (Hübner, 1809)　　Sharp-angled Peacock

Resident; woodland, heathland; local and scarce.

July.

A rather local species found principally on the Bagshot sands where it would appear to be scarce but regular at the static traps in the area. Outside this area there is a recent record from Leigh on the weald, and a few slightly older records from the greensand.

RECORDS – **Windlesham RES**, 1977 (1), 79 (2) (JAB); **Horsell**, 2.8.76 (CGMdeW); **Chobham Common**, 22.6.87 (AJ); **Thorpe**, regular (PJB); **Woking**, common 1985-88 (SCP); **Wisley Common**, 15.7.85 (2) (SCP); **Leigh**, 5.8.90 (RF).

Semiothisa liturata (Clerck, 1759)　　Tawny-barred Angle

Resident; pine woods, heathland; widespread and common.

Probably **univoltine**; mid-May to August, peak July.

Foodplant – Scots pine.

A surprisingly widely distributed species, considering the foodplant – it is presumably able to exist on small groups of pine and probably individual trees in gardens. Some specimens, especially from north-east Surrey, have a rather darker ground colour than the type, but the extreme melanic f. *nigrofulvata* Collins appears to be distinctly scarce; I have only ever taken two examples that I would consider to be of this form, and it is also recorded from Buckland (CH).

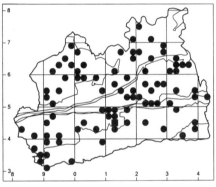

Semiothisa clathrata (Linnaeus, 1758) **Latticed Heath**

ssp. *clathrata* (Linnaeus, 1758)
Resident; commons, downland; fairly
  widespread and fairly common.
Bivoltine; May and June, and July and
  August.
The Latticed Heath has been recorded from
much of the county with the exception of the
western and southern borders; possibly these
areas are too heavily wooded. It is regular at
most of the static traps and often disturbed
by day. The melanic ab. *alboguttata* Fettig
appears to be very scarce, being recorded from
Nutfield, 2.6.1992 (PAC), and White Downs, 4.6.1979 (CH).

Semiothisa brunneata (Thunberg, 1784) **Rannoch Looper**

Migrant; very rare.
The Rannoch Looper, as its name implies, is resident in Britain in the Scottish highlands,
but also occurs in the south-east as a rare migrant. These individuals are usually considerably
larger than the native examples. The moth has been recorded in Surrey on four occasions,
all at light.

1955 – **Ottershaw**, 11.7 (RFB).
1960 – **Wimbledon**, 25.6 (JVD); **Wormley**, 27.6 (JLM).
1992 – **Lingfield**, 11.6 (JC).

Semiothisa wauaria (Linnaeus, 1758) **V-Moth**

Resident; gardens, commons; fairly
  widespread but uncommon.
Univoltine; July.
Foodplant – (currant).
A fairly widely distributed species that would
appear to have declined in frequency in recent
years, possibly as a result of pesticide spraying
in gardens or the decline in popularity of its
foodplants. Several observers note that it has
not been seen by them recently, especially in
the south London area.

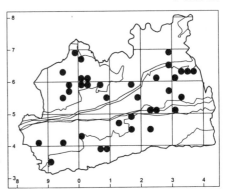

[*Isturgia limbaria* (Fabricius, 1775) Frosted Yellow

Erroneous.

The Frosted Yellow occurred in Britain in Scotland, East Anglia and Kent, but was extinct by 1915. Barrett (1901) mentions that J.W. Douglas, writing in 1851, had recorded it as being formerly plentiful amongst broom at Birch Wood, Surrey. Whilst there are many places known as Birch Wood, the most famous entomologically was near Swanley in Kent, and it is far more likely that the record refers to that locality (see Chalmers-Hunt, 1968-81).]

Cepphis advenaria (Hübner, 1790) Little Thorn

Notable/Nb

Resident; open woodland; local and
  uncommon.

Univoltine; late May to mid-June.

Foodplant – bilberry.

A rather local species, restricted to open woodland in the south-west of the county. The Little Thorn is often noted by day, but also comes to light in numbers. Bretherton (1957) has no records for north-west Surrey for this century, and Evans (1973) gives Westhumble and Betchworth (on the edge of its current

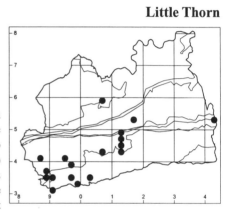

range), and Limpsfield Chart as recently as 1971. Two examples were found there, 9.6.1996, after an absence of 25 years. The melanic ab. *fulva* Guttmer was taken at Friday Street, 1970 (BS).

Petrophora chlorosata (Scopoli, 1763) Brown Silver-line

Resident; woodland, commons;
  widespread and common.

Univoltine; May to early July.

Foodplant – bracken.

The Brown Silver-line is a very common species almost everywhere and is frequently disturbed from bracken by day, although apparently venturing further afield at night when it also comes to light. The larva can be swept at night, often in numbers, but appears to make little impression on its invasive foodplant.

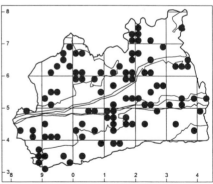

Plagodis pulveraria (Linnaeus, 1758)   Barred Umber

Resident; woodland, commons; local and scarce.

Univoltine; May and early June.

A rather local species, recorded most often from the woods of the weald and greensand. The only recent records from north of the chalk are: Wimbledon, 19.6.1982 (JVD); and Windlesham RES, 1981 (1) (JAB), also in 1978 and 79. Even in its favoured localities the moth is scarce; I have only seen it once in Surrey, and it may be that it is better found by dusking than at the light trap.

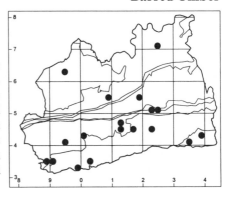

Plagodis dolabraria (Linnaeus, 1767)   Scorched Wing

Resident; woodland; widespread and fairly common.

Univoltine; late May to early July.

The Scorched Wing is a fairly common species found in well-wooded areas including the parks and commons of south London.

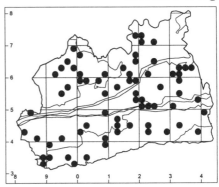

Pachycnemia hippocastanaria (Hübner, 1799)   Horse Chestnut

Notable/Nb

Resident; heathland, open woodland; restricted but fairly common.

Bivoltine; April and May, and late July and August.

Foodplant – heather, cross-leaved heath.

A rather common species on all the major heaths of west Surrey. It has only been recorded once recently from the east of the county: Leigh, 1983 (1) (RF), probably a wanderer from the heathy woods 10 km to the west. It was also recorded in 1973 from

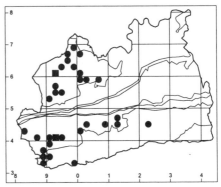

Banstead Wood (RFMcC). Prior to this it was known from the heathland at Addington Hills and the examples recorded from Addiscombe in 1966 (Evans, 1973) were probably from there.

Opisthograptis luteolata (Linnaeus, 1758) — Brimstone Moth

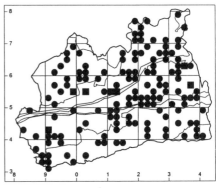

Resident; woodland, commons, heathland, downland; widespread and common.

Mid-May to September.

Foodplant – sloe, hawthorn, (plum, oak, wayfaring-tree).

A very common and widespread species. Some idea of its frequency can be gained from the following trap counts: Bramley, 1985 (50), 86 (123), 90 (RFB); Mitcham, 1981 (56), 82 (117), 83 (108) (RKAM); South Croydon, 1983 (89), 84 (87), 85 (96) (GAC); Selsdon, 1980 (141) (EHW). The voltinism of this species is somewhat complicated; adults can be found in any month from May to September and the winter can be passed either as a nearly full-grown larva or as a pupa.

Epione repandaria (Hufnagel, 1767) — Bordered Beauty

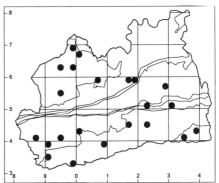

Resident; woodland, commons; fairly widespread but scarce.

Univoltine; July and August.

The Bordered Beauty has been recorded throughout the county with the exception of the London area and much of the chalk. It is, however, only ever seen in very small numbers; even those static traps at which it appears in most years never record more than two or three examples annually. A specimen recorded at Wormley on 3.10.1972 (JLM) may have been an example of a partial second brood.

Pseudopanthera macularia (Linnaeus, 1758)   Speckled Yellow

Resident; woodland, downland; restricted but rather common.

Univoltine; May to mid-June.

An often rather common day-flying species which is restricted to the woods of the south-west, the chalk, especially the woods above the scarp of the North Downs, and heathy woods in the Oxshott area. Occasional examples are noted at light traps, possibly disturbed from nearby vegetation.

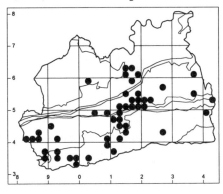

Apeira syringaria (Linnaeus, 1758)   Lilac Beauty

Resident; woodland, commons, gardens; fairly widespread and fairly common.

Univoltine; late June and July.

Foodplant – honeysuckle, garden privet.

A fairly generally distributed species which does though seem to be absent from the more urban parts of London. In rural areas and suburban gardens it is seen in reasonable numbers, but rarely as commonly as at Windlesham RES where the annual trap counts were: 1980 (8), 81 (10) (JAB).

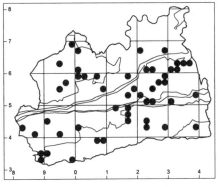

Specimens recorded at Addington, 29.8.1989 (BS), and Milford on 4.9.1992 (DWB) represent a partial second brood, examples of which are easily produced in captivity.

[*Ennomos autumnaria* (Werneburg, 1859)   Large Thorn

Erroneous.

This species is listed in Oldaker (1951) as being common. The species intended was *Ennomos quercinaria* (August Thorn) and there remains, perhaps rather surprisingly, no record of the Large Thorn from Surrey.]

Ennomos quercinaria (Hufnagel, 1767)   August Thorn

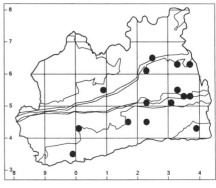

Resident; woodland, commons; restricted and scarce.

Univoltine; late July and early August.

The August Thorn is currently a local species apparently restricted to the chalk and the weald. Although described by the *VCH* as "the commonest species of the genus", the exact status is obscured by the fact that *E. erosaria* is frequently misidentified as this species both by recorders and in museums (Chalmers-Hunt, 1968-81, and Plant, 1993).

RECORDS – **Canterbury Copse**, 6.8.87 (AJ); **Bramley**, 1979 (1), 83 (1) (RFB); **East Horsley**, 3.8.76 (LJDW); **Holmwood Common**, 10.8.84, 19.7.85 (PC); **Buckland**, 10.8.94 (CH); **Leigh**, 20.7.87 (RF); **Banstead**, 26.7.90, 29.7-20.8.91, 10.8.92 (SWG); **North Cheam**, 2.7.82 (RFMcC); **South Croydon**, 25.7.85, 2.8.87, 7-14.8.88, 30.7.90, 22.7.94, 2.8.95 (GAC); **Addington**, most years 1985-96 (BS); **Nutfield**, 1991 (16), 92 (14), 18.7.94, 4-8.8.96 (3) (PAC); **Caterham**, 28-29.7.78 (JC); **Pilgrim Fort**, 20.7.89 (GAC); **South Hawke**, 12.8.78, 3.9.78 (RGS); **Lingfield**, 30.7.93 (JC).

Ennomos alniaria (Linnaeus, 1758)   Canary-shouldered Thorn

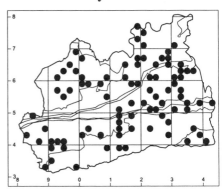

Resident; commons, woodland; widespread and common.

Univoltine; August and September.

Foodplant – silver birch.

A very widely distributed Thorn, found rather commonly everywhere but probably more frequent in rural areas. Trap counts show: Bramley, 1985 (29), 86 (34) (RFB); Mitcham, 1981 (2), 82 (9), 83 (9), 84 (RKAM); South Croydon, 1983 (12), 84 (9), 85 (8) (GAC).

Ennomos fuscantaria (Haworth, 1809)   **Dusky Thorn**

Resident; commons, woodland;
    widespread and common.

Univoltine; August to early October.

Foodplant – (ash).

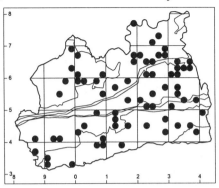

Another common Thorn which, like the last species, is found almost everywhere although there are rather fewer records from the western border. This is certainly the commoner species in London. Comparative trap counts are: Bramley, 1985 (64), 86 (18) (RFB); Mitcham, 1981 (19), 82 (16), 83 (25) (RKAM); South Croydon, 1983 (40), 84 (47), 85 (40) (GAC).

Ennomos erosaria ([Denis & Schiffermüller], 1775)   **September Thorn**

Resident; commons, woodland;
    widespread and common.

Univoltine; July to September.

Foodplant – oak, (hazel, lime).

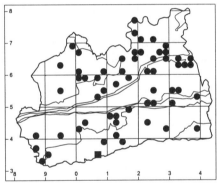

The September Thorn is fairly widely distributed but scarcer locally than the previous two species, and again not much recorded from the western edge of the county. Although recorded from many sites in the London area it has not been noted at South Croydon since 1988.

Selenia dentaria (Fabricius, 1775)   PLATE 4   **Early Thorn**

Resident; woodland, commons;
    widespread and common.

Bivoltine; April, and August.

Foodplant – bramble, (oak, elm).

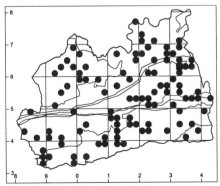

The Early Thorn is one of the commonest members of this group, found throughout the county without any apparent preference for habitat type. There are two broods; the summer one is more numerous than the spring.

Selenia lunularia (Hübner, 1788)   **Lunar Thorn**

Resident; woodland; very local and rare. June.

The Lunar Thorn is our rarest species of Thorn, recorded from only a single site in the last 20 years. There is a small number of records in Bretherton (1957), all from the static traps, and it was taken at Woking in 1961 (JACG). It was also recorded from: Dormansland, June 1912 (coll. H. Jeddere-Fisher); Charterhouse, 1939 and 1953 (Perrins, 1959), and more recently from; East Horsley, 29.6.1973 (LJDW), and Thorpe, 9.6.1975 (PJB). The localization of most of the records to the north-west of the county, despite their very low number, suggests that the moth is probably resident at low density.

RECORDS – **Wisley RES**, 20.6.79, 28.5.82 (AJH).

Selenia tetralunaria (Hufnagel, 1767)   **Purple Thorn**

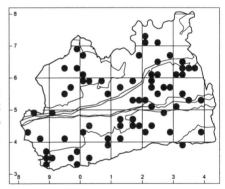

Resident; woodland, commons, widespread and fairly common.

Bivoltine; April and early May, and late July and early August.

Foodplant – (lime).

The Purple Thorn is a fairly common species which is widespread, but of infrequent occurrence in urban London. There are two broods which are very distinct in appearance.

Odontopera bidentata (Clerck, 1759) Scalloped Hazel

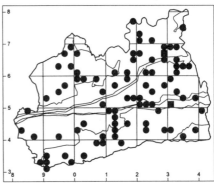

Resident; commons, woodland;
    widespread and common.
Univoltine; mid-May to June.
Foodplant – hawthorn, birch, (privet, ash,
    lilac, laurel, traveller's joy,
    juniper).
The Scalloped Hazel is a common species
throughout much of the county. It is a regular
attendee at light traps, and seems to be
particularly attracted to those of the
Rothamsted type. The melanic form, ab. *nigra*
Prout, has occurred in north-east Surrey.

Crocallis elinguaria (Linnaeus, 1758) Scalloped Oak

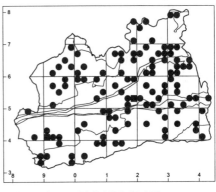

Resident; woodland, commons,
    widespread and common.
Univoltine; mid-July to August.
Foodplant – privet, birch, (hawthorn, oak,
    alder).
An extremely common species found all over
the county. If anything it is rather commoner
in the Selsdon area than anywhere else, as
the following trap counts show: Bramley,
1985 (25), 86 (55) (RFB); Windlesham RES,
1980 (44), 81 (10) (JAB); South Croydon,
1983 (39), 84 (73), 85 (81) (GAC); Selsdon,
1980 (112) (EHW). A melanic form has occurred at Reigate, 20.9.1978 (RAC).

Ourapteryx sambucaria (Linnaeus, 1758) Swallow-tailed Moth

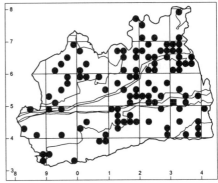

Resident; woodland, commons, gardens;
    widespread and common.
Univoltine; July and August.
Foodplant – ivy, (horse-chestnut).
The Swallow-tailed Moth is a rather common
species everywhere. A count of 118 at Selsdon
in 1980 (EHW) is exceptional but it is still a
frequent species at light, although there does
seem to be some reluctance to actually enter
the trap. A second brood example was noted
at Addiscombe, 22.10.1980 (KGWE).

Colotois pennaria (Linnaeus, 1761)   **Feathered Thorn**

Resident; woodland, commons;
  widespread and common.
Univoltine; October and November.
Foodplant – sloe, oak, hawthorn, wych
  elm, (apple, alder, buckthorn).
The Feathered Thorn is a common and
frequently observed species, despite its late
flight period. Specimens are rather variable
in the amount of speckling, and quite dark
forms occur.

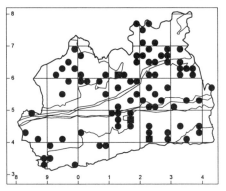

Angerona prunaria (Linnaeus, 1758)   PLATE 9   **Orange Moth**

Resident; woodland; local and uncommon.
Univoltine; June and early July.
Foodplant – (honeysuckle).
The Orange Moth is restricted mainly to the
wealden woods but is also recorded on
occasion in central Surrey, also on the clay.
The banded form, f. *corylaria* Thunberg, has
been recorded from Staffhurst Wood (Evans,
1973), but the typical form is certainly the
commoner one.

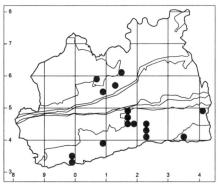

Apocheima hispidaria ([Denis & Schiffermüller], 1775) **Small Brindled Beauty**

Resident; woodland; widespread and
  common.
Univoltine; February to early April.
Foodplant – oak.
A rather widespread species which is
undoubtedly overlooked due to its very early
flight period. However a suitable night in
March amongst mature oak woodland will
usually produce good numbers of specimens.
The females, being wingless, are seldom
reported and are apparently extremely difficult
to find (BS, *pers. com.*). The typical form is
rather dark, and a melanic form with unicolorous forewings is not uncommon.

Apocheima pilosaria ([Denis & Schiffermüller], 1775)   **Pale Brindled Beauty**

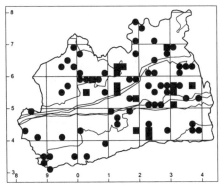

Resident; woodland, commons;
  widespread and common.
Univoltine; January to March.
Foodplant – oak, birch, lime, ash, hazel,
  sloe, field maple, wych elm,
  English elm, lime, hawthorn,
  aspen, (buckthorn, crab apple).
The Pale Brindled Beauty is another species
with a very early flight period and hence
possibly under-recorded. Where noted
though, it is often common, including in the
south London suburbs. The larva is widely
polyphagous on deciduous trees and shrubs, and frequently noted when beating for larvae
in the spring. Both pale, mottled and unicolorous forms occur, but the melanic ab. *monacharia*
Staudinger is currently very scarce, being noted from Hooley, 26.2.1976 (CH).

Lycia hirtaria (Clerck, 1759)   **Brindled Beauty**

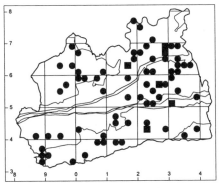

Resident; woodland, commons;
  widespread and common.
Univoltine; April and early May.
Foodplant – English elm, Lombardy
  poplar, birch, (lime, beech,
  maple, oak, lilac, horse-
  chestnut).
A common species everywhere, recorded at
both rural and suburban static traps, often in
large numbers: Bramley, 1985 (176), 86 (133)
(RFB); South Croydon, 1983 (41), 84 (150),
85 (99) (GAC); Mitcham, 1981 (69), 82 (12),
83 (106), 84 (317) (RKAM). The female, although not wingless as in the previous two
species, is just as infrequently observed and possibly never flies. There are also comparatively
few larval records for such a common species. The melanic f. *nigra* Cockayne was taken at
Weybridge, 13.4.1957 (JLM), but does not seem to have been noted in recent years.

Biston strataria (Hufnagel, 1767)   Oak Beauty

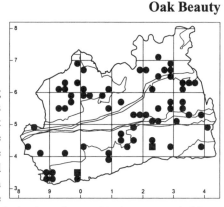

Resident; woodland, wooded commons; widespread and fairly common.

Univoltine; March to mid-April.

Foodplant – aspen, (oak, hazel, alder).

Generally a rather common early spring species occurring in wooded areas everywhere. The males appear regularly at light traps, often in some numbers; 32 were recorded at Bramley in 1985 (RFB). The female is hardly ever recorded at light and possibly may fly only rarely. A form in which the brown coloration covers the whole of the forewing is not uncommon, and the fully melanic ab. *melanaria* Koch was recorded from Chobham, 24.3.1972 (EHW).

Biston betularia (Linnaeus, 1758)   Peppered Moth

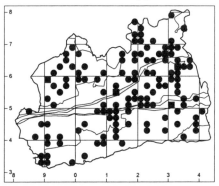

Resident; woodland, commons, heathland; widespread and common.

Univoltine; June to mid-August.

Foodplant – alder buckthorn, lime, oak, Michaelmas daisy, broom, birch, sallow, hawthorn, elm, (poplar, willow, plum, rose, privet, rowan, mugwort).

A very common species throughout the county and probably familiar even to non-naturalists. The female is not often recorded, although hardly as rarely seen as the last species, but the male is one of the commoner geometers at regularly run light traps. The following trap counts illustrate this: Bramley, 1985 (105), 86 (109) (RFB); South Croydon, 1983 (105), 84 (133), 85 (174) (GAC); Mitcham, 1981 (56), 82 (48), 83 (37), 84 (27) (RKAM). The attraction to Rothamsted traps is considerably weaker and annual trap counts in single figures are the norm. The three principal forms are the type, the melanic f. *carbonaria* Jordan, and the intermediate f. *insularia* Thierry-Mieg, although my series from South Croydon shows an almost complete gradation from black to white. Kettlewell (1973) classified the *insularia* complex into five subdivisions: the lightest resembling the type and the darkest being close to *carbonaria* – thus the separation of forms must be to some extent subjective. The first occurrence of *carbonaria* in Surrey is probably an "almost black example" taken at Camberwell and exhibited at a meeting of the SLENHS (Turner, *Proc. SLENHS* **1901**:36), and it was regular at Wimbledon Common by 1905-6 (Smallman, *Ent. Rec.* **20**:61). Bretherton, writing of the period 1946-55 at Ottershaw, lists the occurrence of the forms as: *carbonaria* 80%, *insularia* 6%, and the type 14% (sample size not given), while at Bramley in 1964 there were 41.5% melanic and 45.5% typical. Evans (1973) gives figures comparable with Ottershaw for the forms at Addiscombe in 1969 (n=318), although in a more rural area (Staffhurst Wood, 1970: n=129) they compare more favourably with Bramley, the percentage of *carbonaria* falling to 49% and of the type rising to 43%. Counts from Mitcham in 1981-83 suggest a reduction to 66% for *carbonaria* and an increase in the typical form to 24% (n=141). A subjective analysis of the last ten years suggests that *carbonaria* is greatly outnumbered by paler forms, many more of which are apparently *insularia*.

Agriopis leucophaearia ([Denis & Schiffermüller], 1775)   **Spring Usher**

Resident; woodland, wooded commons; widespread and fairly common.

Univoltine; January to March.

Foodplant – oak.

A fairly widespread moth which, as its English name suggests, is often one of the first species to appear in the spring. The flight period undoubtedly results in under-recording, especially as it seldom occurs far from wooded habitats. The species is rather variable and all the forms illustrated in Skinner (1984) have been found in Surrey.

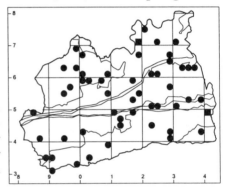

Agriopis aurantiaria (Hübner, 1799)   **Scarce Umber**

Resident; woodland, wooded commons; fairly widespread and not uncommon.

Univoltine; November.

Foodplant – oak, sallow, (hazel, hawthorn, lime, sloe, aspen, honeysuckle).

This species is fairly widespread and certainly not as scarce as its English name implies. It comes to light but does not appear to fly far from the woods where it occurs, and consequently must be somewhat overlooked.

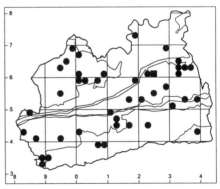

Searching the bare twigs with a paraffin lantern should reveal its presence. Ab. *fumipennaria* Hellweger is a melanic form which occurs regularly on Mitcham Common (BS), and was also recorded from Milford in 1992 (DWB).

Agriopis marginaria (Fabricius, 1777)   Dotted Border

Resident; woodland, wooded commons; widespread and fairly common.
Univoltine; March and early April.
Foodplant – sloe, (lime, oak, hazel, hawthorn, sallow, aspen, elm, ash, birch, honeysuckle).
The Dotted Border is found throughout much of the county, although light-trap records do tend to underestimate its frequency. Searching woodland edges and rides is the best method of finding it, the males on twigs and the wingless females on tree trunks. The species is rather variable and melanic forms have been noted, including ab. *fuscata* Mosley from Mitcham (PMS).

Erannis defoliaria (Clerck, 1759)   Mottled Umber

Resident; woodland, commons; widespread and common.
Univoltine; late October to December.
Foodplant – sloe, sallow, aspen, sycamore, birch, oak, wych elm, hawthorn, hazel, field maple, beech, sweet chestnut, lime, rose, (plum, honeysuckle).
A common species which, like the preceding species of the genus *Agriopis*, would be regarded as uncommon based on light trap records. The larva is widely polyphagous on deciduous trees and shrubs, and larval records form a large proportion of the total. The male is rather variable and many different forms can occur within one population.

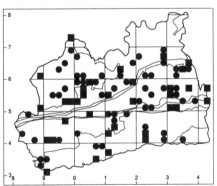

Menophra abruptaria (Thunberg, 1792) **Waved Umber**

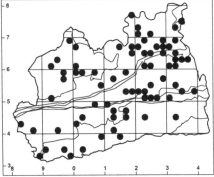

Resident; woodland, gardens; widespread and fairly common.

Univoltine; late April to mid-June.

Foodplant – (privet)

A widespread species which is probably commonest in suburban gardens in the London area; for example, trap counts at Mitcham show 1981 (5), 82 (23), 83 (13) (RKAM). The melanic form, ab. *fuscata* Tutt, has been recorded from South Croydon (GAC), Mitcham (RKAM), Banstead (RFMcC), Chessington (JP), Nunhead (BS), and Wimbledon (JVD). Occasional specimens recorded from late July to the beginning of September probably represent a second brood, which is easily produced in captivity.

Peribatodes rhomboidaria ([Denis & Schiffermüller], 1775) **Willow Beauty**

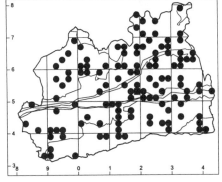

Resident; woodland, wooded commons, gardens; widespread and common.

Probably **bivoltine**; June to September, peaks in July and September.

Foodplant – wild privet, yew, (hawthorn). This species is widespread and often abundant, although the female is seldom seen. Regularly run traps produce counts as follows: South Croydon, 1983 (151), 84 (145), 85 (59) (GAC); Mitcham, 1981 (59), 82 (78), 83 (123) (RKAM); Bramley, 1985 (47), 86 (110) (RFB). Also at acl at Ashtead, 1987 (225), 88 (103), 89 (106) (GG), and at the Rothamsted trap at Wisley, 1986 (27), 87 (31) (AJH). The moth occurs throughout the summer and early autumn, but peak counts in July and again in September suggest a bivoltine pattern; larval records are too few to provide supporting evidence. Most specimens are referable to f. *perfumaria* Newman, and the melanic ab. *rebeli* Aigner has been recorded from Nutfield, 8.8.1988 (PAC).

Peribatodes secundaria (Esper, 1794)   Feathered Beauty

Status uncertain; probably vagrant.

July.

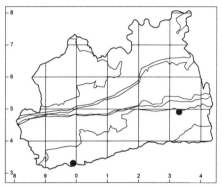

The Feathered Beauty is a species recently established in this country, first found in Kent in 1981 (Skinner, 1981) and West Sussex in 1982. It has subsequently been found in a wood in East Sussex, and as a solitary example in Essex. The future of the Kent colony is in some doubt following extensive storm damage to the conifers in 1987. Two specimens from two distinct areas have been found in Surrey.

RECORDS – **Tugley Wood**, 22.7.85 (1 male) (SCP) [this area of woodland is contiguous with the West Sussex colony]; **Bransland Wood**, 23.7.88 (1 worn specimen) (GAC), in a wood with various conifer species, searched for but not seen in 1989 and 90.

Selidosema brunnearia (Villers, 1789)   Bordered Grey
ssp. *scandinavaria* Staudinger, 1901

Notable/Na

Resident; heathland; local and uncommon.

Univoltine; August.

Foodplant – heather.

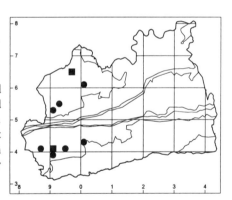

The Bordered Grey is a local species found on heathland, both on the greensand and Bagshot beds, although rarely in any numbers. The larva has been swept from heather at Thursley Common (SHC), and at Chobham Common (PJB). The adult is most frequently noted by day, but will also come to light.

RECORDS – **Chobham Common**, 1988-89 a few larvae (PJB), 11.8.90, 27.7.91 (DY); **Horsell Common**, 12.8.76 (CGMdeW), 12.8.79 (AJH); **Wyke Common**, 17.8.96 (GAC); **Pirbright Common**, 1983 (PC); **Rushmoor**, 2-3.8.82, 8.8.83, 14.8.84 (PAD); **Thursley Common**, 13.5.81 larvae (SHC), 8.8.81, 30.7.82, 3.8.89, 91 (5), 21.8.93 (DWB), 13.8.91 (RFMcC); **Milford**, 11.8.91 (2) (DWB); **Bramley**, 5.8.81 (RFB).

Deileptenia ribeata (Clerck, 1759)   **Satin Beauty**

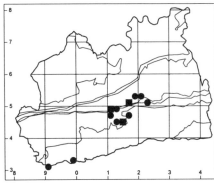

Resident; woodland and downland; local and uncommon.

Univoltine; June and July.

Foodplant – yew, Scots pine.

A local species which is rarely seen in any numbers, most often found in the woods of central Surrey, but also occurring in the extreme south-west. The predominant form is f. *sericearia* Curtis, but the fully melanic form f. *nigra* Cockayne occurs at Box Hill where the larvae are associated with yew. Elsewhere the larva has been recorded on Scots pine at Redlands Wood (GAC).

RECORDS – **Haslemere** (SHC); **Tugley Wood**, 22.7.85, 10.7.86, 14.7.90 (SCP); **Oaken Wood**, 20.7.95 (GAC); **Friday Street**, 7.7.81 (RKAM); **Abinger**, 9.7.76 (RFMcC); **White Downs**, 5.82 larvae on yew (JP), 10.7.95 (DC); **Westcott Downs**, 13.7.83 (GAC); **Headley Warren**, 4.8.94, 5-29.7.95 (GAC); **Box Hill**, 1978 larvae on yew (BS), 1988 larvae on yew (PAC), 1995 f. *nigra* (RMP); **Dawcombe**, 13-28.7.90, 5.7-9.8.91, 30.6-31.7.92 (DC); **Buckland**, 1980s, not seen for about nine years (CH); **Redlands Wood**, 14.5.89 larva on Scots pine (GAC); **Holmwood Common**, 27.6.76 (JP).

Alcis repandata (Linnaeus, 1758)   **Mottled Beauty**

ssp. *repandata* (Linnaeus, 1758)

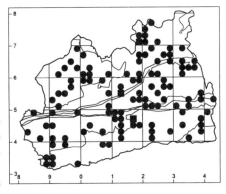

Resident; woodland, commons, heathland, gardens; widespread and common.

Univoltine; June to mid-August.

Foodplant – sloe, traveller's joy, heather, bilberry, birch, oak, (hawthorn, yew, juniper).

A common species found throughout the county in a wide variety of habitat types. The banded form f. *conversaria* Hübner occurs as a very small percentage of some populations. The larva is probably polyphagous and has been recorded from a range of plants.

[Alcis jubata (Thunberg, 1788) **Dotted Carpet**

Doubtful.

A specimen of this predominantly western species is recorded in the Charterhouse list: Grayswood 10.6.1936 by H. Stroyan (Perrins, 1959). There is no other Surrey record, although Barrett (1901) records taking it himself at Woolmer Forest, Hampshire, only a few miles from the Surrey border. However, the record is over a month earlier than the normal emergence period, and in the absence of a voucher specimen this record must be considered doubtful.]

Hypomecis roboraria ([Denis & Schiffermüller], 1775) PLATE 9 **Great Oak Beauty**

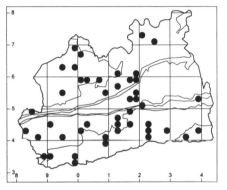

Notable/Nb

Resident; woodland; fairly widespread and fairly common.

Univoltine; mid-June to mid-July.

The Great Oak Beauty is fairly widespread in Surrey. With the exception of a few examples captured at Richmond Park and Wimbledon, it occurs no closer to London than at Ashtead Common, and it is also virtually absent from the north-east of the county. Elsewhere in the south and west of the county it can be found in most of the larger oak woods and can be fairly common, for example: Bramley, 1985 (7), 86 (13) (RFB); and Windlesham RES where as many as 46 were recorded in 1976 (JAB). Specimens from Richmond and Wimbledon are referable to f. *infuscata* Staudinger, which has also been recorded from central Surrey, and an example similar to f. *melaina* Schulze was taken at Wimbledon, 2.7.1967 (JVD).

Serraca punctinalis (Scopoli, 1763) **Pale Oak Beauty**

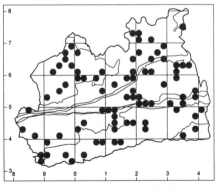

Resident; woodland, commons; widespread and common.

Univoltine; June.

The Pale Oak Beauty is found all across the county and, unlike the previous species with which it may be confused, is widely distributed in the London area albeit at a relatively low density. In rural areas it can be very common as the following trap counts show: Bramley, 1985 (33), 86 (59) (RFB); Milford, 1992 (19) (DWB); Banstead Downs, 1989 (17) (DC). The melanic ab. *humperti* Humpert has occurred at South Croydon (GAC), Friday Street and Ranmore (BS).

Cleorodes lichenaria (Hufnagel, 1767)   **Brussels Lace**

Status uncertain; only one record since the 1950s.
Evidently this species was once fairly widespread in Surrey. The *VCH* gives Haslemere, Gomshall, Box Hill, Redhill, and Ashtead, and in the same period it was recorded from Chertsey, 20.7.1863 (Clarke, *Week. Ent.* 2:212), and the larvae were well known from the Bishop's fence at Addington from where they were reared in 1875 and 1876 (West, *Ent. Rec.* **18**:172). Larvae were found at the SLENHS field meeting at Cutt Mill on 8.5.1938. By the middle of this century it had declined almost to extinction, the last recorded examples being: Box Hill, larvae on 23.5.1948 (Eagles, *Proc. SLENHS* **1948-49**); Ranmore, a series taken in the early 1950s; Juniper Bottom, 19.9.1957 larvae, not reared (Spreadbury in Evans, 1973) [the larvae would have been very small at this date and, as the moth was not reared, this record must be considered unconfirmed]. The situation in Kent is similar (Chalmers-Hunt, 1968-81). In mainland Hampshire it was stated to have become very scarce (Goater, 1974) although it would appear that in recent years, in the New Forest at least, this trend has been reversed (Goater, 1992). This general decline in the south-east of England may be due to climatic conditions or possibly pollution affecting the lichens on which the larva feeds. A single example, of uncertain origin, has been taken recently.

RECORDS – **Nutfield**, 3.7.94 (PAC).

Ectropis bistortata (Goeze, 1781)   **Engrailed**

Resident; woodland, commons; widespread and common.

Bivoltine; April, and July and early August.

Foodplant – birch, sloe, oak, bramble, hazel.

This species and the following one are subject to a considerable degree of confusion; indeed their claim to distinct species status is open to question. The adults, their genitalia, and their larvae are very similar, and the best guide to separating them is the flight period;

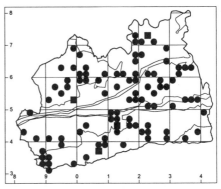

bistortata is double brooded appearing in April and July, whereas *crepuscularia* is single brooded flying from mid-May to mid-June. There is very little overlap especially when the condition of the specimen is taken into account. The Engrailed is a generally distributed and common species. Occasional examples of a third brood have been known, one taken at Friday Street, 14.9.1991 (GAC) being an example.

Ectropis crepuscularia ([Denis & Schiffermüller], 1775)   **Small Engrailed**

Resident; woodland, commons; local and scarce.

Univoltine; mid-May to mid-June.

The Small Engrailed is a moth that is frequently misidentified for the Engrailed (*q.v.*). Compared to that species it is local and generally scarce, most records being of a single example. In view of this all the records are given.

RECORDS – **Rushmoor**, 20.6.83, 3-4.6.85 (PAD); **Haslemere**, 5.89, 5.90 (EE); **Wyke Common**, 25.5.91 (PJS); **Milford**, 25.5.93 (DWB); **Sidney Wood**, 29.5.87 (AJ); **Bramley**, 1984 (3) (RFB); **Virginia Water**, 20-28.5.82 (AG); **Ewhurst**, 3.6.86 (SFI); **East Horsley**, 23.5.76 (LJDW); **Friday Street**, 1980-86 (BS), 22.5.93, 27.5.95 (DC); **Holmwood Common**, 11.6.83 (PC); **Dawcombe**, 8.5.90 (DC).

Paradarisa consonaria (Hübner, 1799)   **Square Spot**

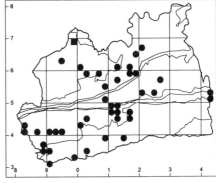

Resident; woodland; restricted and uncommon.

Univoltine; May to mid-June.

Foodplant – lime.

The Square Spot is more or less restricted to central and south-western Surrey. Outside this area it has occurred at Limpsfield Chart on 6.7.1978 (DCL) and 1.6.1986 (GAC), and in the extreme north-west at Thorpe and Windlesham. This suggests that it has to some extent been overlooked, especially in the wealden woods. It is, however, nowhere common with even the regularly run traps recording no more than two or three a year.

Paradarisa extersaria (Hübner, 1799)   **Brindled White-spot**

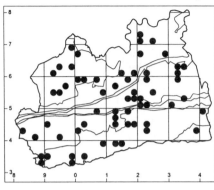

Resident; woodland, commons;
widespread and fairly common.

Univoltine; June and early July.

The Brindled White-spot is a rather widespread species found in suitable habitat across the county, and is probably commoner now than during the period covered by both the north-west and north-east Surrey lists. Although occurring quite well into the metropolis it is here only taken in small numbers; in rural areas it can be quite numerous: Bramley 1985 (4), 86 (17) (RFB); Pirbright RES 1980 (12), 81 (6) (ED).

Aethalura punctulata ([Denis & Schiffermüller], 1775)   **Grey Birch**

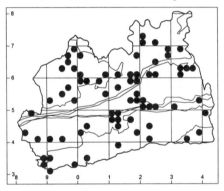

Resident; commons, heathland, woodland;
widespread but uncommon.

Univoltine; May and June.

The Grey Birch is found over much of the county, although reference to the distribution map shows that there are several fairly large areas from which it has not been recorded. In the rural ones at least, it has probably been overlooked as it is never a common species, the static traps recording only single figures annually. An extreme melanic, referable to ab. *obscuraria* Paux, was taken at Friday Street, 7.5.76 (D. O'Keefe per BS).

Ematurga atomaria (Linnaeus, 1758)   **Common Heath**

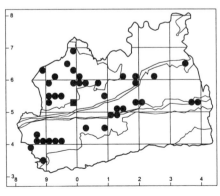

Resident; heathland, chalk grassland;
restricted but common.

Bivoltine; May and June, and late July and August.

Foodplant – heather.

The Common Heath has a restricted distribution due to its habitat preferences. On the heathland of west Surrey it is a common species, found occasionally at light traps but mostly flying by day; it can evidently exist on quite small areas as it is found on the relict heath at Addington Hills. Elsewhere it occurs, but rather less commonly, on the downs around Dorking and Oxted, and at Banstead. The larvae clearly have a different foodplant on the chalk but it has not been recorded.

Bupalus piniaria (Linnaeus, 1758)   Bordered White

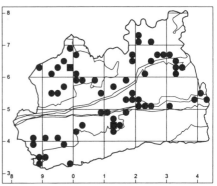

Resident; woodland, heathland, gardens; restricted but fairly common.
Univoltine; June and July.
Foodplant – Scots pine.
As one would expect of a pine feeder the Bordered White is widely distributed on the heathland and pine plantations of west Surrey. It is virtually absent from the weald and very local on the chalk. In the London area it is to be found on commons and in gardens and probably breeds on isolated trees in such areas. Both sexes come to light and the males are often seen flying around the tops of pine trees in the afternoon. Occasionally specimens of the male have been taken in which the ground colour is very pale and closer to Scottish examples than typical southern ones. A form of the female with a melanic underside has been recorded from Richmond Park, 6.6.1992 (AJ), and Leith Hill, 13.6.1992 (CWP).

Cabera pusaria (Linnaeus, 1758)   Common White Wave

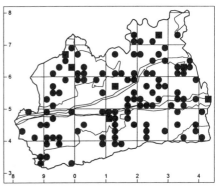

Resident; commons, heathland, woodland; widespread and common.
Possibly **bivoltine**; May to August, peak July.
Foodplant – birch, alder.
A very widely distributed and common species, the Common White Wave is perhaps commoner in rural areas as the following trap counts show: Windlesham RES, 1980 (46), 81 (26) (JAB); Bramley, 1985 (7), 86 (27) (RFB); Wisley RES, 1986 (12), 87 (18), 90 (8), 91 (12) (AJH); Mitcham, 1981 (15), 82 (10), 83 (16) (RKAM); South Croydon, 1983 (8), 84 (3), 85 (4) (GAC). The species is probably double brooded but has been found almost continuously from May to August; the larva, although often noted, has only been recorded in September.

Cabera exanthemata (Scopoli, 1763)   Common Wave

Resident; woodland, commons; widespread and fairly common.

Possibly **bivoltine**; May to August, peak July.

Foodplant – sallow.

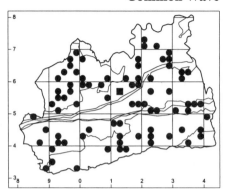

The Common Wave is found throughout the county but is slightly more local than the preceding species due to its preference for damper areas in woods and on commons. It is thus much less frequent on the bulk of the chalk. Although overall less common than *pusaria* it can outnumber it locally as the following, comparative trap counts show: Windlesham RES, 1980 (12), 81 (19) (JAB); Bramley, 1985 (50), 86 (93) (RFB); Wisley RES, 1986 (11), 87 (6), 90 (3), 91 (5) (AJH); Mitcham, 1981 (1), 82 (19), 83 (10) (RKAM); South Croydon, 1983 (1), 85 (1) (GAC).

Lomographa bimaculata (Fabricius, 1775)   White-pinion Spotted

Resident; woodland, commons; widespread and fairly common.

Univoltine; late May and June.

Foodplant – hawthorn.

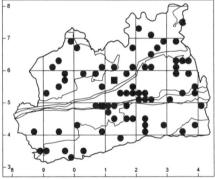

The White-pinion Spotted occurs generally over much of the county but rarely in any numbers. Certainly there is no record of extreme abundance such as the one in Evans (1973). The statement in Evans (*loc. cit.*) that it is very local off the chalk bears no resemblance to the current status of the moth and is probably an artefact of his chosen recording area. Bretherton (1957) considered it a rare insect, but it does occur fairly widely in the north-west although avoiding the heaths.

Lomographa temerata ([Denis & Schiffermüller], 1775)   Clouded Silver

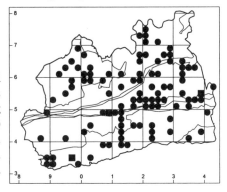

Resident; woodland, commons, downland; widespread and common.

Univoltine; May to July.

Foodplant – hawthorn.

The Clouded Silver is a widely distributed and very common species. Some idea of its frequency can be gained from the following trap counts: Bramley, 1985 (112), 86 (167) (RFB); Banstead Downs ,1989 (201), 90 (75), 91 (25) (DC); Mitcham, 1981 (22), 82 (57), 83 (34) (RKAM); South Croydon, 1983 (20), 84 (20), 85 (9) (GAC).

Aleucis distinctata (Herrich-Schäffer, 1839)   Sloe Carpet

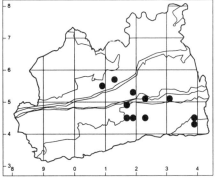

Notable/Nb

Resident; commons; very local and scarce.

Univoltine; late April and early May.

Foodplant – sloe

The Sloe Carpet is a very local species in Surrey and restricted to two areas: the weald, and the London clay around Bookham and Effingham. A typical site would be scrubby grassland with a good growth of sloe, as isolated bushes rather than thickets, on which the adults can be found resting; the appearance of the sloe blossom being a good guide to when the species emerges. Effingham Common is the classic site for this species but it does not seem to have been recorded from there since 1972. As the moth requires searching for rather than relying on the moth trap, it is quite possible that is has to some extent been overlooked. A suitable method for locating it is for one person to hold a lamp whilst others tap the sloe bushes and catch the moths as they are disturbed.

RECORDS – **East Horsley**, 8.5.76 (LJDW); **Bookham Common**, 10.4.93 (1), 17.4.93 (4) (GAC), 11.4.95 (20) (JC), 11-14.4.96 (SCP); **Little Bookham Common**, 19.4.93 (JP); **Holmwood Common**, 17.5.85 (PC); **Dorking**, 3.5.84 (DAT); **Headley Warren**, 31.3.95 (GAC); **Newdigate**, 4.5.78 (RAC); **Buckland**, 3.5.86, 25.4.96 (CH); **Nutfield**, 5.4.77 (PAC); **Leigh**, 1986, 88, 12.4.91 (RF); **Lingfield**, 19.4.92, 2-10.5.95 (JC).

Theria primaria (Haworth, 1809)   Early Moth

Resident; woodland, commons; fairly widespread and fairly common.

Univoltine; January and February.

Foodplant – sloe, hawthorn.

The Early Moth emerges very early in the year and the adult is rather sluggish and consequently requires to be specifically searched for. There is no doubt that it is under-recorded, but its apparent absence from the more built-up areas of London is probably real. The larva is distinctive and can be beaten in May.

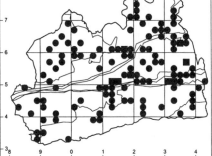

Campaea margaritata (Linnaeus, 1767)   Light Emerald

Resident; woodland, commons; widespread and common.

Univoltine; late June and July.

Foodplant – sloe, beech, ash, bilberry, wild privet, sallow, yew, (hawthorn, birch).

A very common and widely distributed species, occurring everywhere that there are trees. Very occasional second-brood specimens have been recorded as follows: Milford, 19-30.9.1992 (2), 4.9.1994, 17-19.9.1995 (DWB); South Croydon, 10.10.1985, and 25.9.1994 (GAC), and the species does not appear to be regularly double-brooded as it apparently is in north-west Kent (West, 1988).

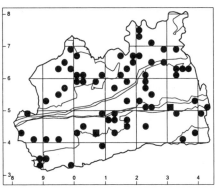

Hylaea fasciaria (Linnaeus, 1758)   Barred Red

Resident; woodland, heathland; widespread and fairly common.

Univoltine; June and July.

Foodplant – Scots pine, Norway spruce.

A rather widespread species, undoubtedly commonest in areas of coniferous woodland, but evidently capable of existing on isolated pines in suburban gardens; a situation found in many of the pine feeders. The typical red form occurs widely, but in south London is replaced by darker and greyer forms, some of which are probably referable to ab. *grisearia* Fuchs. A female example of the green form, ab. *prasinaria* Denis & Schiffermüller, taken at Nutfield, 16.7.1991 (PAC), is the only record of this form from Surrey.

Gnophos obscurata ([Denis & Schiffermüller], 1775)   **Annulet**

Resident; heathland; very local and rare.

Univoltine; August.

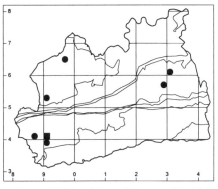

The Annulet is an example of a species that has declined from being relatively common to near extinction. The *VCH* describes it as being "common at Haslemere, Oxshott, Esher, and elsewhere on the heaths, and the pale form occurs on the chalk". Bretherton (1957, and 1965) considered it locally common on the heaths and recorded singletons from many of the static traps. In north-east Surrey it was known from Streatham Vale, 1964-69, and Westhumble in 1950, Box Hill in 1961, and Banstead in 1962 (Evans, 1973). The last east Surrey record was Hooley in 1978, and in north-west Surrey it has only been seen twice recently.

RECORDS – **Rushmoor**, 3.8.82, 8.8.83, 25.7.85 (PAD); **Thursley Common**, 13.5.81 larvae (SHC), 13.8.91 (RFMcC); **Wyke Common**, 16.8.96 (DWB); **Chobham Common**, 30.7.85 (CH), 28.7.95 (DC); **Hooley**, 22.8.78 (CH); **Purley**, 26.8.77 (PMS).

Aspitates gilvaria ([Denis & Schiffermüller], 1775)   PLATE 14   **Straw Belle**

ssp. *gilvaria* ([Denis & Schiffermüller], 1775)

RDB3

Resident; chalk downland; very local but sometimes common.

Univoltine; late July and August.

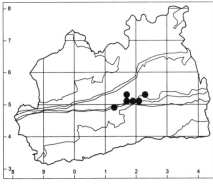

The Straw Belle is a very local species confined to the scarp slope of the North Downs. Its principal centre is those downs between Dorking and Reigate, and in Evans (1973) Bretherton states that he was unable to find it west of the Dorking gap "despite much search". Since then it has been found at Westcott Downs. In addition to the chalk records, Bretherton (1957) lists a record from Longcross in 1949 by C.W. Pierce, who also noted the next species from there. In the absence of a voucher specimen, this record must be considered dubious.

RECORDS – **Westcott Downs**, 1.8.76 (PAM), 11.8.76 (RFB), 21.8.76 (CGMdeW),

5.8.81 (RGS); **Box Hill**, 14.8.78 (8) (JP), 26.7.83 (RKAM), 13.8.84 (GAC), 3.8.94 (2) (JP); **Brockham Warren**, 9.8.94 (3) (DWB), 1.9.96 (8) (DC); **Betchworth**, 24.7.90, 28.7.92 (20) (BS); **Juniper Hill**, 10.8.83 (KNAA).

Aspitates ochrearia (Rossi, 1794)   Yellow Belle

Vagrant; three records only.
Bretherton (1957) lists three specimens: New Haw, 25.8.1954; Longcross, 1948 and 1949 (Pierce). Presumably he was satisfied as to the accuracy of them.

Dyscia fagaria (Thunberg, 1784)   Grey Scalloped Bar

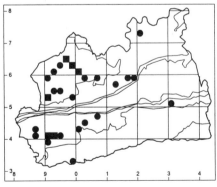

Resident; heathland; very local and scarce.
Univoltine; May and early June.
Foodplant – heather.
A very local heathland species recorded from only six sites during the survey period. The status seems to have changed very little since Bretherton's list; possibly it is slightly reduced. The habitat requirement seems to be for short heather (Bretherton, 1957) (*c.f. Xestia agathina*).

RECORDS – **Rushmoor**, 8.5.85 (PAD); **Thursley Common**, 19.5.81 (SHC), 5.6.83 (DWB); **Pirbright RES**, 1976 (3), 80 (4), 81 (4) (ED); **Chobham Common**, 4.9.82 larvae (SHC); **Horsell Common**, 24.3-12.4.78 larvae (RFMcC); **Thorpe**, 1984 (PJB).

Perconia strigillaria (Hübner, 1787)   Grass Wave

Notable/Nb
Resident; heathland, heathy commons; restricted, but fairly common.
Univoltine; June.
Foodplant – heather, (petty whin).
The Grass Wave is a typical species of the Surrey heaths and here may be found quite commonly, at least as a larva. The adult comes to light and may be easily put up during the day. In addition to heathland sites it is known from heathy woods and commons such as Tugley Wood, and Ashtead and Bookham Commons. It is virtually absent from the London area (Plant, 1993), but was taken at Richmond Park on 6.6.1992 (GAC).

SPHINGIDAE – Hawk-moths

A family of medium-sized to very large moths of which about half the species recorded in Surrey are migrants. The Bee Hawks and the Humming-bird Hawk are day-flying species. The rest are nocturnal and strongly attracted to light. The larvae are mostly brightly coloured and can be distinguished by the dorsal horn on the eleventh segment. The pupae are subterranean and the resident, tree-feeding species can be found by digging beneath the relevant foodplant during the winter.

Agrius convolvuli (Linnaeus, 1758)   Convolvulus Hawk

Migrant; not infrequent.

Foodplant – field bindweed.

The Convolvulus Hawk is a migrant species which occurs in Surrey every few years or so, usually in the autumn although there are a couple of July records. The larva has been found once but it is doubtful if successful breeding could occur.

1976 – **Wormley**, 23-27.8 (3) (JLM); **Selsdon**, 28.8 (EHW); **Wotton**, 8.9 (JDH); **Thorpe**, 27.9 (PJB); **Reigate**, 16.10 (RAC).
1981 – **Leigh**, 26-28.9 (2) (RF), **Chiddingfold**, 29.9 (SHC).
1983 – **Shirley**, 23.8 netted at *Nicotiana* (KMG); **Bramley**, 7.9 (RFB); **Nutfield**, 12.9 (PAC); **Leigh**, 15.9-3.10 (3) (RF); **Oxted**, 23.9 (TD); **Ashtead**, 25.9 (ASW); **Rushmoor**, 23.9-1.10 (4) (PAD); **Tolworth**, 27.9 (JP); **Putney**, 1.10 (Sealey in Plant, *L.N.* **64**:55).
1984 – **Leigh**, 23.7 (RF).
1986 – **Mickleham**, 14.10 (SBRC).
1987 – **Woking**, 11.8 (J. Pontin); **Mickleham**, 25.8 (SBRC); **Nutfield**, 16.9 (PAC); **Wisley**, 9.10 (AJH).
1990 – **Hindhead**, 27.8 (EE); **Buckland Hills**, 29.8 larva on field bindweed (PAC).
1991 – **Milford**, 30.9 (J. Secrett per DWB); **Leigh**, 2.10 (RF).
1992 – **Cobham**, 31.8 (JP); **Leigh**, 2.9 (RF).
1995 – **Nutfield**, 5.7 (PAC); **Buckland**, 11.10 (CH).

Acherontia atropos (Linnaeus, 1758)   Death's-head Hawk

Migrant; scarce.

Foodplant – jasmine, potato, (buddleia).

The Death's-head Hawk owes its presence in the county purely to migration, but is considerably scarcer than the previous species with only a dozen records during the survey period. It would appear to be less frequent than in the past, as the *VCH* described it as "not uncommon throughout the county, especially in the larval state", and in 1950 a number of larvae and pupae were found in north-west Surrey (Bretherton, 1957). This may reflect a decline in local potato-growing as this species is more often noted in the larval stage than as an adult.

1976 – **Putney**, August, a larva on jasmine (Delay in de Worms, *L.N.* **57**:85); **Normandy**, autumn (per CGMdeW).

1977 – **Wormley**, 27.4 (JLM).
1978 – **Tolworth**, 29.6 (JP).
1980 – **Thorpe**, 31.8 (Boon, *Bull. AES* **40**:15).
1982 – **Ashtead**, 2.9, dead in beehive (ASW); **Wandsworth**, 7.9 (Messenbird in Plant, *L.N.* **65**:25); **Betchworth**, 14.9 (J. Colombé, *Ent. Rec.* **95**:146).
1984 – **Haslemere**, 26.8, a larva (Tidmarsh, *Ent. Rec.* **97**:225.); **Ripley**, 8.9, full-grown larva on potato (AJH).
1987 – **Ewhurst**, 18.6 (MR).
1991 – **Selhurst**, 5.9 full-grown larva (Clayton per BS).

Sphinx ligustri Linnaeus, 1758   Privet Hawk

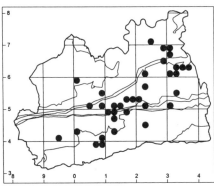

Resident; downland, gardens, woodland; restricted and uncommon.
Univoltine; mid-June to mid-July.
Foodplant – buddleia, (privet, lilac, ash, forsythia, wayfaring-tree, spiraea).

The Privet Hawk is a species that seems to have declined rather during the survey period, and is at present restricted to the North Downs, the gardens of south London, and a few areas in south-western Surrey. Bretherton (1957) described it as fairly common at all the fixed traps, but it has only been recorded once from his area during the last 20 years. It still has a similar distribution in north-east Surrey to that given in Evans (1973), although it is certainly less common. This decline seems to have occurred mainly during the 1970s; at Bramley it was recorded fairly commonly up to 1976, falling to two examples in 1985 and none in 1986, and the trap counts for Selsdon (1972-81) illustrate a similar decline: 1972 (21), 73 (4), 74 (9), 75 (1), 77 (1), 78 (2) (EHW). It is probably now commonest on the scarp of the downs between Guildford and Reigate.

Hyloicus pinastri (Linnaeus, 1758)   Pine Hawk

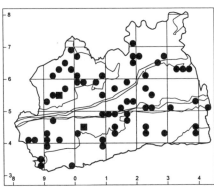

Resident; woodland, heathland; fairly widespread and fairly common.
Univoltine; late May to early August.
Foodplant – Scots pine.

The Pine Hawk is fairly widespread in Surrey although scarcer in the east of the county. The moth was recorded from Esher as early as the beginning of the nineteenth century but was not considered as a breeding species in Britain until the second half of that century, when a larva was found near Wimbledon (*E.M.M.*

25:159). A specimen was recorded from Hindhead on 18.7.1925 (*Ent.* **84**:23) and a further one was taken in that area on 24.6.1946 (Mere, *Ent.* **79**:270). Colonization of Surrey took place in the late 1940s; the first examples for north-west Surrey were at Bagshot and Pirbright in 1948 (Bretherton, 1957) and a larva at Ash Vale in 1949 (Haynes, *Proc. SLENHS* **1949-50**:78), and it had been found as far east as Croydon on 2.8.1949 (Jarvis, *Ent. Rec.* **61**:94). Currently the moth is fairly common in the pine woods and on heathland in the west as the following trap counts show: Milford 1990 (10), 91 (12), 92 (8) (DWB); Bramley 1985 (9), 86 (6) (RFB).

Mimas tiliae (Linnaeus, 1758) Lime Hawk

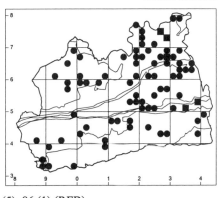

Resident; gardens, woodland; fairly widespread and common.
Univoltine; May to mid-July.
Foodplant – (lime, elm, cultivated maple, birch).
The Lime Hawk is very much an urban species and rather uncommon in rural areas. It is most frequent in the south London district where the following trap counts are typical: Mitcham, 1981 (17), 82 (19), 83 (16), 84 (12) (RKAM); South Croydon, 1983 (27), 84 (15), 85 (12), 86 (10) (GAC). As a comparison, at Bramley the moth was seen as follows: 1985 (5), 86 (1) (RFB).

Smerinthus ocellata (Linnaeus, 1758) Eyed Hawk

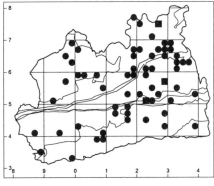

Resident; commons, gardens; widespread and common.
Univoltine; June to mid-July.
Foodplant – apple, sallow, willow, laurel.
As with the previous species, the Eyed Hawk is probably commonest on the commons and in gardens in suburban London. It is, though, a regular species in more rural areas and the apparent absence from areas of west Surrey is likely to be due to under-recording; it has certainly been found on some of the heaths, the larva feeding on small sallows alongside the rides. Trap counts show: Mitcham, 1981 (7), 82 (8), 83 (7) (RKAM); South Croydon, 1983 (16), 84 (10), 85 (16), 86 (7) (GAC); Bramley, 1985 (5), 86 (4) (RFB). In addition to the usual foodplants, several larvae were found feeding on a hedge of laurel at Croydon and reared through on it (WL).

Laothoe populi (Linnaeus, 1758)   Poplar Hawk

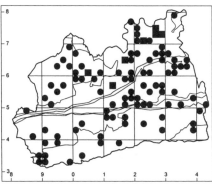

Resident; commons, woodland;
widespread and common.
Possibly **bivoltine**; May to August, peaks
late May and July.
Foodplant – Lombardy poplar, aspen,
sallow.
The Poplar Hawk occurs throughout the
county, widely in the parks and commons of
south London where poplars are often planted,
and also in rural areas where it is more often
associated with aspen and sallow. At some of
the static traps it can be an abundant species:
Bramley, 1985 (79), 86 (84) (RFB); Mitcham, 1981 (14), 82 (22), 83 (24) (RKAM); South
Croydon, 1983 (33), 84 (11), 85 (18) (GAC). The species' voltinism is difficult to determine;
there are apparently two peaks of emergence with moths recorded from May to August, but
larvae have only been noted from July to September.

Hemaris tityus (Linnaeus, 1758)   PLATE 1   Narrow-bordered Bee Hawk

Extinct; not recorded since 1953.
This species and the next are very similar when on the wing, and have, in the past, both
shared the name *bombyliformis*. Some confusion, especially in the earlier records, may
have occurred but it is certain that this moth was once a resident and equally certain that it
is now extinct. Barrett (1895) considered this species more northern than *fuciformis* and
scarce in Surrey but apparently spreading southwards. Tutt (1902) however was able to list
a number of localities across the county: Haslemere, Redhill, Coombe Wood, Wimbledon
Common, Leatherhead, Dorking area, Guildford, and Oxshott, and in 1918 it was sufficiently
common in the Chiddingfold area for a series of 42 to be taken (Tullett, *Ent. Rec.* **32**:55).
By the middle of this century it was known from central and north-western Surrey: Fetcham
Downs, 1945, and Ashtead, 1947 (EHW); Banstead Wood, 1947 (Johnson); Bookham
Common (Rumsey) (Plant, 1993). Also Pirbright, 20.6.1944; Clasford Common, rather
numerous 1945/46 (Bretherton, 1957), and Box Hill, 9.6.1953 (Sankey, *E.M.M.* **89**:286).
This latter record appears to be the last sighting of the species in Surrey. No doubt land
drainage and house building have taken their toll on this moth, but the species has also
shown a national decline and a retreat to more western localities.

Hemaris fuciformis (Linnaeus, 1758) PLATES 5,10 **Broad-bordered Bee Hawk**

Notable/Nb
Resident; woodland; very local and
    uncommon.
Univoltine; late May and early June.
Foodplant – wild honeysuckle.

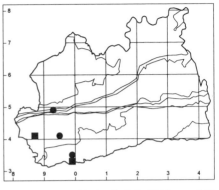

The Broad-bordered Bee Hawk has, like the
previous species, undergone a serious decline
in Surrey. It does manage to hold on in a few
sites in the extreme south-west of the county
where it is sometimes not uncommon as
larvae. Tutt (1902) described it as common
and generally distributed, although all the sites
in the *VCH* are in the western half of the county, and near Hambledon in July 1919 over 100
larvae were found (Tullett, *Ent. Rec.* **32**:55). Larvae were found at Ranmore Common,
26.6.1937 (*Proc. SLENHS* **1937-38**:42). Bretherton (1957) gave several sites in the north-
west including breeding records from Pirbright, and Evans (1973) gives breeding records
from Westhumble (1947) and Morden (1950). It was recorded from Prince's Coverts, 1947-
50 (CGMdeW), and at Bookham Common at the same period ova and larvae were described
as common every year (Wheeler, 1955); larvae were last noted there on 11.7.1966 (BS).

RECORDS – **Rushmoor**, 1983-85 larvae (PAD); **Milford**, 2.6.80 (1) (DWB);
Fisherlane Wood, 23.5.76, 1.6.77 (RFB), 19.7.91 larvae on honeysuckle (GAC), 24.5.92
(SWG); **Tugley Wood**, 2.6.85, 17.5.90, 31.5.96 (SCP), 7.6.96 (RMP); **Botany Bay**,
10.7.77 (DWB); **Oaken Wood**, 1.7.95 larvae, 23.6.96 larvae (GAC); **Hog's Back**,
13.5.96 (DWB).

Macroglossum stellatarum (Linnaeus, 1758)   **Humming-bird Hawk**

Migrant; usually uncommon.
Foodplant – (lady's bedstraw).

The Humming-bird Hawk is another of the migrant species, but one of the more regular
occurring in most years. It is principally day-flying and thus comes to the attention of the
general naturalist more than other migrants might. 1996 was a excellent year for the moth
with adults recorded from April to the end of August; local breeding may well have occurred
although the larva has not been recorded during the survey period.

1976 – **Selsdon** (2) (EHW); **Tadworth**, August-September (3) (*L.N.* **57**:81-90).

1977 – **Wimbledon**, 2.3 (N.D. Riley); **Thursley Common**, June (SBRC).

1980 – **Leigh** (RF).

1982 – **Headley**, 11.9 (RDH); **Cranleigh**, 16.9 (PC).

1983 – **Leigh** (RF); **Addington**, 13.6 at honeysuckle (RGS); **Woking**, August
    (J. Pontin); **Mitcham**, 1-15.8 (PAM); **Bookham Common**, 14.8 (Bratton in
    Plant, 1986); **Rushmoor**, 14.9 (PAD); **Purley**, 16.9 (DCL).

1984 – **Thorpe** (2) (PJB); **Croham Hurst**, 29.7 (GBC).

1986 – **Wotton**, July (JDH); **Clapham**, 19.7 (Miss N. Tyson per CWP).

1987 – **Tolworth**, April, at light (Falconer per JP); **Oxted**, 19.6 (TD).
1989 – **Cranleigh**, 20.9 (PC); **Nutfield**, 27.10 (PAC).
1990 – **Thorpe** (PJB); **Nutfield**, 28.4, 13.8 (PAC); **White Downs**, 20.7 (DWB); **Leigh**, 21.8, 2.9 (RF).
1992 – **Leigh**, 17.8 (RF); **Farnham**, September (JKH); **Wyke Common**, 3.9 (F. Blackburn per PJS); **Guildford**, 11.9 (DWB).
1993 – **Streatham**, 19.9 (Lockwood per CWP).
1994 – **Thorpe** (PJB); **Headley**, 7.7 (JP); **Streatham**, 12.8 (Lockwood per CWP); **Banstead**, 27.8 at honeysuckle (SWG).
1996 – **St. Martha's Hill**, 11.4 (DWB); **North Cheam**, 7.6 (DC); **Buckland**, 9-16.6 (3) (CH); **Newlands Corner**, 14.6 (DWB); **Ranmore**, 15.6 (GJ); **Rowhills**, 17-24.6 (JKH); **Nutfield**, 23.6 (PAC); **Banstead**, 26.7, 19-28.8 (SWG); **Chessington**, 3.8, 11.9 (JP); **Tolworth**, 8.8 (JTS); **Kenley Common**, 16.8 (ME); **Guildford**, 16.8 (DWB); **Epsom Downs**, 19.8 (BG); **Cranleigh**, 26.8 (PC); **Wotton**, 26.8 (JDH); **Merrow**, 28.8 (Clark per S. Curson).

Daphnis nerii (Linnaeus, 1758)   Oleander Hawk

Migrant; very rare.

The Oleander Hawk is one of our rarest migrant Hawks of which there are only a few Surrey records, none of them in the last 50 years. It has been known to be misidentified and a voucher specimen has not always been kept. The following records have appeared in the literature:

19th century – **Addlestone**, 1870 by Mr Smith (Bretherton, 1957).
[1910 – **Sydenham**, "Surrey" 24.9 (*Ent.* **43**:316) *teste* Plant (1993) should probably be Kent (Chalmers-Hunt, 1962-7).]
1935 – **Addiscombe**, 28.6 (*Ent. Rec.* **47**:91).
[1946 – **Dulwich**, 27.7 (*Ent.* **79**:256) *teste* Plant (1993) – the reference given does not refer to this species, nor is there any record of it in the *Entomologist* for that year.]

Hyles euphorbiae (Linnaeus, 1758)   Spurge Hawk

Migrant or introduction; very rare.

There are only three records for this very rare migrant, all of which are open to some question as to their origin or accuracy. Two pupae were found under an oak tree at Kew Gardens, 2.3.1907 (Lucas, *Ent.* **40**:212), either progeny of an earlier migrant or more likely introduced with foreign plants. At Woldingham, 23.9.1939, a larva was found on green field-speedwell (Comber, *Ent.* **72**:260), the identity confirmed by L.W. Newman – the foodplant is not included in any of the text books including Newman and Leeds (1913). Finally one was taken at Selsdon, 26.5.1973 (EHW), in a year of much migrant activity, although this was the only example of the Spurge Hawk recorded in the country that year and it should also be borne in mind that pupae were readily available from various butterfly farms at that time.

Hyles gallii (Rottemburg, 1775)   **Bedstraw Hawk**

Migrant; rare.

The Bedstraw Hawk is a rare immigrant, recorded as three individuals during the survey period and with not many more earlier records.

19th century – **Tooting**, 12.8.1870 (Leslie, *Ent.* **5**:82); **Weybridge**, August 1875, two flying over flowers (Milne, *Ent.* **8**:271).

1929 – **Warlingham** (3) (Bell in de Worms, 1954-58).

1938 – **Pirbright**, 14.7 (Lawson, *Ent.* **71**:238).

1955 – **Dorking**, 29.7 (Howard, *Ent. Rec.* **67**:236); **Chiddingfold**, 18.8 (*Ent.* **89**:177); **Mitcham Common**, a full-grown larva, moth reared (Christie, in Evans, 1973).

1956 – **Chiddingfold**, 30.5 (*Ent.* **90**:234).

1961 – **Chiddingfold**, 21.7 (*Ent.* **96**:36); **Ottershaw**, infertile female, 24.7 (Bretherton, 1965).

1973 – **Thorpe**, 18.7 (PJB).

1975 – **Selsdon**, 14.8 (EHW).

1976 – **Thorpe**, 7.7 (PJB); **Purley**, 22.8 (PMS).

1989 – **Milford**, 30.7 (DWB).

Hyles livornica (Esper, 1780) =*lineata* auctt. PLATE 7 **Striped Hawk**

Migrant; scarce.

Foodplant – (dock).

The Striped Hawk is a scarce migrant, recorded in only two years of the survey period, but nevertheless more frequent than the Bedstraw or Silver-striped Hawks. It has also been known to breed in Surrey although not recently. It should be noted that *lineata* Fabricius is the species occurring in North America, and that the European species is *livornica* Esper.

19th century – **St. George's Hill, Weybridge**, 1.8.1868 (Barton, *Ent.* **4**:149); **Cheam**, September 1869 (Brown, *Ent.* **4**:365); **Box Hill**, June 1883 (Paskell, *Ent.* **16**:234); **Kenley**, 15.10.1898 (Snell, *Ent.* **31**:292); **Limpsfield**, 19.8.1899 (Frohawk, *Ent.* **32**:235).

1906 – **Epsom**, 19.6 (Penn, *Ent.* **39**:262); **Woking**, 8.8 (Smith, *E.M.M.* **43**:211).

1911 – **Purley**, 3.8 (Russell, *Ent. Rec.* **24**:147).

1922 – **Merton**, 15.5 (Coulson, *Ent.* **55**:163).

1931 – **Addington**, 12.5 (Palmer); **Caterham**, 8.7 (Bell in de Worms 1954-58).

1941 – **Ewhurst**, 22.6 (*Ent.* **74**:185).

1943 – **Cranleigh**, 23.8, and one bred from a larva found on dock (Kettlewell, *Proc. SLENHS* **1943-44**:17).

1945 – Surrey (3) (*Ent.* **79**:107).

1949 – **Purley** (Norris, *Ent.* **82**:235), Surrey (3) (*Ent.* **83**:131).

1958 – **Horsell**, 9.5 (de Worms, *Ent.* **91**:162).

1964 – **Woldingham**, 14.5 (Halford, *Ent. Gaz.* **15**:96).

[1965 – **Tolworth**, May (JP) - record withdrawn.]

1966 – **Wormley**, 24.5 (JLM).

1985 – **Rushmoor**, 2.4 (PAD); **Bramley**, 10.4 (RFB).

1996 – **Nutfield**, 7.6 (PAC); **Milford**, 8.6 (DWB).

Deilephila elpenor (Linnaeus, 1758) — Elephant Hawk

Resident; woodland, commons, gardens; widespread and common.

Univoltine; mid-June to July.

Foodplant – rosebay willowherb, great willowherb, bogbean, fuchsia, *Impatiens roylei*, (orange balsam, marsh bedstraw, hoary willowherb).

Overall the Elephant Hawk is probably the commonest and most widespread of the family, and can be very common to abundant at some of the static traps as the following counts show: Milford, 1992 (176) (DWB); Bramley, 1985 (24), 86 (105) (RFB); South Croydon, 1983 (25), 84 (33), 85 (16), 86 (14) (GAC). An untimely example was noted at Wyke Common, 14.10.1995 (GAC).

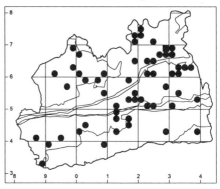

Deilephila porcellus (Linnaeus, 1758) — Small Elephant Hawk

Resident; chalk grassland, commons, heathland; restricted but fairly common.

Univoltine; mid-May to early July.

Foodplant – lady's bedstraw.

The Small Elephant Hawk is rather more restricted than its congener, showing preference for lighter soils and being virtually absent from the weald. It is a regular species on the commons of south London, and at Mitcham has been recorded in abundance: 1981 (52), 82 (67), 83 (63), 84 (103) (RKAM); such numbers though are unusual.

Hippotion celerio (Linnaeus, 1758) — Silver-striped Hawk

Migrant; very rare.

The Silver-striped Hawk is a rare migrant of which only six examples have been recorded from Surrey, none in recent years.

19th century – **Ewell**, August 1898 (Frohawk, *Ent.* **32**:39).

1935 – **Purley**, 5.11 (Garratt, *Ent.* **69**:15).

1955 – **Wandsworth**, 14.11 (Lyn Jones, *Ent.* **89**:103).

1963 – **Wormley**, 25.10 (JLM); **Chiddingfold**, 6.11 (2) (Mere, *Ent. Rec.* **76**:28).

NOTODONTIDAE – Prominents

The Notodontidae are a family of medium-sized to large moths, of which 20 species are resident in Surrey. The males at least are strongly attracted to light, but in some species the females are scarcely seen by this method. The adults cannot feed, so are not to be found at sugar or flowers. The larvae, often adorned by various fleshy humps, feed on the leaves of trees and shrubs and frequently rest with the head and anal segments raised.

Phalera bucephala (Linnaeus, 1758)   **Buff-tip**

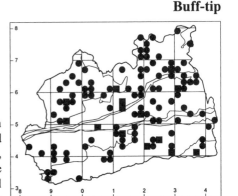

Resident; woodland, commons, heathland; widespread and common.

Univoltine; mid-June to July.

Foodplant – oak, sallow, osier, beech, lime, birch, hazel, (poplar, elm).

The Buff-tip occurs throughout Surrey in a variety of habitats. The larvae feed gregariously and are frequently observed, although possibly less commonly in the London area than formerly. The adult is still fairly regular at light as the following counts show: Mitcham, 1981 (12), 82 (6), 83 (11) (RKAM); South Croydon, 1983 (11), 84 (7), 85 (15), 86 (14) (GAC). In some areas, noticeably the south-west, it can be abundant: Bramley, 1985 (138), 86 (254) (RFB); Milford, 1992 (156) (DWB). The adult is remarkably invariable but a melanic form from Putney was exhibited at the 1951 exhibition of the SLENHS (Swain, *Proc. SLENHS* **1951-52**:plate IV).

Cerura vinula (Linnaeus, 1758)   **Puss Moth**

Resident; woodland, commons, heathland; fairly widespread but uncommon.

Univoltine; May and June.

Foodplant – sallow, aspen, poplar.

The Puss Moth is fairly widespread in the county but is scarce on the chalk and apparently absent from a large area of western Surrey. The adult is only weakly attracted to light, noted at most in ones and twos even at regularly run traps, and many records refer to the ova or larvae. There has evidently been a decline in the London area where the larva used to be a common sight on the commons

(Evans, 1973), and the only records from this area in the last decade are: Addington, one at light in 1985 (BS); Mitcham Common, larvae on aspen in 1990 and 1991 (DCL); and East Sheen, 6.6.1995 (D. Couzens). Elsewhere, north of the chalk, it has only been noted in this period as larvae from Wisley (AJH), and Chobham Common (DCL); as both these sites are on heathland this suggests that the lack of records from the west is due to under-recording.

Furcula bicuspis (Borkhausen, 1790)   **Alder Kitten**

Notable/Nb

Resident; commons, open woodland; very local and scarce.

Univoltine; June.

Foodplant – ([birch]).

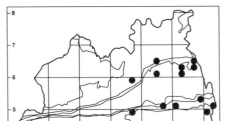

The Alder Kitten is a very local species, being confined to the extreme east of the county. Most records are of single specimens, but there does seem to have been an increase in its range and frequency in the last ten years. Limpsfield Chart, following a prediction in Evans (1973), was a well known site in the 1970s but does not seem to have been worked recently. It was apparently unknown to Barrett as a Surrey species although it was common in Tilgate Forest just a few miles south of the county boundary. The only other reference to its occurrence in Surrey is of a larva of this genus beaten from birch at Camberley but not reared (Green, *Ent. Rec.* 51:23). Bretherton (1965) includes it in his supplement to the north-west Surrey list but rightly assigns some element of doubt to it.

RECORDS – **Dorking**, 24.5.92 (DAT); **Ashtead Common**, 6.6.92 (DC); **North Cheam**, 4.6.82 (RFMcC); **Banstead Downs**, 16.6.86 (RFMcC); **Reigate**, 16.6.79 (DAT); **Purley**, 27.6.86, 15.6.90 (PJS); **South Croydon**, 27.5.92, 8.6.93, 31.5-6.6.94, 22.5.95 (2), 26.6.96, 22-29.5.97 (7) (GAC); **Addington**, 10.6.93 (BS); **Shirley**, 16.6.96 (AJW); **Nutfield**, 22.6.76, 9.7.83, 19.6.89, 28.4.90, 1993 (3), 94 (2), 26.6.95, 25-29.6.96 (2) (PAC); **Lingfield**, 21.5.90, 1991 (3), 28.5-1.6.92, 19.6.95 (JC); **Staffhurst Wood**, 13.6.81 (RKAM); **Oxted**, 8.6.82, 6.95, 6.96 (TD); **Limpsfield Chart**, 3.7.76 (TD).

Furcula furcula (Clerck, 1759)   Sallow Kitten

Resident; commons, heathland; widespread and fairly common.

Bivoltine; May, and July and August.

Foodplant – sallow.

The Sallow Kitten is the commonest and most widely distributed member of the genus, occurring almost everywhere but only scarce on the chalk. Numbers at regularly run traps seldom exceed single figures as the following counts show: Bramley, 1985 (3), 86 (5) (RFB); Milford, 1989 (11), 90 (11), 92 (25) (DWB); Mitcham, 1981 (1), 82 (14), 83 (8) (RKAM); South Croydon, 1983 (11), 84 (3), 85 (1), 86 (1) (GAC); Selsdon, 1980 (1) (EHW).

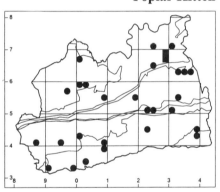

Furcula bifida (Brahm, 1787)   Poplar Kitten

Resident; commons, woodland; local and uncommon.

Univoltine; May to August; peak early June.

Foodplant – white poplar, (Lombardy poplar, hybrid black poplar, aspen).

A local species, occurring most commonly in the south London area, but very widely distributed throughout Surrey. It may prove to be more common if poplar plantations are specifically searched, but the bulk of records are of singletons at light. The species is apparently univoltine with a prolonged emergence, although the possibility of a partial second brood cannot be ruled out.

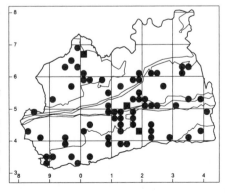

Stauropus fagi (Linnaeus, 1758)   PLATE 5   Lobster Moth

Resident; woodland; fairly widespread and fairly common.

Univoltine; mid-May to mid-July.

Foodplant – beech, alder, hazel, (apple, oak, birch).

A fairly widespread species which is however apparently absent from the London area. Elsewhere it is principally a woodland species and is commonest in beech woods in central and southern Surrey, although the larva is by no means confined to this pabulum. Trap counts show: Bramley, 1985 (11), 86 (20) (RFB); South Croydon, 1983 (3), 84 (7), 85 (4), 86 (3) (GAC). Most examples are to some degree melanic and many are referable to f. *obscura* Rebel.

Notodonta dromedarius (Linnaeus, 1767)   Iron Prominent

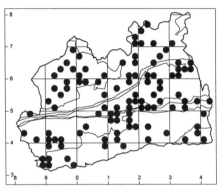

Resident; woodland, commons, heathland; widespread and common.

Bivoltine; May and June, and mid-July to August.

Foodplant – birch, hazel.

The Iron Prominent is found throughout Surrey, often very commonly as the following trap counts show: Bramley, 1985 (36), 86 (51) (RFB); Mitcham, 1981 (12), 82 (23), 83 (17), 84 (RKAM); South Croydon, 1983 (43), 84 (27), 85 (15) (GAC).

Eligmodonta ziczac (Linnaeus, 1758)   Pebble Prominent

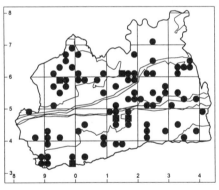

Resident; commons, woodland; fairly widespread and common.

Bivoltine; May and June, and August.

Foodplant – sallow, aspen.

The Pebble Prominent is a fairly widespread species but is absent from much of the London area. In rural areas at least it can be a very common species, but declines rapidly in more built-up areas: Bramley, 1985 (82), 86 (94) (RFB); South Croydon, 1983 (8), 84 (11), 85 (4), 86 (1) (GAC). It was unrecorded from Mitcham and noted but once from Wimbledon during the survey period, despite the amount of foodplant on the nearby commons.

Peridea anceps (Goeze, 1781)   **Great Prominent**

Resident; woodland; restricted but fairly common.

Univoltine; May and early June.

Foodplant – oak.

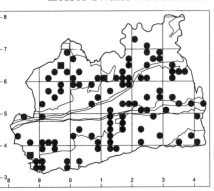

The Great Prominent is absent from the north and much of the east of the county but can be found in well-wooded areas in much of the rest of Surrey. Static trap counts from these areas show it to be a fairly common species: Bramley, 1985 (46), 86 (2) (RFB); Milford, 1992 (34) (DWB), and even on the extreme north-eastern edge of its range it can be quite common, for example at Bookham Common.

Pheosia gnoma (Fabricius, 1777)   **Lesser Swallow Prominent**

Resident; commons, woodland, heathland; widespread and common.

Bivoltine; mid-April to May, and July and August.

Foodplant – birch.

This species and its rather similar congener are to be found throughout much of the county, although the Lesser Swallow Prominent has a greater number of records. The commoner species at a particular site depends on the availability of the respective foodplants. At Bramley roughly similar numbers are recorded, at South Croydon *gnoma* is much the commoner species whilst at Mitcham the reverse is true.

Pheosia tremula (Clerck, 1759)   **Swallow Prominent**

Resident; commons, woodland; fairly widespread and common.

Bivoltine; May and June, and August.

Foodplant – aspen, (Lombardy poplar, hybrid black poplar).

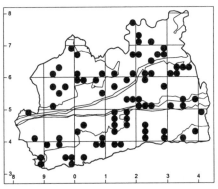

The Swallow Prominent is slightly less well distributed than its congener, and seems to be particularly scarce on the heaths. Otherwise it is fairly general and in the vicinity of its foodplant can be very common: Bramley, 1985 (135), 86 (145) (RFB).

Ptilodon capucina (Linnaeus, 1758) Coxcomb Prominent

Resident; commons, woodland, heathland; widespread and common.

Bivoltine; May and June, and August.

Foodplant – sallow, lime, birch, (hawthorn, elm, beech).

The Coxcomb Prominent is probably the most widespread species of Prominent, although numbers seen are usually lower than the other common species. The larva appears to be polyphagous on deciduous trees which no doubt allows it to utilize various habitats.

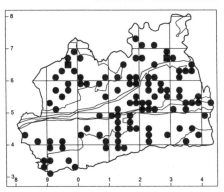

Ptilodontella cucullina ([Denis & Schiffermüller], 1775) Maple Prominent

Status uncertain; possibly only vagrant.

The only old record of this species in Surrey is of a few reared from Caterham by Bell (de Worms, *L.N.* **38**:43). The record is undated but other records by Bell refer to the 1920s and early 1930s, and it would appear to be reliable. Larvae were also stated to have been taken in July/August 1923-25 in the Haslemere district (Oldaker, *Ent.* **59**:37), a record which may equally well refer to West Sussex or North Hants as to Surrey. It is most surprising that this species is not resident in the county as there is much suitable habitat and it has been recently recorded from most if not all of the counties adjacent to Surrey. The single recent record is from a site only a mile or so from the Kent border.

RECORDS – **Addington**, 1.7.94 (BS).

Odontosia carmelita (Esper, 1799) Scarce Prominent

Resident; heathland, commons; fairly widespread and fairly common.

Univoltine; April and early May.

Foodplant – (birch).

The Scarce Prominent is currently fairly widespread in Surrey with the exception of the London area. The discovery of mercury vapour light as an attractant in the 1950s revealed this species to be much commoner than previously thought, but there does also appear to have been a genuine increase in range since this period. Bretherton (1957)

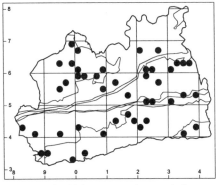

describes it as very scarce in the north-west, even at the light traps, whereas it is now common. Evans (1973) had only three records from the very south of his area, but it has now been taken all along the northern edge of the chalk. The following totals were seen in a single night's trapping: Chobham Common, 29.4.1985 (20+) (GAC); Tugley Wood, 30.4.1987 (25+) (SCP).

Pterostoma palpina (Clerck, 1759)   Pale Prominent

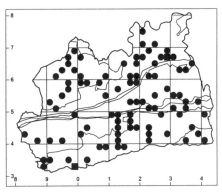

Resident; commons, woodland; widespread and fairly common.

Bivoltine; mid-May to June, and late July and August.

Foodplant – poplar, (sallow, aspen).

The Pale Prominent is another widespread Prominent found in suitable habitats throughout the county. It is perhaps slightly less frequent than some of the other Prominents although still fairly common: Bramley, 1985 (18), 86 (23) (RFB); Mitcham, 1981 (7), 82 (19), 83 (26) (RKAM); South Croydon, 1983 (2), 85 (1), 86 (1) (GAC).

Ptilophora plumigera ([Denis & Schiffermüller], 1775)   Plumed Prominent

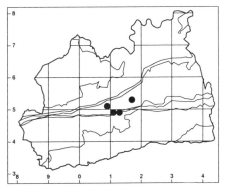

Notable/Na

Resident; woodland on chalk; very local but fairly common.

Univoltine; November.

Foodplant – (field maple, Norway maple).

The Plumed Prominent is an absurdly local insect currently known in Surrey from a few sites all within a few miles of each other. It was previously recorded from Godalming, some way from the chalk, in November 1923 by Kettlewell (*Ent. Rec.* **36**:27), and again in 1924 (*Ent. Rec.* **37**:13); he also mentions two males taken at Charterhouse in 1888. Although the foodplant is quite a common species on the chalk, one factor that may be responsible for the distribution is that at the main sites the maple is in the form of trees with trunks some 50 cm in diameter. The very variable weather that can occur during its flight period makes its appearance somewhat uncertain, but on a good night it can be quite common. The ground colour varies from pale straw through grey to reddish brown, but the wings are always variegated.

RECORDS – **Sheepleas**, 22.11.80 (AJH); **Westcott Downs**, 11.11.84, 16.11.90 (12) (GAC); **White Downs**, many records, the more recent being: 7.11.85 (4), 9.11.88 (34) (SCP), 16.11.90 (5) (GAC), 5.11.92 (25) (DC), 29.11.96 (6) (GAC); **Mickleham**, 30.10.85 (SBRC).

Drymonia dodonaea ([Denis & Schiffermüller], 1775)   **Marbled Brown**

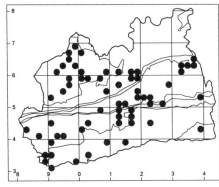

Resident; woodland; fairly widespread and fairly common.

Univoltine; late May and June.

Foodplant – (oak).

The Marbled Brown is fairly well distributed in Surrey but is absent from the London area and only local in the east. It is more widespread in central and western Surrey but usually not seen in large numbers; even the most well-attended traps only record the following annual counts: Bramley, 1985 (6), 86 (17) (RFB); Selsdon, 1980 (10) (EHW).

A melanic form has occurred in the Horsell area (de Worms, 1979), and indeed most Surrey specimens tend to melanism.

Drymonia ruficornis (Hufnagel, 1767)   **Lunar Marbled Brown**

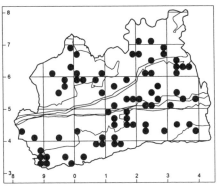

Resident; woodland; fairly widespread and common.

Univoltine; April to mid-May.

Foodplant – (oak).

Compared with its congener, the Lunar Marbled Brown is most local in the extreme west of the county and more widespread in the east, including the London area where it is not uncommon. A melanic form, referable to ab. *nigrescens* Lempke, was taken at Friday Street, 12.5.1979 (2), and again on 6.5.1986 (BS).

Clostera pigra (Hufnagel, 1766)   **Small Chocolate-tip**

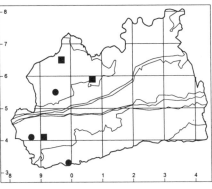

Notable/Nb

Resident; heathland, woodland; local and scarce.

Bivoltine; May, and late July and early August.

Foodplant – sallow, creeping willow.

The Small Chocolate-tip is a very local, but possibly overlooked species, found principally on heathland in west Surrey. It has also been taken in woodland in the south-west where it may be associated with aspen. Bretherton (1957) considered it very scarce at all except one of the static traps but had many larval records, and it is highly likely that searching for the larva would reveal the moth to be rather more widespread.

RECORDS – **Rushmoor**, 19.7.82, 9.8.83 (PAD); **Thursley Common**, 20.6.82 larva on creeping willow (DWB); **Tugley Wood**, 22.7.85, 30.4.87 (SCP); **Oaken Wood**, 20.7.95 (GAC); **Pirbright RES**, 1980 (2), 81 (1), 82 (1) (ED); **Chobham Common**, 1980 (2) (DCL), 13.7.85 larva (AJH); **Wisley**, 9.83 larva on sallow (AJH).

Clostera curtula (Linnaeus, 1758)   Chocolate-tip

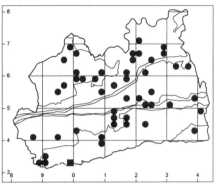

Resident; commons, woodland; fairly widespread but uncommon.

Bivoltine; May, and August.

Foodplant – aspen, (poplar).

The Chocolate-tip is fairly widely but thinly spread in Surrey, but does appear to be absent from fairly large areas in both the east and west of the county. It probably comes to light more readily than its congener but is only recorded in any numbers in the vicinity of its foodplant, for example: Bramley, 1985 (16), 86 (9) (RFB); Milford, 1990 (1), 91 (2), 92 (10) (DWB); Mitcham, 1981 (1), 82 (2), 83 (2), 84 (2) (RKAM). At other traps it is little more than occasional.

Diloba caeruleocephala (Linnaeus, 1758)   Figure of Eight

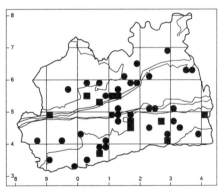

Resident; commons, woodland; restricted but locally common.

Univoltine; October.

Foodplant – sloe, hawthorn, bird cherry, (apple, damson, laurel).

The Figure of Eight has not been recorded from the chalk or from the Bagshot sands during the survey period, and is also virtually absent from London being recorded only from Mitcham once: 4.10.1984 (RKAM). On the weald and the London clay in the Leatherhead district it is a locally common species, the conspicuous larva being often noticed. The adult moth can be common at light placed well into its habitats, and is recorded in good numbers at one of the static traps: Bramley, 1985 (61), 86 (44) (RFB).

LYMANTRIIDAE – Tussocks

The Lymantriidae is a large family of which most species are tropical. There are seven species resident in our county. The genus *Orgyia* has males that fly by day and wingless females, the other species being nocturnal and frequently seen at light. The larvae feed exposed on trees and shrubs and are densely hairy, many possessing dorsal hair tufts or "tussocks". The larvae of the Brown-tail, currently rather common in the London area, are severely urticating and should be avoided.

Orgyia recens (Hübner, 1819)   Scarce Vapourer

Extinct; not recorded this century.

The Scarce Vapourer is given in the *VCH* as being formerly common near Veitch's Nursery on Wimbledon Common but not seen for many years. Barrett (1895) also mentions Coombe Wood in the 1850s.

Orgyia antiqua (Linnaeus, 1758)   Vapourer

Resident; commons, gardens, woodland; fairly widespread and common.
Probably **univoltine**; July to mid-October.
Foodplant – sallow, oak, birch, hazel, sweet chestnut, alder buckthorn, laburnum, bramble, lime, London plane, (horse-chestnut, poplar, cherry, plum, honeysuckle, rose, meadowsweet, laurel).

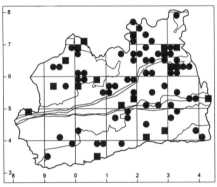

The Vapourer is a fairly widely distributed species which is probably commonest close to the metropolis and scarcest away from it. The male is mainly diurnal and quite good numbers can be assembled to a virgin female, but it will also fly at night and many records are of specimens in the light trap. The female is wingless and at Bookham Common, 12.9.1991, one was beaten from oak (GAC). The voltinism is not clear; the larva has been found as late as September 26th and adults are recorded for October. These late examples may be a partial second brood or merely a result of protracted hatching of the eggs (Barrett, 1895).

Dicallomera fascelina (Linnaeus, 1758)   **Dark Tussock**

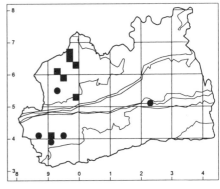

Resident; heathland; local and uncommon.
Univoltine; mid-July to mid-August.
Foodplant – heather, (broom).
In Surrey the Dark Tussock is restricted to heathland but probably occurs on all the major heaths in the west. There is one record from Buckland and this may be evidence of an isolated colony on perhaps Reigate Heath or Headley Heath. The larvae are not uncommonly swept in the autumn but are considerably scarcer in the spring, and are none too easy to rear, many being parasitized.

RECORDS – **Rushmoor**, 1982-85 (PAD); **Thursley Common**, 6.8.76 (JP), 11.7.79 (AJ), 13.5.81 larvae (SHC), 13.8.91 (RFMcC); **Milford**, 19-23.7.85, 29.7.86, 14.8.86, 91 (5), 92 (5), 93 (1) (DWB); **Whitmoor Common**, 21.9.93 larva (GAC); **Pirbright Common**, 7.7.83 (PC); **Lucas Green**, 2.10.88 larva on heather (GAC); **Bisley**, 2.10.88 larva on heather (GAC); **Chobham Common**, 28.3.76 larva (JP), 4.9.82 larva (SHC), 26.5.85 larva (AJH), 30.4.83 larvae, 17.9.88 larva, 25.7.89, 19.9.91 larvae, 18.4.92 larvae (GAC), 28.7.95 (DC); **Buckland**, 9.8.91 (CH).

Calliteara pudibunda (Linnaeus, 1758)   **Pale Tussock**

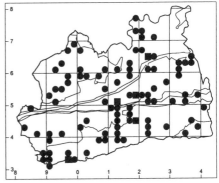

Resident; woodland, wooded commons, widespread and common.
Univoltine; mid-May to June.
Foodplant – birch, (sallow).
The Pale Tussock is rather a common species in wooded districts throughout the county. Males are common at light but the females are rarely seen. Melanic specimens are not uncommon especially in central and north-east Surrey. Unseasonal examples include: Addiscombe, 9-18.8.1968 (KGWE), and Rowhills, 17.12.1994 (JKH) – in view of the extremely long duration of the larval stage it is likely that the Addiscombe specimens represented a delayed emergence rather than a second brood.

Euproctis chrysorrhoea (Linnaeus, 1758)   PLATE 5   **Brown-tail**

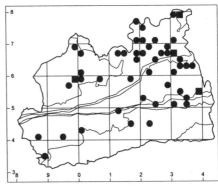

Resident; gardens, commons; fairly widespread but uncommon.

Univoltine; July.

Foodplant – hawthorn, ornamental cherry.

The Brown-tail is a species which is subject to much variation in its numbers nationally, at times scarce and restricted to the coast, and at other times as a pest species whose larvae were destroyed in huge numbers. It is principally coastal but when on the increase spreads into the London area and into Surrey. Bretherton (1957) had no records, and Evans (1973) knew of only six examples from four sites and these all in the period 1967-72. Additionally, eight specimens were recorded from Selsdon in 1972 (EHW). Since then, possibly in two waves, it has become not uncommon in the London area and has been recorded widely in Surrey, including breeding records from Woking where the larvae were first noticed in 1986 and were still present in 1996 (AJH), and from Oxted Downs, 1994 (GAC).

Euproctis similis (Fuessly, 1775)   **Yellow-tail**

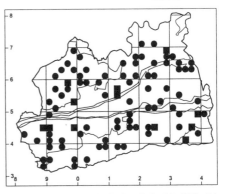

Resident; woodland, commons, heathland; widespread and common.

Univoltine; July and August.

Foodplant – apple, oak, bramble, sallow, alder buckthorn, hawthorn, sloe, lime, alder, meadow- sweet, (birch, elm, rose, mugwort).

The Yellow-tail is a fairly generally distributed species, although there is evidence that it is not keen on chalk soils. At many sites it is a common species as the following trap counts show: Bramley, 1985 (88), 86 (130) (RFB); Wisley RES, 1986 (31), 87 (24), 90 (28), 91 (21) (AJH); Mitcham, 1981 (18), 82 (16), 83 (28) (RKAM). Surprisingly though, only four individuals have been noted at South Croydon in 15 years. Very rarely, examples appear in September and October, such as Buckland, 9.10.95 (CH).

Leucoma salicis (Linnaeus, 1758)   White Satin

Resident; commons, gardens; local and uncommon.

Univoltine; July.

Foodplant – (Lombardy poplar).

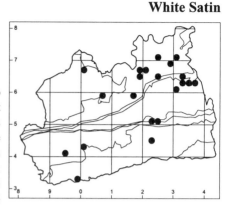

The White Satin is more or less restricted to the commons of suburban south London, but it is prone to wander and isolated examples have been recorded from most parts of the county. In the early 1980s at least it was recorded in reasonable numbers, from: Mitcham, 1981 (7), 82 (6), 83 (13), 84 (8) (RKAM), and South Croydon, 1983 (4), 84 (4) (GAC). Since then it has only been taken twice at South Croydon and not at all at Mitcham despite regular trapping in the last few years, and it may be in decline as the *VCH* says "common everywhere on sallow, willow, and poplar".

Lymantria monacha (Linnaeus, 1758)   Black Arches

Resident; woodland; restricted but fairly common.

Univoltine; late July and August.

Foodplant – oak.

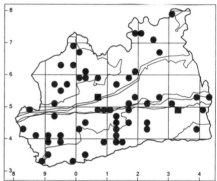

The Black Arches has not been recorded from the chalk, and, with the exception of an individual in a building in Lambeth, 6.8.1986 (RFMcC) has only been noted from the London area at Mitcham, Richmond Park and Wimbledon, all comparatively recently. Elsewhere it is widely distributed but never particularly common, single figures being the norm for annual light trap captures. Bretherton (1957) considered it very scarce, and Evans (1973) had no records later than 1962. It has undoubtedly increased since then as there are sites within both these survey areas where it is now regular.

ARCTIIDAE – Tigers and Footman Moths

The Arctiidae is a very large family of mainly tropical species, 17 of which are resident in Surrey. Several species are immigrants, but only two have been recorded in recent years. The larvae are covered with dense tufts of setae arising from verrucae; those of the subfamily Arctiinae feed on shrubs and low plants, and those of the subfamily Lithosiinae eat lichens and hence occur in damper habitats.

Thumatha senex (Hübner, 1808)   PLATE 12   Round-winged Muslin

Resident; wetland, damp woodland, wet heathland; fairly widespread but uncommon.

Univoltine; July.

The distribution of this species is necessarily limited by its need for wet places, but it occurs in suitable habitat throughout the county. It is only noticed commonly when a light is run in its immediate locality, and to some extent must be overlooked.

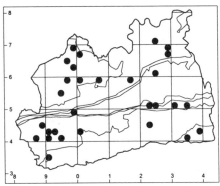

Setina irrorella (Linnaeus, 1758)   Dew Moth

Notable/Na

Resident; chalk downland; very local and scarce.

Univoltine; July.

A very local species which, with the exception of one wanderer, is confined to the scarp of the North Downs. There is only one recent occasion when it has been seen in any numbers and it has probably declined somewhat since the middle years of this century, prior to which it could often be found commonly flying by day. Bretherton (1957) lists four wanderers which occurred at Ottershaw and New Haw between 1948 and 1950, years when it appeared to be common in its known haunts (Evans, 1973), and he also took it himself; Bramley, 26.6.1973 (RFB).

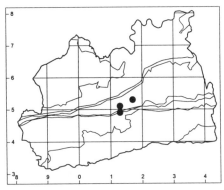

RECORDS – **Westcott Downs**, 10.7.82 (19) (BC), 13.7.83 (GAC), 8.7.87 (RF); **Juniper Hall**, 7.85 (R Softly (per CWP)).

Miltochrista miniata (Forster, 1771)   **Rosy Footman**

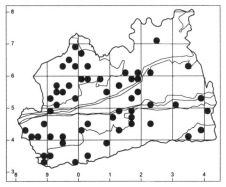

Resident; woodland; fairly widespread and common.

Univoltine; July.

Although virtually absent from north-east Surrey, the Rosy Footman is widespread and rather common elsewhere. The following trap counts demonstrate this and also show that there is considerable fluctuation in numbers from year to year, presumably due to variation in humidity levels during the larval period: Bramley, 1985 (4), 86 (6) (RFB); Milford, 1991 (5), 92 (47) (DWB); Wisley RES, 1986 (19), 87 (11), 90 (3), 91 (3) (AJH). The yellow ab. *flava* Bigneau was recorded at Ashtead, 2.7.1993 (GAC).

Nudaria mundana (Linnaeus, 1761)   **Muslin Footman**

Status uncertain; possible former resident.

A record of this species from Chertsey, 15.7.1863 (Clarke, *Week. Ent.* **2**:212) is considered by Bretherton to be in error for *Thumatha senex* (Bretherton, 1957). However the *VCH* gives Reigate Hill, and as being in Barrett's list from Haslemere, while Barrett (1895) says generally distributed in the south of England. Interestingly, Barrett (*loc. cit.*) doesn't specifically quote Surrey for *senex* and the *VCH* gives only Redhill (Webb). Either some of the most experienced lepidopterists of their day confused the two species or else there has been a reversal in their fortunes. The Muslin Footman does not appear to have been recorded in this century from Surrey.

Atolmis rubricollis (Linnaeus, 1758)   **Red-necked Footman**

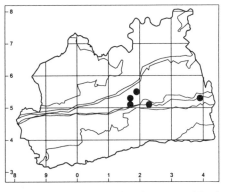

Notable/Nb

Resident; woodland on chalk; very local and rare.

Late June and early July.

Foodplant – (lichens on yew).

The Red-necked Footman has been recorded during the survey period at the rate of one or two a decade, and its future in Surrey is clearly very precarious. Nationally it has also declined during this period, especially in the south-east. Barrett (1895) considered it probably common, in its favourite years, in almost all the woods in the south of England. The *VCH* gives "formerly abundant at Buckland Hills among the yew trees, also near Haslemere and elsewhere". In more recent times it was recorded from Ashtead [undated] (de Worms *L.N.* **33**:137), Weybridge trap, 13.6.1952

(Bretherton, 1957), White Downs, 11.6.1956 (RFB), Abinger, 1967 (RF), and from the Box Hill area where it just about hangs on. It is interesting to notice that the years in which it has occurred recently were extremely good ones for lepidoptera in general.
RECORDS – **Nower Wood**, 26.6.76 (JP); **Juniper Hall**, 5.7.83 (JHFC); **Box Hill**, 27.6.92 (PJB); **Buckland**, 13.7.96 (CH); **Oxted**, "a couple in the 1980s" (TD).

Cybosia mesomella (Linnaeus, 1758)   **Four-dotted Footman**

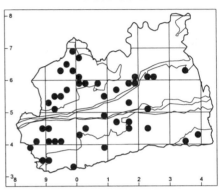

Resident; woodland, commons, heathland; fairly widespread and fairly common.

Univoltine; late June and July.

Although scarce in eastern Surrey, the Four-dotted Footman is of rather general distribution in the rest of the county and found in a variety of habitats. The yellow form, f. *flava* de Graaf, is regular at some sites.

Eilema sororcula (Hufnagel, 1766)   PLATE 10   **Orange Footman**

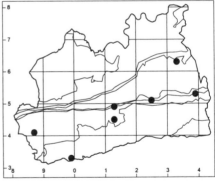

Notable/Nb

Resident, and possible migrant; woodland; very local and rare.

Univoltine; June to mid-August.

The Orange Footman has been recorded on only a very few occasions recently, and the origin of some of the specimens is not entirely clear. It has certainly declined considerably since the turn of the century, but several recent records have been from areas where it was formerly more frequent and probably represent relict populations. Barrett (1895) described it as not scarce in oak woods in Surrey, although the *VCH* gives only sparingly at Box Hill and Reigate Hill. The north-west list gives Ottershaw, 24.5.1953; Weybridge, 14-16.5.1952 (3), 24.5.1953; Horsell, 11.5.1954; Pirbright trap, once; Bagshot, 23.5.1949 (Bretherton, 1957). Evans (1973) gives several records from the Box Hill area from 1948-54, and Ashtead in 1953. At the same period it was found commonly at car lights at Bookham Common (Wheeler, 1955), and at White Downs, June 1948, and Chiddingfold, 28.5.1955 (3) (JLM). More recently it was taken at Ranmore on 27.5.1960 (JVD); Holmwood Common, 26.5.1966 (RF); East Horsley, 25.6.1973 (LJDW); and Thorpe, 13.7.1975 (PJB). The record from South Croydon, although in an area of suitable habitat, is considered to be a probable migrant; the moth is smaller than resident specimens, and several examples were recorded in the same period from areas where they had never been taken before, and a number were seen on the Dorset coast with other migrants (D.C. Brown, *pers. com.*).

RECORDS – **Rushmoor**, 17.7-15.8.84 (PAD); **Oaken Wood**, 2.6.95 (2) (DC); **Tugley Wood**, 1994, 23.5.95 (DY); **Friday Street**, 3.7.76 (EHW); **White Downs**, 5-17.6.85 (BS); **Reigate**, 23.5.89 (RAC); **South Croydon**, 29.5.92 (GAC); **Oxted**, 4.6.83 (TD).

Eilema griseola (Hübner, 1803)   Dingy Footman

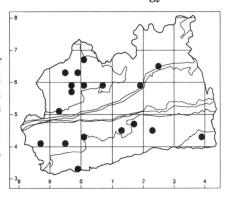

Resident; heathland, woodland; restricted but fairly common.
Univoltine; mid-July to mid-August.
The Dingy Footman is typically a species of damp areas and consequently is unrecorded from the chalk; it is also not resident in south London. It can be locally common as the following counts show: Bramley, 1985 (2), 86 (50) (RFB); Milford, 1992 (22) (DWB); Wisley, 1986 (15), 87 (15), 90 (9), 91 (10) (AJH).

Eilema complana (Linnaeus, 1758)   Scarce Footman

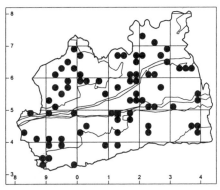

Resident; woodland, commons, heathland; widespread and fairly common.
Univoltine; July to mid-August.
Foodplant – lichens on wayfaring-tree.
This species and the Common Footman are rather similar and require careful examination to distinguish them, although in life they sit quite differently. Overall the Scarce Footman is slightly less widely distributed and numerically very much less common than *lurideola*. The one exception to this is that *lurideola* is very scarce in the built-up areas of London and at South Croydon, for example, the current species is the commoner. Trap counts are: Bramley, 1985 (7), 86 (7) (RFB); Wisley RES, 1986 (8), 87 (5), 90 (2), 91 (4) (AJH); South Croydon, 1983 (11), 84 (9), 85 (2) (GAC). Several larvae found on the trunks of wayfaring-tree at White Downs on 11.4.1992 proved to be this species (MP).

Eilema deplana (Esper, 1787)   **Buff Footman**

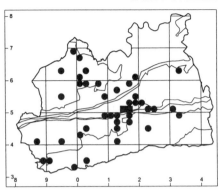

Resident; woodland; restricted and
uncommon.
Univoltine; mid-July to August.
Foodplant – lichens on yew.
The distribution of the Buff Footman is rather
restricted, it being regular only in central
Surrey. It is absent from the north-east and
only occasional elsewhere. Compared to the
Dingy Footman, which it resembles, this
species prefers drier and more wooded
habitats and the two are seldom found
together. A melanic form, f. *plumbia*
Cockayne, exists in a polymorphism at Bransland Wood, and has been recorded occasionally
elsewhere.

Eilema lurideola (Zincken, 1817)   **Common Footman**

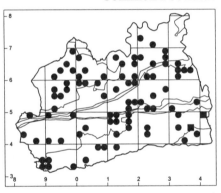

Resident; woodland, commons, heathland;
widespread and common.
Univoltine; mid-July to mid-August.
Foodplant – (lichen on a wall).
A very widespread and common species.
Often much commoner than *complana* (*c.f.*)
as the following counts show: Bramley, 1985
(54), 86 (263) (RFB); Wisley RES, 1986
(154), 87 (89), 90 (47), 91 (74) (AJH); but at
South Croydon, 1983 (5), 84 (3), 85 (-)
(GAC). Larvae were found on damp willow
trunks at Blindley Heath, 23.4.1993 (GAC),
where they were presumably feeding on microscopic algae.

Lithosia quadra (Linnaeus, 1758)   **Four-spotted Footman**

Migrant; scarce.
The Four-spotted Footman is a fairly regular migrant which becomes temporarily established
from time to time. It is likely that most Surrey records relate to primary migrants although
it was recorded at Wormley from 1962-75, following the migration of 1962 in which some
80 individuals were recorded nationally; all these specimens were males but their frequency
hints at the possibility of the establishment of a temporary breeding population during the
1960s.

1929 – **Warlingham**, July (Bell in de Worms, 1954-58).
1951 – **Chiddingfold**, (3) (Mere, *Ent. Gaz.* **3**:179).
1955 – **Chiddingfold**, 20.9 (*Ent.* **89**:175).

1956 – **Leigh**, 14.7 (RF); **Hook Heath**, 15-16.7 (3) (Bretherton, 1965).
1957 – **Weybridge**, 21.7 (JLM).
1958 – **Westhumble**, 14.9 (Cole in Evans, 1973).
1962 – **Chiddingfold**, 13-30.7 (4) (*Ent.***97**:126); **Wormley**, 26.7 (JLM).
1964 – **Wormley**, 15.7, 3.8 (JLM).
1965 – **Wormley**, 14.7 (JLM).
1966 – **Wormley**, 13.6 (JLM).
1973 – **Wormley**, 7.7 (JLM); **East Horsley**, 20.9 (LJDW).
1975 – **Wormley**, 20.7 (JLM).
1976 – **East Horsley**, 30.6 (LJDW).
1982 – **Buckland**, 28.6 (CH); **Dorking**, 11-14.7 (2) (DAT).
1984 – **Rushmoor**, 29-30.7 (2) (PAD).

Coscinia cribraria (Linnaeus, 1758)　　　　　Speckled Footman

Vagrant; not recorded this century.
Barrett (1895) mentions a record of this species, currently restricted to the heaths on the Hampshire/Dorset border, from Wimbledon Common in 1872 but gives no further details. As the subspecies is unknown it is not possible to say whether, assuming the record is genuine, it was a migrant or a vagrant from resident colonies.

Utetheisa pulchella (Linnaeus, 1758)　　　　　Crimson Speckled

Migrant; very rare.
The Crimson Speckled is a rare migrant, a few examples of which were noted in Surrey earlier this century. More recently only one has been recorded inland in Surrey, in a year in which some 30 individuals were recorded along the south coast.

1901 – **Clapham**, 1-15.7 (4) (*Ent.* **34**:230, 297; South, 1961).
1913 – **"Surrey Downs"**, 14.6 (Castle-Russell, *Ent. Rec.* **25**:198).
1923 – **Godalming**, August (Frisby, *Ent.* **59**:37).
1991 – **Buckland**, 6.10 (CH).

Parasemia plantaginis (Linnaeus, 1758)　　PLATE 1　　Wood Tiger
ssp. *plantaginis* (Linnaeus, 1758)

Extinct; not seen since 1951.
The Wood Tiger has undergone a serious decline in the south-east of England and has not been recorded in Surrey since 1951. The *VCH* says that it occurred sparingly in the woods near Horsley and elsewhere on the North Downs. Other former localities were: Hydon Ball, 1920 (4) (JLM); Warlingham [undated]; Godstone, 17.6.1941; Earlswood, prior to 1950 (Evans, 1973); seen flying on the downs near Carshalton, June 1951 (Booker in de Worms, *L.N.* **33**:135). This latter record presumably refers to Banstead Downs.

Arctia caja (Linnaeus, 1758)

Garden Tiger

Resident; gardens, commons; widespread and fairly common.

Univoltine; mid-July to August.

Foodplant – dandelion, (common nettle, bramble, hollyhock, radish, yarrow).

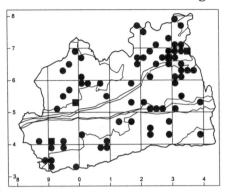

The Garden Tiger is fairly generally distributed in more open habitats throughout Surrey, but, with the exception of the London area where it can be abundant, is rarely more than fairly common. Comparison of rural mv traps with those from the suburbs of south London shows: Bramley, 1985 (6), 86 (32) (RFB); Milford, 1992 (14) (DWB); South Croydon, 1983 (160), 84 (166), 85 (60) (GAC); Mitcham, 1981 (200), 82 (499), 83 (445) (RKAM).

Arctia villica (Linnaeus, 1758)

Cream-spot Tiger

ssp. *britannica* Oberthür, 1911

Resident; downland, woodland; local and rare.

Univoltine; June.

Foodplant – (foxglove).

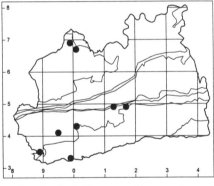

The Cream-spot Tiger appears to have declined in recent years, and in the last decade has only been found in south-west and central Surrey, and then only as singletons. Writing in 1952, Cockayne (*Ent. Rec.* **64**:302) stated that some years earlier Kettlewell had found larvae not uncommonly in the hedgerows round Cranleigh, and that by assembling to reared females he had attracted large numbers of males including a small percentage of ab. *ursula* Schultz. A further example of this aberration was taken at Caterham in 1948 (EHW).

RECORDS – **Hindhead**, 16.6.83 (JTS); **Milford**, 19.5.82 (DWB); **Tugley Wood**, 7.6.87 (SCP); **Bramley**, 19.6.84 (RFB); **White Downs**, 5-17.6.85 (BS); **Westcott Downs**, 16.6.84 (GAC); **Dorking**, 5.6.84 (DAT); **Thorpe**, scarce; not since 1978 (PJB); **Virginia Water**, 7.81 (J. Pontin).

Diacrisia sannio (Linnaeus, 1758)   **Clouded Buff**

Resident; heathland, chalk grassland;
    restricted but fairly common.
Univoltine; mid-June to early July.
Foodplant – heather.
As a resident of heathland this species occurs
on all the larger heaths where it is fairly
common, the males frequently flying by day
when they are very noticeable. It also occurs
on chalk grassland in a few places and has
been recorded as follows: Hackhurst Downs,
4.7.1979 (GAC); White Downs, 28.6.1986
(AJH); Ranmore, 16.6.1977 (TJD), 4.7.1977,
9.6.1978 (JP), 10.6.1978 (PAM), 29.6.1979 (GAC); North Cheam, 30.6.1984 (RFMcC);
Banstead Downs, 13.6.1988, 89 (1), 90 (5), 91 (8) (DC). In the hot summer of 1976 one was
taken at Leigh towards the end of August, probably representing a partial second brood
(RF).

Spilosoma lubricipeda (Linnaeus, 1758)   **White Ermine**

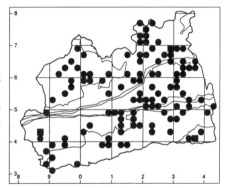

Resident; commons, woodland, gardens;
    widespread and common.
Univoltine; May to July.
Foodplant – (dock, knotgrass).
The White Ermine is very widely distributed
in the county and frequently very common,
e.g. Bramley 1985 (241), 86 (251) (RFB). The
larva is less frequently observed, usually
racing across open ground prior to pupation,
and consequently knowledge of its foodplants
is rather poor.

Spilosoma luteum (Hufnagel, 1766)   Buff Ermine

Resident; commons, woodland, gardens; widespread and common.
Univoltine; mid-May to mid-August.
Foodplant – common nettle, (bindweed, buddleia, dock, ivy, burdock, orache).
The Buff Ermine is also very widespread and, although marginally less frequent than *lubricipeda* where trap counts are kept, still a very common species. A second-brood example was noted at Mitcham, 11.9.1981 (RKAM). A melanic specimen, described as ab. *totinigra* Seitz, was taken at Ottershaw, 10.8.1962 (RFB); otherwise this species is pretty invariable.

Spilosoma urticae (Esper, 1789)   PLATE 1   Water Ermine

Extinct; not seen since 1959.
The Water Ermine was formerly known from the Ottershaw, New Haw, Horsell, Pirbright traps, very scarce; Egham 17.6.1934; Woking 1911/14 (Bretherton, 1957), and Horsell Park, 1959 (JACG in Bretherton, 1965). A further specimen was taken at White Downs, 14.7.56 (RFB). There is also an undated record from Merton Park (de Worms, *L.N.* **33**:134), and Barrett (1895) gives it as occurring "formerly in marshy places near London, especially about the Croydon Canal". The moth is an inhabitant of wet places and has no doubt suffered from drainage and development of its sites.

Diaphora mendica (Clerck, 1759)   Muslin Moth

Resident; commons, woodland; widespread and common.
Univoltine; mid-May to early June.
Foodplant – (sallow).
The grey males of this species are a common sight in the moth trap in spring, and show the moth to be widely distributed. The white female has been observed occasionally flying by day. Ab. *rustica* Hübner, in which the male resembles the female, has been recorded from Nutfield, 8.5.1970 (PAC), and Bramley, 1974 (RFB). A bilateral gynandromorph was taken at Horsell, 7.5.1961 (CGMdeW).

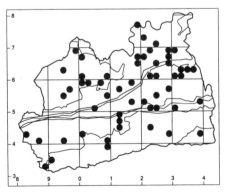

Phragmatobia fuliginosa (Linnaeus, 1758)　　　**Ruby Tiger**
ssp. *fuliginosa* (Linnaeus, 1758)

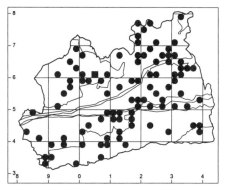

Resident; commons, heathland, downland; widespread and common.

Bivoltine; May, and mid-July to August.

Foodplant – [heather], (ragwort).

A rather common species everywhere. The vast majority of records are of second-brood moths at light traps, and it seems that this brood has different habits to the first which is noted more by day. Because of this difference in behaviour it is difficult to compare numbers of the two broods but it seems likely that the second really is more numerous and that probably there is heavy larval mortality during the winter. A specimen taken at South Croydon, 23.7.1989, has the hindwings normal but the forewings approaching the colour of the northern subspecies *borealis* Staudinger (GAC). An aberration with the red colour replaced with a dull orange was taken at Wimbledon, 26.7.1996 (JVD).

Callimorpha dominula (Linnaeus, 1758)　　　**Scarlet Tiger**

Status uncertain; unlikely to be resident.

The *VCH* gave this species as occurring at Redhill, very sparingly, since when it has been recorded as follows: Weybridge, 30.6.1952 (JLM); Abinger Hammer, 3.7.1976 in a pub (EHW); and Banstead Downs, 10.7.1989 (DC). These records may refer to vagrants or to escapees as it is unlikely that such an obvious moth would be overlooked if breeding in Surrey, although there is potentially suitable habitat along the Mole and the Wey and its tributaries. Writing in 1941, Green (*Ent. Rec.* **53**:30), stated that he had "turned down" larvae of this species in his garden at Camberley, but considered the introduction unsuccessful. Kettlewell also introduced a colony into his garden at Cranleigh in 1939 which was still thriving 30 years later (Kettlewell, 1973).

Tyria jacobaeae (Linnaeus, 1758)　　PLATE 5　　　**Cinnabar**

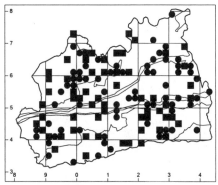

Resident; commons, grassland; widespread and common.

Univoltine; June.

Foodplant – ragwort, hoary ragwort, Oxford ragwort, marsh ragwort, groundsel, (colt's-foot).

This moth, and in particular its very obvious and distinctive larva, is to be found throughout the county, often very commonly. The adults have been observed both by day and at the moth trap.

DAVID WILSON

Extinct, and probably extinct, species

1. *Zygaena trifolii decreta* Five-spot Burnet (marsh form)   **2.** *Eriogaster lanestris* Small Eggar
3. *Eupithecia irriguata* Marbled Pug   **4.** *Hemaris tityus* Narrow-bordered Bee Hawk
5. *Trichopteryx polycommata* Barred Tooth-striped   **6.** *Parasemia plantaginis* Wood Tiger
7. *Pachetra sagittigera* Feathered Ear   **8.** *Spilosoma urticae* Water Ermine
9. *Heliophobus reticulata* Bordered Gothic   **10.** *Jodia croceago* Orange Upperwing
11. *Cosmia diffinis* White-spotted Pinion   **12.** *Tyta luctuosa* Four-spotted

PLATE 1

Family Hepialidae   Gold Swift

Family Cossidae   Goat Moth

Family Zygaenidae   Narrow-bordered
Five-spot Burnet

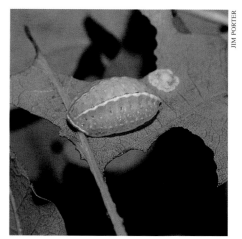

Family Limacodidae   Festoon

Larvae – family representatives

PLATE 2

Family Lasiocampidae   Lackey

Family Sesiidae   Hornet Clearwing

Family Saturniidae   Emperor Moth

Family Drepanidae   Oak Hook-tip

Larvae – family representatives

PLATE 3

Family Thyatiridae   Frosted Green

Family Geometridae   Sloe Pug

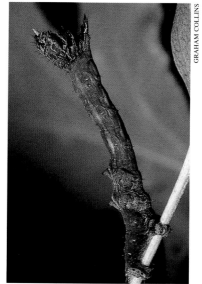

Family Geometridae   Beautiful Carpet

Family Geometridae   Early Thorn

Larvae – family representatives

PLATE 4

Family Notodontidae   Lobster Moth

Family Sphingidae   Broad-bordered Bee Hawk

Family Arctiidae   Cinnabar

Family Lymantriidae   Brown-tail

Larvae – family representatives

PLATE 5

Family Nolidae   Short-cloaked

Family Noctuidae   Beautiful Yellow
                         Underwing

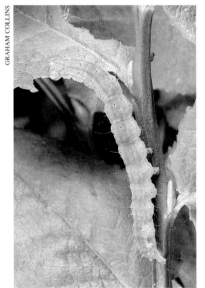

Family Noctuidae   Beautiful Snout

Family Noctuidae   Blossom Underwing

Larvae – family representatives

PLATE 6

Hyles livornica   Striped Hawk

Rhodometra sacraria   Vestal

Heliothis peltigera   Bordered Straw

Mythimna albipuncta   White-point

Migrant species

PLATE 7

Ashtead Common

Dichonia aprilina   Merveille du Jour

Dicycla oo   Heart moth

Mythimna turca   Double Line

Parkland species

PLATE 8

Edolphs Copse

Angerona prunaria   Orange Moth

Hypomecis roboraria   Great Oak Beauty

Synanthedon vespiformis Yellow-legged
                                              Clearwing

Woodland species

PLATE 9

Hemaris fuciformis   Broad-bordered Bee Hawk

Eilema sororcula   Orange Footman

Meganola strigula   Small Black Arches

Paracolax tristalis   Clay Fan-foot

Woodland species

PLATE 10

Chobham Common

Cossus cossus   Goat Moth

Heliothis maritima Shoulder-striped Clover

Xestia agathina   Heath Rustic

Heathland species

PLATE 11

River Wey Navigation, Send

Xanthorhoe biriviata   Balsam Carpet

Thumatha senex   Round-winged Muslin

Hedgecourt Lake

Wetland species

PLATE 12

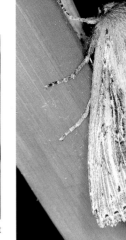

Celaena leucostigma   Crescent

Nonagria typhae   Bulrush Wainscot

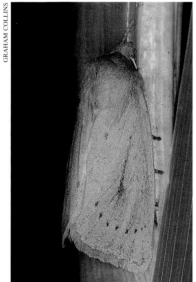

Plusia festucae   Gold Spot

Archanara algae   Rush Wainscot

Wetland species

PLATE 13

Westcott Downs

Scopula ornata   Lace Border

Aspitates gilvaria   Straw Belle

Synanthedon andrenaeformis Orange-tailed
Clearwing

Chalk downland species

PLATE 14

Eupithecia intricata   Freyer's Pug

Hadena compta   Varied Coronet

Polychrysia moneta   Golden Plusia

Lithophane leautieri   Blair's Shoulder-knot

Garden species

PLATE 15

Sesia apiformis   Hornet Clearwing

Scopula marginepunctata   Mullein Wave

Idaea vulpinaria   Least Carpet

Eupithecia millefoliata   Yarrow Pug

"South London" species

PLATE 16

NOLIDAE

The Nolidae is a family of small moths, of which four are resident in Surrey. The adults have characteristic raised tufts of scales on the forewing. They are nocturnal and come rather freely to light. The larvae have the first pair of prolegs absent and are adorned with short tufts of setae arising from verrucae.

Meganola strigula ([Denis & Schiffermüller], 1775) PLATE 10 Small Black Arches

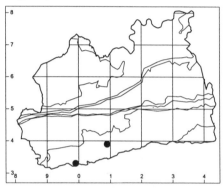

Notable/Na

Resident; woodland, very local and rare.

July.

There appear to be only a handful of records for the Small Black Arches in Surrey, with only two sites known during the survey period; yet it is apparently not uncommon in some of the Sussex woods in the Plaistow region, just over the county boundary. The *VCH* gives Redstone Wood, Reigate Hill, Gomshall and Haslemere, to which can be added: New Haw trap, 5.7.1952 (Bretherton, 1957); Chiddingfold, 29.6.1957; Wormley, 18.7.1961 and 14.7.1964 (JLM); and Bramley, 12.7.65 (RFB).

RECORDS – **Oaken Wood**, 30.6-20.7.95 (GAC); **Ewhurst**, 29.7.81 (SFI).

Meganola albula ([Denis & Schiffermüller], 1775) Kent Black Arches

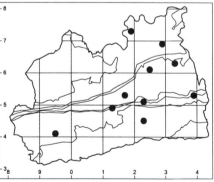

Notable/Nb

Resident; chalk downland; very local and
       uncommon.

Univoltine; July.

From the frequency and distribution of the records it would seem that the Kent Black Arches is resident on the downs around Dorking. It is also occasionally recorded from elsewhere in the county, but whether these specimens represent wanderers from the downs or are primary migrants is unknown.

RECORDS – **Milford**, 11.7.92 (DWB);
Westcott Downs, 13.7.83 (20) (GAC); **Juniper Hall**, 7.85 (R. Softly (per CWP)); **Buckland**, 1.8.85, 31.7.86, 21.7.94 (CH); **Leigh**, 1980, 88 (RF); **Oxted**, 26.7.86 (TD); **Banstead Downs**, 10.7.89 (DC); **South Croydon**, 22.7.93 (GAC); **Mitcham**, 14.7.81 (RKAM); **Richmond Park**, 5.7.95 (MP).

Nola cucullatella (Linnaeus, 1758) PLATE 6 Short-cloaked

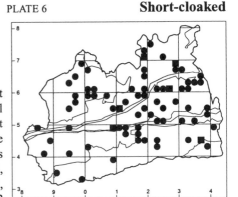

Resident; commons, woodland;
widespread and common.
Univoltine; July.
Foodplant – sloe, hawthorn.

A very widespread species which, on account of its small size and unexceptional appearance, is probably to some extent overlooked. The larvae can be found quite easily by beating in the spring and the adults are fairly common at light: Bramley, 1985 (8), 86 (17) (RFB); Wisley RES, 1986 (3), 87 (9), 90 (4), 91 (3) (AJH); Mitcham, 1981 (15), 82 (18), 83 (33) (RKAM); South Croydon, 1983 (16), 84 (14), 85 (4) (GAC). The melanic ab. *fuliginalis* Stephens was recorded at Ashtead, 2.7.1993 (GAC), but does not appear to have been otherwise noted.

Nola confusalis (Herrich-Schäffer, 1847) Least Black Arches

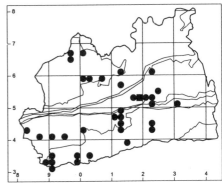

Resident; woodland, wooded commons;
restricted but fairly common.
Univoltine; mid-May to mid-June.
Foodplant – hawthorn.

The Least Black Arches is absent from the east of the county, but in well-wooded areas of central and western Surrey it is a regularly seen species. Trap counts show: Milford, 1992 (15) (DWB); Bramley, 1985 (7), 86 (8) (RFB).

NOCTUIDAE

The Noctuidae is the largest family of British macrolepidoptera and comprises mostly rather dull, medium-sized moths. All come to light traps, and most can also be taken at sugar and on flowers. The larvae are rather variable; most have four pairs of prolegs but in the subfamilies Plusiinae and Hypeninae some pairs are vestigial. Habits are very variable, as one might expect of such a large family; trees, shrubs and grasses are utilized, some species feeding internally or being subterranean.

Euxoa tritici (Linnaeus, 1761)   **White-line Dart**

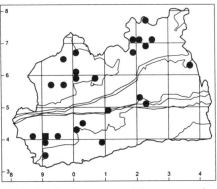

Resident; heathland, gardens; local and uncommon.

Univoltine; late July and August.

The White-line Dart is commonest on the heaths of south-west Surrey, but also occurs in widely spaced localities across the north of the county. Many of these are gardens but all are fairly close to areas of heathland, albeit some of them rather vestigial. Bretherton (1965) considered that there were two distinct forms, one larger, flying earlier in the season, and occurring in gardens and cultivated areas, the other smaller, flying later and associated with the heaths; he suspected that two species may have been involved. The species varies greatly across its range and even within a single population, and there is currently debate over the status of some forms. It would be useful to have voucher specimens from as many sites and habitats as possible.

Euxoa nigricans (Linnaeus, 1761)   **Garden Dart**

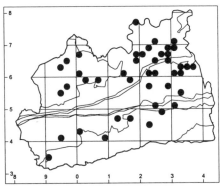

Resident; gardens; restricted but fairly common.

Univoltine; late July and August.

Although taken occasionally in other habitats the Garden Dart is principally a species of gardens and cultivated areas and in Surrey is commonest in the north-east. Trap counts from this area show it to be fairly common: Carshalton, 1988 (25), 89 (13), 90 (9) (DC); South Croydon, 1983 (9), 84 (25), 85 (10) (GAC); Selsdon, 1980 (31) (EHW).

Agrotis cinerea ([Denis & Schiffermüller], 1775)   Light Feathered Rustic

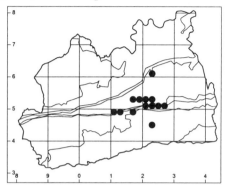

Notable/Nb
Resident; chalk downland; very local and
    uncommon.
Univoltine; May and early June.
In Surrey the Light Feathered Rustic is
confined to the area of the North Downs
around Dorking, although occasional
wanderers turn up at sites a few miles away.
It is rarely recorded in any numbers although
access to its breeding grounds is not always
easy. Some examples are a rather unicolorous
brown, illustrated in Skinner (1984).

RECORDS – **White Downs**, 4.6.79 (RFMcC), 5-17.6.85 (BS); **Dorking**, 21.5.87 (DAT);
Juniper Hall, 24.5.82, 7.6.83 (JHFC); **Headley Warren**, 19.5.94 (HM-P), 5-27.5.95
(GAC); **Betchworth**, 2.6.79 (RAC); **Dawcombe**, 1-22.5.90 (81), 11.5-10.6.91 (36),
19.5.92 (4) (DC); **Buckland**, 25.5.88 (ID), 7.5.95 (2) (CH); **Buckland Quarry**, 1-7.6.83
(CH); **Reigate**, 6.6.76, 13.6.78 (DAT), 9-18.5.76, 25.5.78, 1987 (RAC); **Leigh**, 11.6.77,
24.5.92 (RF); **Banstead**, 23-24.6.90 (SWG).

Agrotis vestigialis (Hufnagel, 1766)   Archer's Dart

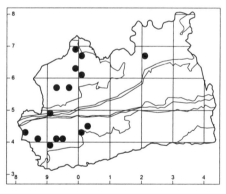

Resident; heathland; local and uncommon.
Univoltine; late July and August.
In Surrey Archer's Dart is typically a
heathland insect and is probably found on all
the larger heaths. It is likely to be more
widespread on the north-western heaths on
areas owned by the army and where very little
recording has been done. Some specimens,
especially from Blackheath, are particularly
dark – f. *nigra* Tutt (*teste* Kettlewell, 1973).
The origin of the example recorded at
Tolworth is uncertain; there may be an
undiscovered population nearby, or it may just
have been a vagrant.

RECORDS – **Boundstone**, 3.8.84 (BH); **Rushmoor**, 1982-85 (PAD); **Thursley
Common**, 13.8.91 (RFMcC); **Witley Common**, 21.8.93 (GAC); **Milford**, 17.8.80, 83
(2), 85 (4), 86 (2), 90 (1), 91 (2), 92 (3), 93 (3), 94 (2), 96 (2) (DWB); **Bramley**, 23.8.83
(RFB); **Blackheath**, 20-30.8.87 (BS), 16.8.91 (GAC); **Wanborough Wood**, 17.7.94
(GAC); **Bisley Ranges**, 16-17.8.96 (MRH); **Horsell**, 7.8.77 (CGMdeW); **Woking**, 1.8.93
(J. Pontin); **Chobham Common**, 7.8.82 (RKAM), 14.8.85 (GAC); **Virginia Water**,
7.8.82 (AG); **Thorpe**, scarce; 1987, 89, 92 (PJB); **Tolworth**, 30.7.90 (JTS).

Agrotis segetum ([Denis & Schiffermüller], 1775) **Turnip Moth**

Resident; gardens, commons; widespread and common.

Bivoltine; June and July, and September and October.

A widespread and common species occurring in a variety of habitats especially gardens and cultivated habitats.

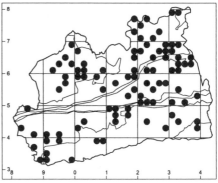

Agrotis clavis (Hufnagel, 1766) **Heart and Club**

Resident; gardens, commons; widespread and common.

Univoltine; July.

The Heart and Club is found throughout much of Surrey and is often an abundant species especially in the suburbs of south London. Trap counts show: Milford, 1992 (470) (DWB); Bramley, 1985 (226), 86 (111) (RFB); South Croydon, 1983 (709), 84 (866), 85 (682) (GAC); Selsdon, 1980 (189) (EHW).

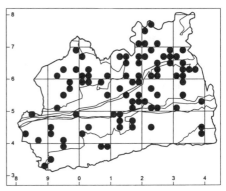

Agrotis exclamationis (Linnaeus, 1758) **Heart and Dart**

Resident; gardens, commons, downland, woodland; widespread and very common.

Univoltine; mid-May to August.

Foodplant – (ground-ivy).

The Heart and Dart is a very widespread species in Surrey. In rural areas it is regular but not always common, whereas in gardens, especially those in suburbia, it is abundant and often the commonest species. Trap counts show: Bramley, 1985 (1124), 86 (124) (RFB); Milford, 1992 (685) (DWB); and even at an

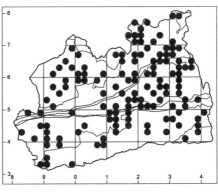

actinic trap at Ashtead, 1987 (443), 88 (412), 89 (382) (GG). In south London even larger numbers are recorded: Banstead, 1990 (5112), 92 (2189) (SWG); South Croydon, 1983

(3910), 84 (5263), 85 (2593) (GAC); and in the exceptional summer of 1976 at Selsdon no less than 10260 were noted (EHW). Occasionally fresh examples are noted well after the main emergence, and these may represent a partial second brood. The moth is very variable and many different forms have occurred including bilateral gynandromorphs at Addington, 17.6.1984 and 19.6.1988 (BS). Ab. *obsoleta* Tutt , a rare form in which the stigmata are absent and recorded mainly from Surrey, was taken at West Norwood, 1965 (BS).

Agrotis ipsilon (Hufnagel, 1766)   Dark Sword-grass

Migrant; recorded annually.

The Dark Sword-grass occurs every year in Surrey but with a considerable variation in numbers. The peak time of appearance is from mid-July to mid-October; some of the later examples are no doubt locally bred but there is no direct evidence of survival during the winter. An early specimen at South Croydon on 29.4.1985 was probably migrant as it was associated with an influx of the Striped Hawk (*q.v.*), two of which were taken in Surrey during that period.

Agrotis puta (Hübner, 1803)   Shuttle-shaped Dart

ssp. *puta* (Hübner, 1803)

Resident; gardens, commons; widespread and common.

Bivoltine; mid-May to June, and mid-July to early September.

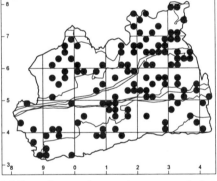

Another very common Dart which, like several of its congeners, is commonest in the gardens of south London. Trap counts show: Bramley, 1985 (152), 86 (28) (RFB); Milford, 1992 (355) (DWB); Mitcham, 1981 (179), 82 (447), 83 (305) (RKAM); South Croydon, 1983 (818), 84 (837), 85 (94) (GAC); Selsdon, 1980 (612) (EHW). In hotter years the species thrives and a small third brood is produced. A bilateral gynandromorph was recorded at Addington, 21.7.1983 (BS).

Axylia putris (Linnaeus, 1761)   Flame

Resident; commons, woodland, downland; widespread and common.

Univoltine; July and early August.

The Flame is found across Surrey in a range of habitats, and, particularly at the static traps, is a common species as the following counts show: Bramley, 1985 (281), 86 (229) (RFB); Mitcham, 1981 (103), 82 (134), 83 (66) (RKAM); South Croydon, 1983 (169), 84 (144), 85 (76) (GAC).

Actebia praecox (Linnaeus, 1758)   Portland Moth

Vagrant; a single record.

A specimen of this normally coastal species was recorded on a lamp at Wandsworth in 1858 (Stevens, *Ent. Wkly. Intell.* **5**:115).

Ochropleura plecta (Linnaeus, 1761)   Flame Shoulder

Resident; widespread and common.

May to September; peak August.

Foodplant – (groundsel).

A very common species everywhere; at Bramley it is one of the dominant species. The voltinism is unclear but there are probably two overlapping broods, the second being much the larger.

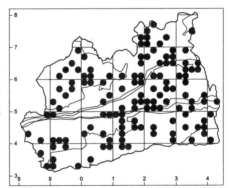

Rhyacia simulans (Hufnagel, 1766)　　　Dotted Rustic

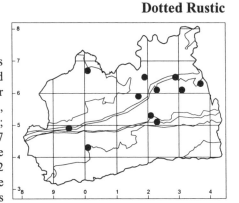

Resident; probably temporary.
Univoltine; July to early October.
Until recently the Dotted Rustic was principally a species of central England and there are only three records from Surrey prior to 1980: Ewell, one taken at buddleia, 4.7.1949 (Tunstall, *Ent. Rec.* **64**:203); Pyrford, 26.8.1971 (JACG); Thorpe, 3.7.1977 (PJB). In the 1980s it has expanded its range greatly and there are many records after 1982 given below. As there have only been three records since 1990 it has been given the status of a temporary resident, although whether it remains established or disappears again only time will tell.

RECORDS – **Wallington**, 17.7.82 (SC); **Tolworth**, 6.9.82 (JTS); **Purley**, 13.9.83 (DCL); **Bramley**, 16.7.83, 12-15.8.85 (2), 2.9.87 (RFB); **Addington**, 4.10.83, 6.7.87 (BS); **Thorpe**, 28.7.84, 26.7.85 (PJB); **Compton**, 25.7.85 (DWB); **Ashtead**, 25.8.87, 18.9.87 (GG); **Dawcombe**, 5.7.91 (DC); **Buckland**, 30.6.92 (CH); **Banstead**, 22.7.96 (SWG).

Noctua pronuba Linnaeus, 1758　　　Large Yellow Underwing

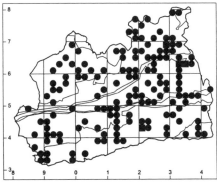

Resident; commons, downland, heathland, woodland; widespread and common.
Univoltine; mid-June to October.
Foodplant – sloe, common nettle, white dead-nettle, (ivy).
The Large Yellow Underwing is an extremely common species found in various habitats throughout the county. At many of the static traps it is a dominant species: Bramley, 1985 (397), 86 (2763) (RFB); South Croydon, 1983 (1842), 84 (1580), 85 (2548) (GAC); Selsdon, 1980 (1912) (EHW). The moth is on the wing from mid-June into the autumn as a single extended brood, and the larvae can be found commonly during the winter feeding in mild weather.

Noctua orbona (Hufnagel, 1766)   Lunar Yellow Underwing

Vagrant; a single reliable record.

This species, the Lunar Yellow Underwing, is subject to misidentification, and to nomenclatural confusion with *N. comes* – both species having been known as *orbona* at times. Barrett (1897) gives it as having been found rarely in Surrey, and other southern counties. Apart from this unconfirmed occurrence there is but one reliable record: New Haw trap, 2.8.1950 (Bretherton, 1957). The species seems to have been declining nationally for some time although there is evidence of a revival in North Hampshire. As it is possible that it may reappear in Surrey in the future, any doubtful examples should be retained as vouchers.

Noctua comes Hübner, 1813   Lesser Yellow Underwing

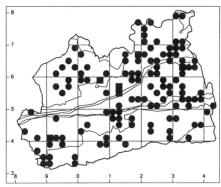

Resident; commons, downland, heathland, woodland; widespread and common.

Univoltine; July to early October.

Foodplant – birch, sloe, bilberry, common nettle, (meadow-grass, sycamore, gorse).

The Lesser Yellow Underwing is another very common species throughout the county although not seen in as large numbers as *pronuba*. The larva is common in the spring on a variety of shrubs and herbaceous plants.

Noctua fimbriata (Schreber, 1759)   Broad-bordered Yellow Underwing

Resident; commons, downland, heathland, woodland; widespread and common.

Univoltine; July to September.

Foodplant – sloe, birch, hawthorn, rowan, bilberry, privet, wayfaring-tree, (sallow, elm, willow-herb, dock).

Although considerably less common than its congeners, the Broad-bordered Yellow Underwing is still regularly found at light traps and as a larva in the spring. Trap counts show: Bramley, 1985 (26), 86 (33) (RFB); South Croydon, 1983 (33), 84 (43), 85 (32) (GAC); Selsdon, 1980 (20) (EHW).

Noctua janthe (Borkhausen, 1792) **Lesser Broad-bordered Yellow Underwing**

Resident; commons, downland, heathland, woodland; widespread and common.

Univoltine; August.

Foodplant – (bramble, dock).

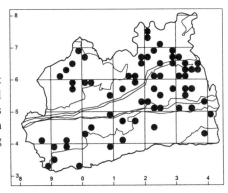

As with its congeners this species is very common and widespread although its flight period is much shorter. Recent work on the continent has discovered a species complex containing three species, the British species being *janthe* rather than *janthina* (Mentzer et al, 1991; Dyer, 1993). The other two species are probably not British, but while this situation is still in flux it would be useful to collect vouchers from as many different sites as possible so that the true situation in Surrey can be ascertained.

Noctua interjecta Hübner, 1803   **Least Yellow Underwing**

ssp. *caliginosa* (Schawerda, 1919)

Resident; commons, downland, woodland; widespread and fairly common.

Univoltine; August.

Foodplant – (common nettle, grasses).

The Least Yellow Underwing is the least frequent of the resident *Noctua* but is still sometimes fairly common. The adult is usually noted at light, but has also been observed feeding at ragwort flowers during the day.

Spaelotis ravida ([Denis & Schiffermüller], 1775)   **Stout Dart**

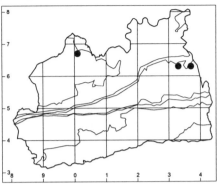

Vagrant; four recent records.

Late August.

The Stout Dart is a resident of the midlands and eastern counties and only eight examples are recorded for Surrey, all from the extreme north of the county. At this frequency it is best considered as a vagrant. Records before the survey period are: Ottershaw trap, 31.8.1960 (Bretherton, 1965); West Norwood, 18.9.1963 (BS); Thorpe, 1973 (2) (PJB).

RECORDS – **Addington**, 14.8.78 (BS); **Thorpe**, 1980 (1) (PJB); **South Croydon**, 1.9.86, 23.8.88 (GAC).

Graphiphora augur (Fabricius, 1775)   **Double Dart**

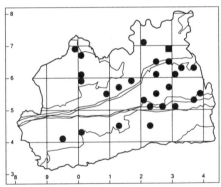

Resident; commons, woodland; restricted and scarce.

Univoltine; late June and July.

Foodplant – sloe.

The Double Dart seems to occur most frequently in the north-east of the county, especially on the chalk. Elsewhere it is scarce and has probably declined in the last decade; at Bramley 45-five were seen in the 1970s and only one since (RFB), and at Leigh it is reported as being seen only on very few occasions recently (RF). It is equally at home on the commons of south London as in more rural areas.

Paradiarsia glareosa (Esper, 1788)   **Autumnal Rustic**

ssp. *glareosa* (Esper, 1788)

Resident; commons, heathland, downland; fairly widespread and fairly common.

Univoltine; September.

Foodplant – birch.

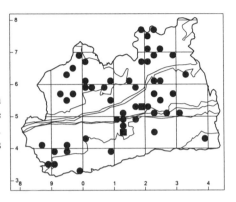

The Autumnal Rustic is fairly widespread in Surrey but does appear to be absent from some areas of the west and much of the weald. Evans (1973) considered that it was perhaps spreading, and the same may be true today.

Lycophotia porphyrea ([Denis & Schiffermüller], 1775)   **True Lover's Knot**

Resident; heathland, gardens; widespread and common.

Univoltine; late June to early August.

Foodplant – heather.

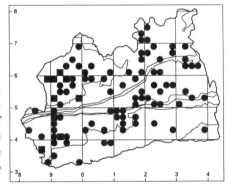

The True Lover's Knot is a common species on the heaths of west Surrey, both as an adult at light and as larvae in the autumn and early spring. It is also not infrequent in the east of the county and, although there is some vestigial wild heather in these areas, the probability is that the larvae are also associated with cultivated heathers in gardens.

Peridroma saucia (Hübner, 1808)   **Pearly Underwing**

Migrant; recorded most years.

The Pearly Underwing is a migratory species which reaches Surrey in most years, but rarely in any numbers. There are no records of the early stages.

Diarsia mendica (Fabricius, 1775)　　　　　Ingrailed Clay

ssp. *mendica* (Fabricius, 1775)

Resident; woodland, commons;
　　widespread and common.
Univoltine; June and early July.
Foodplant – (sloe).
The Ingrailed Clay is very widely distributed
in Surrey and often found rather commonly.
Trap counts for Bramley show: 1985 (66), 87
(53) (RFB), although such abundance at the
other static traps is unusual. The moth prefers
well-wooded districts.

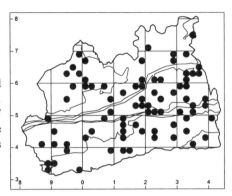

Diarsia dahlii (Hübner, 1813)　　　　　Barred Chestnut

Resident; woodland; very local but fairly
　　common.
Univoltine; late August and early
　　September.
The Barred Chestnut constitutes one of the
species that the late Russell Bretherton
described as "Surrey alpines"; that is, species
that are normally more northern and western
in distribution but occur in Surrey only at
some altitude. The typical habitat in Surrey
is well-wooded areas on the greensand, and
here the moth can be common. Confusion

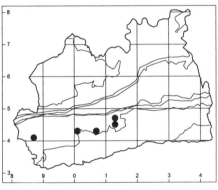

with other species is regular and voucher specimens should be kept.

RECORDS – **Rushmoor**, 25.8.83 (PAD); **Bramley**, 1978 (1) (RFB); **Winterfold**,
20.8.76, 26.8.78 (RFB); **Friday Street**, 6-8.9.77 (13) (JP), 9.9.79 (PMS), 3.9.87 (SCP),
3.9.91 (5) (RFMcC), 28.8.92, 19-29.8.93 (GAC); **Wotton**, scarce; 1976-77 (JDH).

Diarsia brunnea ([Denis & Schiffermüller], 1775)   **Purple Clay**

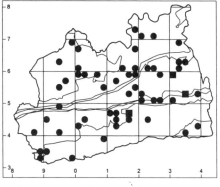

Resident; woodland, commons;
    widespread and fairly common.
Univoltine; late June and July.
Foodplant – sloe, birch, bramble, bilberry,
    common nettle.
The Purple Clay occurs over much of the
county, but does not appear to penetrate far
into urban London and is also poorly recorded
from the weald. It rarely occurs in any
numbers as an adult and single figure annual
catches at light traps are the norm. There are,
however, a number of larval records and this
species would seem to be one of the more regularly encountered early spring larvae.

Diarsia rubi (Vieweg, 1790)   **Small Square-spot**

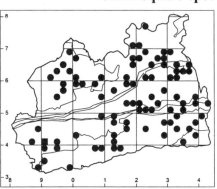

Resident; commons, woodland;
    widespread and common.
Bivoltine; June, and August and
    September.
The Small Square-spot occurs rather
commonly across the county, preferring
slightly more open habitats than some of its
congeners. Trap counts at Mitcham show
1981 (15), 82 (76), 83 (29) (RKAM), but such
numbers are exceptional and at Bramley,
where it was still regarded as abundant, the
numbers were 1985 (7), 86 (25) (RFB).

Xestia c-nigrum (Linnaeus, 1758)   **Setaceous Hebrew Character**

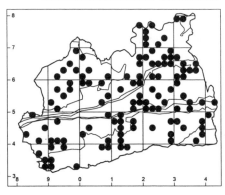

Resident; commons, woodland, heathland;
    widespread and common.
Bivoltine; June to mid-July, and August to
    early October.
Foodplant – heather.
A very common species found throughout the
county. There are two fairly distinct broods,
the second being much more numerous; at
South Croydon the trap counts show the
second brood to be ten times as large as the
first. It is quite likely that the autumnal moths
are reinforced by migrants.

Xestia ditrapezium ([Denis & Schiffermüller], 1775)   Triple-spotted Clay

Resident; woodland, wooded commons; restricted and uncommon.

Univoltine; July.

Foodplant – sloe, birch.

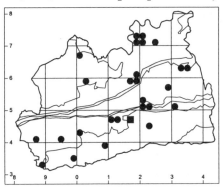

The Triple-spotted Clay is one of the less common species of the genus. Evans (1973) considered it to be increasing in the early 1970s, but the number of records for the last decade suggest that it has declined again and it is currently rather restricted, preferring wooded areas on heavier soils.

Xestia triangulum (Hufnagel, 1766)   Double Square-spot

Resident; commons, woodland; widespread and common.

Univoltine; July and early August.

Foodplant – sloe, (lime, English elm, hawthorn, common nettle, ivy).

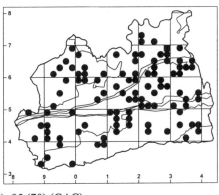

The Double Square-spot is a very common species over much of the county. It probably prefers rural areas but is still very common in suburban London as the following counts show: Bramley, 1985 (204), 86 (274) (RFB); Mitcham, 1981 (48), 82 (127), 83 (27) (RKAM); South Croydon, 1983 (129), 84 (79), 85 (70) (GAC).

Xestia baja ([Denis & Schiffermüller], 1775)   Dotted Clay

Resident; woodland, commons, heathland; widespread and fairly common.

Univoltine; mid-July to August.

Foodplant – birch, common nettle.

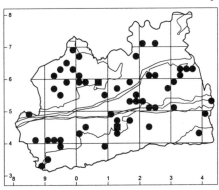

A rather widespread species which is not usually seen in any numbers, although the following counts were made at Milford: 1992 (23), 93 (39), 94 (27) (DWB).

Xestia rhomboidea (Esper, 1790) Square-spotted Clay

Notable/Nb
Resident; wooded downland; very local
  and scarce.
Univoltine; August.

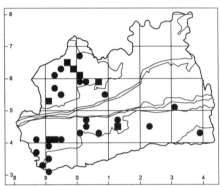

The Square-spotted Clay is certainly a very local species being known recently only from a handful of wooded sites mainly on the crest of the North Downs. It is possibly overlooked to some extent as it prefers flowers, especially of burdock, and sugar to the light trap.

RECORDS – **Milford**, 13.8.94 (DWB); **Bramley**, 7.8.83, 13.8.84 (3) (RFB); **Headley Warren**, 4.8.94 (5), 29.7-3.8.95 (12) (GAC); **Dawcombe**, 9.8.91 (3) (DC); **Buckland**, 19.8.92, 13-29.8.96 (CH).

Xestia castanea (Esper, 1796) Neglected Rustic

Resident; heathland, heathy woods;
  restricted but fairly common.
Univoltine; mid-August to mid-September.
Foodplant – heather.

The Neglected Rustic is principally a species of heathland and open spaces in woods where its foodplant grows. In Surrey it can be found in most suitable habitat in the west of the county but is only occasional in the east. Both the grey and the red forms occur, and a strongly yellow form has been taken at Wormley – 26.8.1968, 17.8.1971 and 4.9.1976 (JLM).

Xestia sexstrigata (Haworth, 1809)   **Six-striped Rustic**

Resident; woodland, grassland;
    widespread and fairly common.

Univoltine; August.

Foodplant – (meadow-grass).

The Six-striped Rustic is found throughout the county, but is restricted to grassy places such as commons and clearings in woodland. In such places it is a fairly common species although at most of the static traps annual counts in excess of single figures are unusual.

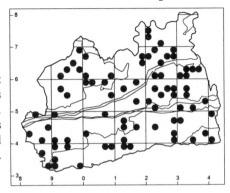

Xestia xanthographa ([Denis & Schiffermüller], 1775)   **Square-spot Rustic**

Resident; commons, grassland, heathland;
    widespread and common.

Univoltine; August and September.

Foodplant – grasses, (timothy).

A very common autumnal species all over the county, favouring almost any habitat where grasses grow. Annual trap counts show that it is perhaps commonest on the commons and in the gardens of south London: Bramley, 1985 (118), 86 (85) (RFB); South Croydon, 1983 (190), 84 (172), 85 (124) (GAC); Mitcham, 1981 (153), 82 (322), 83 (487) (RKAM).

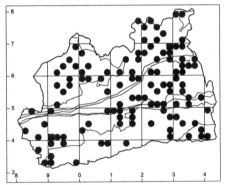

Xestia agathina (Duponchel, 1827)   PLATE 11   **Heath Rustic**
ssp. *agathina* (Duponchel, 1827)

Resident; heathland; very local and scarce.

Univoltine; late August and September.

Foodplant – heather.

The Heath Rustic is a very local species restricted to the heathland of the greensand, and in the last decade only recorded from the extreme south-west of that area. It is stated to prefer heathland with deep heather, so that the frequent fires caused by day-trippers, which result in loss of this older heather and in some cases its replacement by *Molinia*

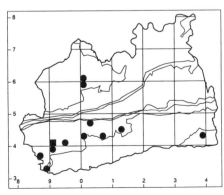

grassland, may pose a threat to its continued existence in Surrey. Elsewhere in Surrey a singleton was recorded at Horsell on 7.9.1978 (CGMdeW), the first record for the Bagshot sands for over 60 years, and another at Woking in 1995 (SCP); earlier records were: Horsell Common, a few at heather bloom in early September 1910, and many larvae in 1911-13 (Champion, *E.M.M.* **48**:45), "not found recently" (Bretherton, 1957), and Oxshott, 24.8.1911 (Russell, *Ent. Rec.* **24**:147). A further example was taken at Foyle Riding on 28.9.1971 (Evans, 1973). It is likely that these records were only of vagrants; the latter one, and the recent record from Lingfield, possibly originate from Ashdown Forest where it is resident.

RECORDS – **Hindhead**, 23.8.90 (EE); **Haslemere**, 8.90 (EE); **Thursley Common**, 13.5.81 larvae (SHC), 4.9.89 (AJ), 14.8.93 (RFMcC), 31.8.96 (GAC); **Milford**, 3.8.82, 21.9.93 (DWB); **Bramley**, 1976 (2), 77 (1), 78 (1) (RFB); **Blackheath**, 23.8.76, 9.9.78 many (RFB); **Winterfold**, 20.8.76, 10.9.77, 26.8.78 (RFB); **Friday Street**, 27.8.76 (JP); **Horsell**, 7.9.78 (CGMdeW); **Woking**, 22.8.95 (SCP); **Lingfield**, 25.8.94 (JC).

Naenia typica (Linnaeus, 1758)   Gothic

Resident; commons, woodland, gardens; fairly widespread but uncommon.

Univoltine; July.

Foodplant – (dock, rosebay willowherb, hollyhock).

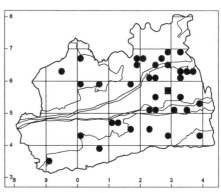

The Gothic is a very uncommon species which has been recorded over much of the county, although perhaps with a bias towards eastern areas. It is a difficult species to obtain and rarely seen in any numbers; annual trap counts of one to three are usual, but in 1986 15 were recorded at Bramley (RFB). At South Croydon only four individuals have been noted in ten years trapping (GAC). Sugar and flowers would appear to be better lures than light.

Eurois occulta (Linnaeus, 1758)   Great Brocade

Migrant; very scarce.

The Great Brocade is resident in Scotland, but only migratory in southern England and of a distinct form with pale grey coloration. Unlike many migrant species they originate in northern Europe and appear here under different climatic conditions. There have been more records during the survey period than at any other time, so it would appear that the incidence of migration is increasing.

19th century – **Wimbledon Common**, (Sinclair, *Ent.* **14**:258).

1945 – **Esher**, 14.8 (Purefoy); **Horsell**, at sugar, 14.8 (de Worms, *Ent.* **78**:144, 174).

1955 – **Wallington**, 9.7 (Taylor, *Ent. Rec.* **67**:275).

1968 – **Wormley**, 30.7 (JLM).

1971 – **Reigate**, 4.9 (DAT).

1972 – **Wormley**, 1.8 (JLM).
1976 – **West Norwood**, 9.9 (BS).
1977 – **Purley**, 13.8 (PMS).
1978 – **Addington**, 20.7 (BS).
1982 – **Purley**, 6.8 (DCL); **Shirley**, 14.8 (KMG).
1983 – **Buckland**, 8.8 (CH); **South Croydon**, 31.8 (GAC); **Oxted**, 1.9 (TD).
1995 – **South Croydon**, 22.8 (GAC).
1996 – **South Croydon**, 2.9 (GAC).

Anaplectoides prasina ([Denis & Schiffermüller], 1775)   Green Arches

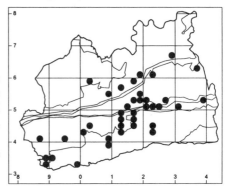

Resident; woodland, wooded commons; restricted and uncommon.
Univoltine; mid-June to mid-July.
Foodplant – (honeysuckle).

The Green Arches has a restricted distribution in Surrey and is virtually absent north of the chalk. It has a preference for well-wooded areas but even here it is rarely common, although recent trap counts for Bramley show: 1985 (23), 86 (58) (RFB); these are exceptionally high.

Cerastis rubricosa ([Denis & Schiffermüller], 1775)   Red Chestnut

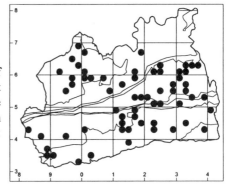

Resident; commons, woodland, heathland; fairly widespread and fairly common.
Univoltine; mid-March to April.

The Red Chestnut occurs through much of Surrey although it does seem to be absent from the environs of London. In suitable habitat it can be a fairly common spring moth as the trap counts from Bramley demonstrate: 1985 (44), 86 (13) (RFB).

Cerastis leucographa ([Denis & Schiffermüller], 1775)   **White-marked**

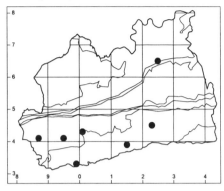

Notable/Nb

Resident; woodland; very local and uncommon.

Univoltine; April.

The White-marked is not an easy moth to obtain, being restricted to woodland in the weald and encroaching onto the greensand. It is also rather uncertain in its appearance partly due to its early flight period. Searching or beating sallow catkins over a sheet would appear to be more effective than light. It is unrecorded in the north-west Surrey list and in the north-east Surrey list, and the presence of a specimen at North Cheam on 12.4.1990 (RFMcC) was rather unexpected.

RECORDS – **Rushmoor**, 2.5.83, 26.4-1.5.84 (PAD); **Milford**, 11.4.81, 2.5.83, 5.5.85, 3.5.86, 24.4.92 (DWB); **Tugley Wood**, 9.4.78 (JP), 30.4.87, 28.3-5.4.88 (SCP), 30.4.95 (DY); **Bramley**, scarce; 1985 (3), 86 (11), 90 (1) (RFB); **Vann Lake**, 5.5.89 (GAC); **Leigh**, 1984 (1), 88 (1), 89 (2) (RF); **North Cheam**, 12.4.90 (RFMcC).

Anarta myrtilli (Linnaeus, 1761)   PLATE 6   **Beautiful Yellow Underwing**

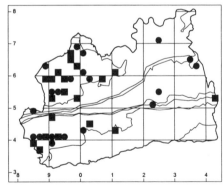

Resident; heathland; restricted but common.

Bivoltine; mid-April to mid-May, and July and August.

Foodplant – heather.

The Beautiful Yellow Underwing is restricted in its distribution by its choice of foodplant. It is however to be found on all the major heaths of west Surrey where it is usually very common, especially as a larva, and also occurs on many relict areas of heath in the north-east of the county such as Wimbledon Common, Addington Hills, and Headley Heath. The moth is essentially a day-flier but examples, particularly of the second brood, will come to light traps, sometimes a little distance from their breeding grounds.

Discestra trifolii (Hufnagel, 1766)   **Nutmeg**

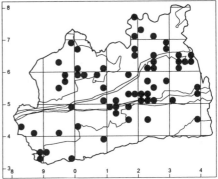

Resident; waste ground, commons; fairly widespread and fairly common.

Bivoltine; June, and August and September.

Foodplant – knotgrass, (wormwood).

In Surrey the Nutmeg is mainly a species of waste ground and other ruderal habitats, and consequently there is a bias in its distribution towards the London area. The moth is rarely common though, the highest annual count during the survey period being 56 in 1992 from Milford (DWB). Other recent counts are usually much lower, and thus contrast with the totals of 187 in 1969 and 316 in 1970 recorded from Addiscombe (Evans, 1973).

Hada plebeja (Linnaeus, 1761) =*nana* (Hufnagel, 1766)   **Shears**

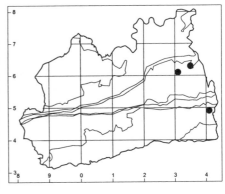

Resident; commons, downland; restricted but fairly common.

Univoltine; mid-May to mid-July.

Foodplant – (hawkweed).

Although occurring widely in much of Surrey, the Shears shows a preference for lighter soils. It can be very common on the downs, but is scarce south of the chalk and especially on the weald.

Polia bombycina (Hufnagel, 1766)   **Pale Shining Brown**

Status uncertain; possibly extinct.

Univoltine; July.

The Pale Shining Brown is an extremely local species which was recorded from several sites in the 1970s but is represented by only a single record since 1980, and is most probably now extinct in Surrey. For several years it was rather common at Selsdon although this was the only place at which its observer (EHW) had ever seen it. In north-east Surrey it was apparently unrecorded before 1967 (Evans, 1973), after which it was noted at:

Addiscombe, 1968-70 (KGWE); Warlingham, 1967-70 (Fletcher); South Croydon, 18.7.1972 (A. Short); Shirley, 20.7.1972 (KMG); Selsdon, 1972 (12), 73 (7), 74 (16), 75 (4), 76 (19) and 81 (1) (EHW); and Nutfield, 2.7.1973 (PAC). In north-west Surrey it was noted during the 1950s with the advent of ultra-violet traps and considered doubtfully resident (Bretherton, 1957 and 1965); later seen at Pyrford, 1970 (JACG) and Tilford, 1971 (Haggett per RFB). In the south-west, at Wormley, it was taken in six years between 1959 and 1973 (JLM). It may be that it was only a temporary resident somewhat akin to the Dotted Rustic (*q.v.*).

RECORDS – **Purley**, 3.7.76 (DCL); **Selsdon**, 1976 (19), 9.7.81 (1) (EHW); **Staffhurst Wood**, 29.6.76 (PAC).

Polia trimaculosa (Esper, 1788)   Silvery Arches

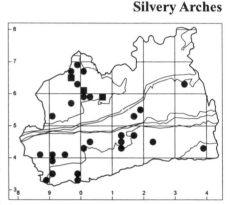

Notable/Nb

Resident; heathland, commons; restricted but fairly common.

Univoltine; mid-June to mid-July.

Foodplant – birch.

The Silvery Arches is a species most at home on heathland with birch scrub and so is commonest in the western half of the county. It has occurred from time to time in the east but is probably only resident in the extreme south-east. The adult is attracted to light but the species is most easily found as a larva in the early spring before the birch leaves are too large, and most of the records have been made in this way.

Polia nebulosa (Hufnagel, 1766)   Grey Arches

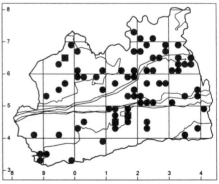

Resident; woodland, commons, heathland; widespread and common.

Univoltine; late June and July.

Foodplant – sloe, bilberry, (birch, honeysuckle).

The Grey Arches is a rather common species throughout the county as the following trap counts show: Bramley, 1985 (7), 86 (18) (RFB); Mitcham, 1981 (7), 82 (7), 83 (4) (RKAM); South Croydon, 1983 (60), 84 (55), 85 (74) (GAC); Selsdon, 1980 (31) (EHW). The distinctive larva has been found several times in the spring.

Pachetra sagittigera (Hufnagel, 1766) PLATE 1 **Feathered Ear**

ssp. *britannica* Turner, 1933

Extinct; not seen since 1960.

The Feathered Ear was always a local species whose principal habitat was the North Downs of Kent and Surrey. The last Surrey specimens were seen in 1960 and the last in Kent in 1963, and in view of the amount of searching for this species that has taken place since then, it is highly probable that it is now extinct. According to Barrett (1897) it was first discovered in Surrey around 1855 by Samuel Stevens at Mickleham Downs and was taken by him over a period of seven or eight years. One was taken at Redhill in 1868, more were seen at Box Hill in 1879 and 1882 (22.5.1882, C. Mackworth-Praed coll.), and another one at Reigate, 9.6.1894 (Adkin, *Proc. SLENHS* **1895**). A female was taken at sugar on Box Hill, 1.6.1913 (Baker-Sly, *Ent. Rec.* **26**:46). More recently it was seen commonly by A.J. Wightman at sugar at the base of Colley Hill in 1927, and a specimen was taken at light at Westhumble on 12.5.1948 by G.A. Cole. At Betchworth a female was knocked out of a hawthorn on 6.6.1949, and on 14.1.1950 some numbers of larvae were found. On the first of June of that year three males were attracted to mvl (RWP *in litt.*), and other specimens were attracted to a paraffin pressure lamp (RF), and for the next decade this area was the centre of attention in Surrey with many larvae being found. Four specimens were seen at a paraffin lamp on 1.6.1960, apparently the last examples to be seen in Surrey. Considerable search has since been made on the downs between Dorking and Reigate but the moth has not been seen again. It would be nice to think that it may still exist undiscovered on the North Downs, but in view of the lack of success in the attempts to relocate it and the apparent extinction of its two main colonies with a few years of each other, the inescapable conclusion is that it has gone forever. The Betchworth site had, in 1950, very short turf heavily grazed by rabbits, but by 1960 was covered in grasses several feet high and was being invaded by hawthorn scrub, the rabbits having been almost wiped out by myxomatosis. This degradation of the habitat must at least have been a causative factor in the decline and extinction of this fine species.

Sideridis albicolon (Hübner, 1813) **White Colon**

Notable/Nb

Resident; heathland; very local and rare.

June.

The White Colon is a species of coastal dunes which also exists in a few inland colonies in the Breck of East Anglia and the heathland of the Surrey/Hampshire border. There are very few records from the survey period and, although it may be overlooked, it would appear to be declining. In the 1950s in north-west Surrey it was known from: Ottershaw, New Haw, Weybridge and Horsell traps, very

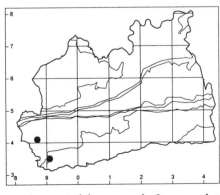

scarce, but annually (Bretherton, 1957), but has not been noted there recently. It occurred at

Frensham, 15.5.1961 (JLM). Evans (1973) mentions several specimens taken at light in Putney in 1951 and it is possible that it was breeding on Wimbledon Common at that time. Alternatively these specimens may have come up the Thames from the east. Further records of this species would be most welcome.

RECORDS – **Rushmoor**, 17.6.83, 6.6-8.7.84, 29.6.85 (PAD); **Haslemere RES**, 1976 (1) (TGW).

Heliophobus reticulata (Goeze, 1781)   PLATE 1   Bordered Gothic
ssp. *marginosa* (Haworth, 1809)
Extinct; not seen since 1964.

The *VCH* listed this species from localities as diverse as Haslemere, Reigate, Worcester Park and Croydon. It was probably commonest on the chalk and there are many records for the 1950s in Evans (1973). At this time it was also noted in north-west Surrey from Ottershaw, New Haw, Weybridge, and Horsell (Bretherton, 1957 and 1965). The most recent record was at Givons Grove, 15.6.1964 (JDH), and it is probably now extinct in Surrey.

Mamestra brassicae (Linnaeus, 1758)   Cabbage Moth

Resident; gardens, allotments; widespread and common.

May to September; peaks in May and September.

Foodplant – traveller's joy, (cabbage, bindweed).

A rather widespread species which is associated with residential and agricultural areas, and is consequently commonest in the London area. Records away from such areas, in woodland or heathland for example, are few and far between. Trap counts indicate:

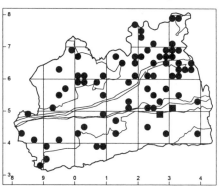

Bramley, 1985 (69), 86 (21) (RFB); South Croydon, 1983 (62), 84 (47), 85 (26) (GAC); Selsdon, 1980 (134) (EHW); Mitcham, 1981 (105), 82 (127), 83 (189) (RKAM). The voltinism of this species is not clear cut; there are possibly two broods, but they overlap to a considerable degree and the autumn emergence is rather larger than at other times.

Melanchra persicariae (Linnaeus, 1761) **Dot Moth**

Resident; gardens, commons; widespread and common.

Univoltine; late June to mid-August.

Foodplant – common nettle, broom, dock, yellow loosestrife, (traveller's joy, sallow, willow, poplar, bindweed, buddleia, birch, Michaelmas daisy, foxglove, thistle, goosefoot, elder, burdock, groundsel, primrose, orache, oak, wormwood).

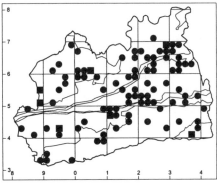

This species, like the last, is commonest in suburban London but overall occurs in a wider range of habitats. The larva is polyphagous and has been recorded from a large number of plant species.

Lacanobia contigua ([Denis & Schiffermüller], 1775) **Beautiful Brocade**

Resident; heathland, downland, commons; fairly widespread but uncommon.

Univoltine; June and early July.

Foodplant – heather, (birch, oak).

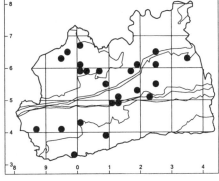

Although found over much of the county, the Beautiful Brocade is not recorded from urban London nor has it been noted from much of the weald, where it may have been overlooked. Heathland and open habitats on chalk are the most likely to produce it. The only record of it occurring in any numbers is from Banstead Downs: 1989 (23), 90 (15), 91 (12), 2.6.92 (15) (DC).

Lacanobia w-latinum (Hufnagel, 1766)   Light Brocade

Resident; commons, heathland;
    widespread and fairly common.
Univoltine; mid-May to June.
Foodplant – bramble, heather, (sallow).
The Light Brocade is a moth of open country
and is found in suitable habitat throughout
the county, but usually in small numbers.

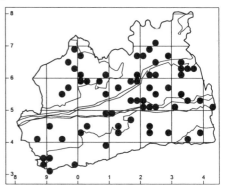

Lacanobia thalassina (Hufnagel, 1766)   Pale-shouldered Brocade

Resident; commons, woodland;
    widespread and fairly common.
Univoltine; late May to early July.
Another Brocade that is found throughout the
county, but unlike its congeners is often found
in more wooded areas.

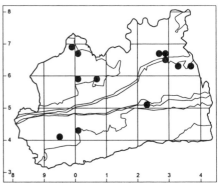

Lacanobia suasa ([Denis & Schiffermüller], 1775)   Dog's Tooth

Resident; waste ground; local and
    uncommon.
Bivoltine; late May, and late July and
    August.
The Dog's Tooth is a species of ruderal
habitats and so is found mostly in the north
of the county, and at some sites is probably
resident or at least temporarily resident.

RECORDS – **Milford**, 12.7.86 (DWB);
Bramley, 18.8.77 (1), 82 (1) (RFB);
Virginia Water, 1-4.8.83 (AG); **Thorpe**,
regular (PJB); **Woking**, 1-2.8.86, 25.7.87
(SCP); **Wisley RES**, 1982 (1), 84 (3) (AJH); **Mitcham**, 5-19.8.91 (8), 1.8.92 (8),
20.8.93, 7-22.8.94 (5) (DC); **Mitcham Common**, 1990-92 (DCL); **Beddington**,

17.5-10.6.93 (13), 14.7.93 (3), 2.7-26.8.94 (24), 10-19.6.95 (6), 17.7-18.8.95 (7) (DC); **Carshalton**, 1991 (3) (DC); **South Croydon**, 3.8.89, 4.8.94, 2.8.95 (GAC); **Addington**, 26.7.89 (BS); **Buckland**, 27.5.82 (CH).

Lacanobia oleracea (Linnaeus, 1758) Bright-line Brown-eye

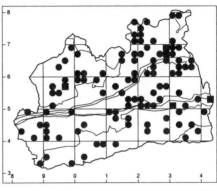

Resident; commons, gardens, heathland; widespread and common.

Univoltine; May to September.

Foodplant – mugwort, fat hen, heather, knotgrass, traveller's joy, yellow loosestrife, tomato, (Michaelmas daisy, cabbage, orache, chickweed, groundsel).

The Bright-line Brown-eye is certainly the most widespread and by far the commonest member of the genus. The commons and gardens of south London appear to suit it especially well as the following trap counts show: Bramley, 1985 (57), 86 (32) (RFB); Milford, 1992 (108) (DWB); South Croydon, 1983 (200), 84 (222), 85 (134) (GAC); Mitcham, 1981 (304), 82 (210), 83 (242) (RKAM). There appears to be but a single brood occurring through much of the summer, although examples taken in September may be a partial second brood.

Ceramica pisi (Linnaeus, 1758) Broom Moth

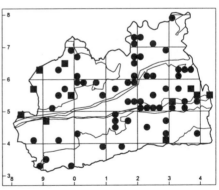

Resident; commons, heathland; widespread and fairly common.

Univoltine; June.

Foodplant – broom, red bartsia, orache, creeping thistle, heather, (sallow, bramble, mugwort, birch).

The Broom Moth occurs throughout Surrey preferring open habitats. It is rarely more than fairly common, even in its favoured sites, as the following trap counts show: Bramley, 1985 (3), 86 (19) (RFB); Mitcham, 1981 (3), 82 (7), 83 (14) (RKAM). The brightly coloured and polyphagous larva is seen almost as often as the adult.

Hecatera bicolorata (Hufnagel, 1766)

Broad-barred White

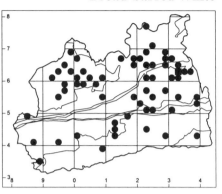

Resident; commons, gardens; fairly widespread and fairly common.

Univoltine; mid-June and July.

Foodplant – sow-thistle.

In the north of the county, especially in the gardens of south London, this is a fairly common species, whereas in central and southern Surrey it is rather scarce. Annual trap counts are usually in single figures but at Banstead it was recorded as follows: 1990 (52), 91 (61), 92 (61) (SWG).

Hecatera dysodea ([Denis & Schiffermüller], 1775)

Small Ranunculus

Extinct; not seen this century.

The Small Ranunculus was, in the last century, a fairly common species in the south-east of England and East Anglia, but had become very scarce by the turn of the century and extinct in the 1930s. Barrett (1897) wrote that "thirty years ago it was one of the most reliable of visitors to the valerian flowers in London suburban gardens"; he also described it as more frequent in Surrey [than in counties further south]. For an account of the decline of this species and the possible causative factors, see Pratt (1986).

Hadena rivularis (Fabricius, 1775)

Campion

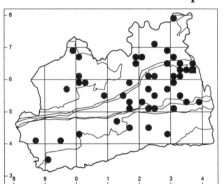

Resident; gardens, commons, fairly widespread and fairly common.

Bivoltine; June, and late July to mid-August.

Foodplant – {sea campion}.

The Campion has been found in much of the county but is only common in the north-east where it is a garden moth. Elsewhere it is only of occasional appearance even at the regularly run traps. The larva has been found on introduced sea campion at Addington (BS).

Hadena perplexa ([Denis & Schiffermüller], 1775)   **Tawny Shears**

ssp. *perplexa* ([Denis & Schiffermüller], 1775)

Resident; chalk grassland, gardens; restricted but fairly common.

Partially **bivoltine**; mid-May to June, and August.

Foodplant – bladder campion.

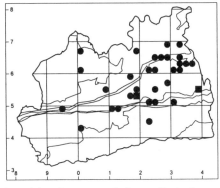

In Surrey the Tawny Shears is more or less restricted to the chalk, with a few records from the gardens of south London and even fewer from outlying areas, these latter examples being no more than just vagrants. Within this area it appears regularly at the static traps although annual counts into double figures are unusual. A partial and rather erratic second brood has been recorded, usually in hotter years.

Hadena compta ([Denis & Schiffermüller], 1775)   PLATE 15   **Varied Coronet**

Resident; gardens, commons; restricted but fairly common.

Univoltine; June and July.

Foodplant – sweet William.

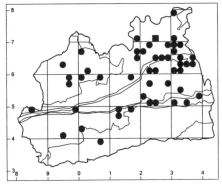

The Varied Coronet is another garden-frequenting species which is found principally in suburban south London and in scattered areas elsewhere where sweet William is grown. The moth didn't establish itself in this country until 1948 when several were taken in Kent, and was first recorded in Surrey at West Norwood, 10.7.1962 (BS). Its subsequent spread has been fairly rapid and it is probably still extending its range south-westwards in Surrey; at its most south-westerly point it did not appear until 1994. The moth is normally univoltine with a peak emergence in the second half of June, but occasional examples are noted later in the year, e.g. Milford on 1.9.1994 (DWB).

Hadena confusa (Hufnagel, 1766)　　Marbled Coronet

Resident; chalk grassland; local and
　　uncommon.
Univoltine; mid-June to mid-July.
Foodplant – bladder campion, sweet
　　William, {sea campion}.

The Marbled Coronet is virtually confined to
the chalk and even here is an uncommon
species that has possibly decreased during the
survey period. It is certainly much scarcer than
compta which it superficially resembles, and
any examples taken away from the chalk
should be critically examined. The larva has
been found on introduced sea campion at Addington (BS).

RECORDS – **Cranleigh**, 1988 a larva on sweet William (PC); **Compton**, 25-29.6.89
(DWB); **Dorking**, 29.6.84 (PC); **Headley**, 2.6.94 (GAC); **Buckland**, 4.7.95 (CH);
Reigate, 27.6.77 (RAC); **Banstead**, 7-18.6.88, 1990 (2), 24.5.92 (SWG); **Banstead
Downs**, 20.6.88, 1989, 90 (4) (DC); **Purley**, 7.7.77 (PMS), 31.6.91 (PJS); **Addington**,
1977-87 (BS); **Selsdon**, 1979 (2) (EHW); **South Croydon**, 1983 (5), 84 (3), 1.7.85,
4.7.87, 2.6.90, 7.6.91, 6.6.92 (GAC); **Mitcham**, 22.8.82, 29.6-5.7.83, 7.6.84 (RKAM);
Wimbledon, 2.6.92 (JVD).

Hadena albimacula (Borkhausen, 1792)　　White Spot

Vagrant; one record only.

An example of this south-eastern coastal species was taken at South Croydon on 3.6.1983.
In view of its extremely tattered condition, it is highly likely that it was transported in the
vehicle of a day-tripper or even another entomologist.

Hadena bicruris (Hufnagel, 1766)　　Lychnis

Resident; commons, downland, gardens;
　　widespread and common.
Bivoltine; mid-May to mid-July, and mid-
　　July and August.
Foodplant – sweet William, bladder
　　campion, white campion, {sea
　　campion}.

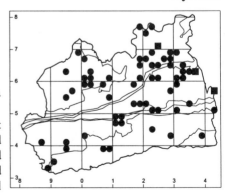

The Lychnis is by far the commonest and most
widespread of its genus in Surrey and is found
throughout the county. The larvae will feed
on various cultivated campions and
consequently the moth is commonest of all
in the vicinity of domestic gardens.

Cerapteryx graminis (Linnaeus, 1758)   **Antler**

Resident; grassland; widespread but uncommon.

Univoltine; August.

This species, which is in some regions a pest, is surprisingly scarce in Surrey. It has been recorded from most areas although there are no records this decade from the weald, but even in its most favoured areas annual counts rarely exceed single figures. The adult has been observed on several occasions feeding from ragwort flowers during the day.

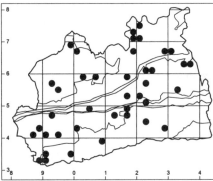

Tholera cespitis ([Denis & Schiffermüller], 1775)   **Hedge Rustic**

Resident; grassland, open woodland; fairly widespread but uncommon.

Univoltine; second half of August.

As reference to the map shows, the Hedge Rustic is found through much of Surrey with a concentration of records in central and north-eastern parts of the county. It is however nowhere common, annual trap counts never exceeding single figures, and more usually seen in ones and twos.

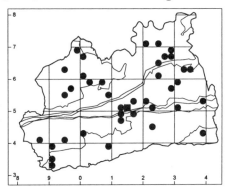

Tholera decimalis (Poda, 1761)   **Feathered Gothic**

Resident; grassland, open woodland; widespread but uncommon.

Univoltine; late August and early September.

The Feathered Gothic is rather more widespread than its congener and perhaps slightly more common. Annual trap counts are also usually in single figures, but at Bramley an average of 28 a year were recorded (RFB).

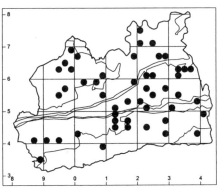

Panolis flammea ([Denis & Schiffermüller], 1775)   Pine Beauty

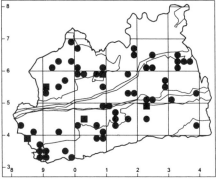

Resident; heathland, coniferous woodland; widespread and fairly common.

Univoltine; April and May.

Foodplant – Scots pine.

The Pine Beauty is probably commonest on the heaths in the west of the county where Scots pine is a common tree, but also occurs further east where there is sufficient foodplant. The apparent absence from much of the south-east of the county may be due to under-recording, but it certainly seems to shun the more built-up parts of London; unlike other pine-feeders it appears to be unable to exist on isolated trees. West (1996) illustrates the three forms: *flammea* D. & S., *griseovariegata* Goeze, and *grisea* Tutt, bred from the same female taken at Friday Street on 23.4.1987 (BS), and his figures for the incidence of the forms is probably similar to the situation in Surrey, *griseovariegata* forming the bulk of the population with the other two being very scarce.

Orthosia cruda ([Denis & Schiffermüller], 1775)   Small Quaker

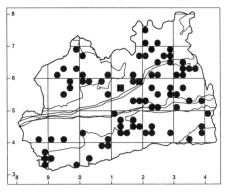

Resident; woodland; widespread and common.

Univoltine; March and April.

Foodplant – oak.

The Small Quaker is found across the whole of the county and in well-wooded districts is often abundant, rivalling the Hebrew Character in numbers. Trap counts show: Bramley, 1985 (556), 86 (169) (RFB); South Croydon, 1983 (20), 84 (31), 85 (35) (GAC); Wisley RES, 1986 (43), 87 (65), 90 (88), 91 (119) (AJH).

Orthosia miniosa ([Denis & Schiffermüller], 1775)   PLATE 5   **Blossom Underwing**

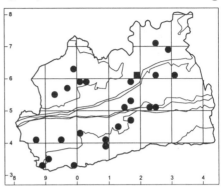

Resident; woodland, wooded commons; restricted and uncommon.

Univoltine; April and early May.

Foodplant – oak.

The Blossom Underwing is most regular in the west of the county, although even here it is uncommon. It would appear to be genuinely absent from the south-east corner and is very local in the north-east, where it has been observed annually at Banstead Downs 1989-91 (DC) and certainly breeds at Ashtead (GAC).

Orthosia opima (Hübner, 1809)   **Northern Drab**

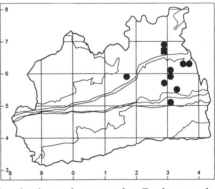

Resident; grassland, golf courses; very local and scarce.

Univoltine; mid-April to May.

The Northern Drab is our rarest *Orthosia*, and in the last decade has only been recorded from a handful of sites, all in the north-east of the county. It has probably declined in numbers and at Mitcham Common, formerly a well-known site, has not been recorded since 1983. There are several records in the north-west Surrey list (Bretherton, 1957) but it has not been recorded there recently, and Evans (1973) considered it to be increasing – a situation that is not the case today. Further search, especially on golf course roughs in the east, is needed to establish the true range of the species.

RECORDS – **Ashtead**, 10.5.89 (GG); **Mitcham Common**, 3.5.80 (BS), 10.5.80 (PAM), 18.5.80 ova (JP); **Mitcham**, 28.4.83 (RKAM); **Purley**, 7.5.76, 6-25.4.77 (4), 14.5.82 (DCL); **Hooley**, 2-3.5.78, 29.5.79 (CH); **Coulsdon**, 22.4.79 (PMS); **Caterham**, 13-21.4.77 (3) (JC); **Selsdon**, 1976 (2), 77 (1) (EHW); **Addington**, 1977-94, most years (BS); **Nutfield**, 1.4.89 (PAC).

Orthosia populeti (Fabricius, 1781)   **Lead-coloured Drab**

Resident; woodland; fairly widespread but uncommon.

Univoltine; late March and April.

Foodplant – aspen.

The Lead-coloured Drab is probably found everywhere its foodplant grows in Surrey and is possibly overlooked amongst forms of the Clouded Drab. It can occasionally be fairly common in the immediate vicinity of aspen groves but most annual trap counts are of one or two examples. The larva feeds between spun leaves and may be found by searching.

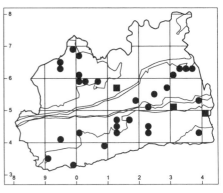

Orthosia gracilis ([Denis & Schiffermüller], 1775)   **Powdered Quaker**

Resident; commons, woodland; widespread and fairly common.

Univoltine; late April and May.

Foodplant – (meadowsweet).

The Powdered Quaker is the least common of the widespread Quakers, and also flies rather later in the spring than most of its congeners. Annual trap counts are usually in single figures with the following exceptions: Bramley, 1985 (10), 86 (17) (RFB); Milford, 1992 (23) (DWB).

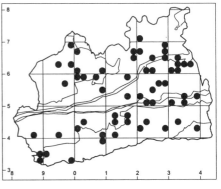

Orthosia cerasi (Fabricius, 1775)   **Common Quaker**

Resident; commons, woodland; widespread and common.

Univoltine; March to mid-May.

Foodplant – oak, birch, bramble, honey-suckle, hazel, wayfaring-tree (lime, elm, hawthorn, aspen, alder, sallow, field maple).

The Common Quaker is a widespread and common species everywhere in Surrey as the following trap counts show: Bramley, 1985 (451), 86 (336) (RFB); South Croydon, 1983 (410), 84 (887), 85 (592) (GAC); Wisley RES,

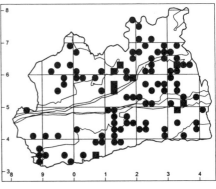

1986 (23), 87 (42), 90 (25) (AJH). Occasional specimens may be recorded during mild spells in the winter, an extreme example being one at South Croydon on 7.11.1992 (GAC).

Orthosia incerta (Hufnagel, 1766)   Clouded Drab

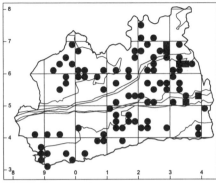

Resident; commons, heathland, woodland; widespread and common.

Univoltine; April to mid-May.

Foodplant – apple, birch, wych elm, traveller's joy, [poplar, lime], (field maple, beech, oak, bramble).

The Clouded Drab is a widespread species in Surrey, preferring open areas, and is the characteristic *Orthosia* of heathland. Although not abundant it is often very common with several annual trap counts in excess of 100 specimens. A wide range of forms occur; mottled examples are commonest on the heaths and intensely black specimens are regular in south London.

Orthosia munda ([Denis & Schiffermüller], 1775)   Twin-spotted Quaker

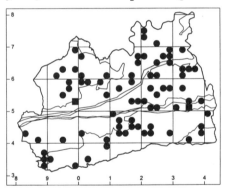

Resident; woodland, commons; widespread and fairly common.

Univoltine; March and April.

Foodplant – oak, (hawthorn, ash).

The Twin-spotted Quaker is another species that is common throughout Surrey but usually seen in smaller numbers than *cerasi, incerta,* or *cruda.* Ab. *immaculata* Staudinger, in which the twin spots are absent, is a regularly occurring form in some districts, while specimens with increased spotting are rare.

Orthosia gothica (Linnaeus, 1758)   Hebrew Character

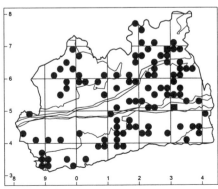

Resident; commons, woodland; widespread and common.

Univoltine; April and May.

Foodplant – (hazel).

A common species everywhere. Annual trap counts show: Bramley, 1985 (595), 86 (235) (RFB); South Croydon, 1983 (283), 84 (655), 85 (511) (GAC); Wisley RES, 1986 (21), 87 (45), 90 (37), 91 (41) (AJH). Variation occurs chiefly in the ground colour, which varies from reddish through buff to dark grey.

Mythimna turca (Linnaeus, 1761)   PLATE 8   Double Line

Notable/Nb

Resident; wooded commons; very local
but common.

Univoltine; July.

Foodplant – creeping soft-grass, common
bent.

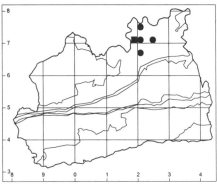

Until recently only four examples of this moth
had been recorded during the survey period
from three sites. The proximity of these
suggested that it was still breeding in the area
albeit at a low density; indeed Richmond Park,
only a few miles from these sites, was once a
noted locality for the moth. A field meeting was held at Richmond on 3.7.1993 to search
specifically for this species, and the first moth seen was *turca*. During the evening no less
than 50 examples were seen at sugar and mvl, and the presence of a considerable colony
confirmed. Larvae were found there in the following spring. The species is principally
western in its distribution and this record represents both the most easterly known examples
and one of the few areas outside the west country and west Wales where it has been taken
recently. The *VCH* gives also Reigate, Leatherhead and Ashtead, and there is a specimen
from Leatherhead, 1914, in the Mackworth-Praed collection. Bretherton (1957) gives a
number of north-west Surrey records and considered it to be resident. It was last seen in that
area at Thorpe on 9.7.1971 (PJB).

RECORDS – **Tolworth**, 11.7.87, 15.7.96 (JTS); **Wimbledon**, 13.7.81, 20.7.91, 18.7.93
(JVD); **Wimbledon Common**, 7.7.82 (AJ); **Richmond Park**, 3.7.93 (50+) (GAC/MP/
DC), 16.5.94 larvae, 4.7.94, 5.7.95 (MP), 12.7.96 (GAC/MP); **East Sheen**, 18.7.95 (D.
Couzens).

Mythimna conigera ([Denis & Schiffermüller], 1775)   Brown-line Bright-eye

Resident; commons, downland; restricted
but fairly common.

Univoltine; July to mid-August.

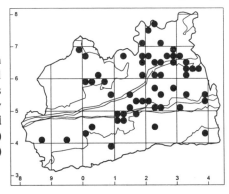

The Brown-line Bright-eye seems to shun
heathland and is represented by only a handful
of examples from the weald, but on the downs
and the commons of south London it is a fairly
common species. Trap counts show: Banstead
Downs, 11.7-15.8.88 (21), 89 (23), 90 (18)
(DC); and Mitcham, 1981 (11), 82 (2), 83 (2)
(RKAM).

Mythimna ferrago (Fabricius, 1787)   Clay

Resident; commons, open woodland, heathland; widespread and common.

Univoltine; July to mid-August.

Foodplant – grasses.

A very widespread and common species, perhaps reaching its greatest numbers on the commons of south London where annual trap counts in excess of 100 individuals are not unusual.

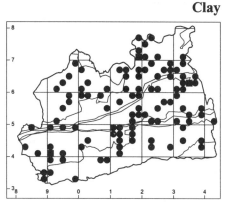

Mythimna albipuncta ([Denis and Schiffermüller], 1775)   PLATE 7   White-point

Migrant; very scarce.

Some eight examples of this migrant species have been noted in Surrey during the survey period, scarcely fewer than during the rest of the century, suggesting that it may be becoming more frequent.

1934 – **Egham**, 15.8 (CGMdeW, in Bretherton, 1957).
1956 – **Ottershaw** trap, 6.9 (Bretherton, 1965); **Chiddingfold**, 9.9 (*Ent.* **90**:234).
1959 – **Wormley**, 4-12.10 (2) (JLM); **Leigh**, 8.10 (RF); **Chiddingfold**, 24.10 (*Ent.* **95**:175).
1960 – **Leigh**, 3.9 (RF); **Wormley**, 8.9 (JLM).
1961 – **Hankley Common**, 2.9 (JLM).
1969 – **Tilford**, 16.8 (G. Haggett); **Leigh**, 14.9 (RF).
1978 – **Nutfield**, 4.10 (PAC).
1986 – **Milford**, 3.9 (DWB).
1990 – **Nutfield**, 13.10 (PAC); **Lingfield**, 18.10 (JC).
1992 – **Lingfield**, 10-21.9 (2) (JC).
1993 – **Lingfield**, 13.9 (JC).
1994 – **Lingfield**, 16.8 (JC).
1995 – **Buckland**, 16.8 (CH).

Mythimna vitellina (Hübner, 1808)   Delicate

Migrant; scarce.

The Delicate is another of the migrant wainscots and, like the previous species, is being recorded more frequently.

1950 – **New Haw** trap, 16.10 (Bretherton, 1957).
1951 – **Chiddingfold**, 1.10 (Mere, *Ent. Gaz.* **3**:179); **Dunsfold**, 27.10 (Goodban, *Ent. Rec.* **64**:57).
1954 – **Chiddingfold**, 24.9 (Mere, *Ent. Gaz.* **5**:234).
1961 – **Chiddingfold**, 15.9 (*Ent.* **96**:37); **Wormley**, 15.9 (JLM).
1962 – **Chiddingfold**, 11.9 (*Ent.* **97**:124); **Leigh**, 6.10 (3) (*ibid.*); **Wormley**, 10.10 (JLM).

1974 – **East Horsley**, 17.8 (LJDW).
1975 – **Ranmore Common**, 1.6 (Grey, *Ent. Rec.* **87**:258).
1976 – **Bramley**, 13.10 (RFB).
1977 – **Nower Wood**, 15.10 (LKE); **Thorpe**, 21.10 (PJB).
1979 – **Thorpe** (PJB); **Bramley**, 23.10 (RFB).
1982 – **Oxted**, 30.10 (TD).
1984 – **Buckland**, 10.11 (CH).
1988 – **Mugswell**, 15.10 (A&OH).
1990 – **Nutfield**, 15.10 (PAC).
1992 – **Lingfield**, 1.9-10.11 (8) (JC); **Milford**, 17.9 (DWB); **Addington**, 25.9 (BS).
1993 – **Lingfield**, 25.6, 14.7 (JC).
1996 – **Milford**, 13-21.10 (2) (DWB).

Mythimna pudorina ([Denis & Schiffermüller], 1775)   Striped Wainscot

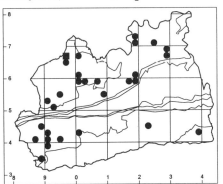

Resident; heathland, commons; rather local but fairly common.

Univoltine; July.

The Striped Wainscot is a rather local species restricted to heathland and commons that are neutral or acidic. It is absent from the chalk, and only recorded once on the weald. It can be fairly common where it occurs and, as well as coming to light, can be found sitting on grass stems after dark, sometimes in numbers as at Wisley Common, 15.7.1985 (AJH).

Mythimna straminea (Treitschke, 1825)   Southern Wainscot

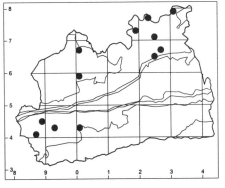

Resident; wetland; very local and scarce.

Univoltine; July.

The Southern Wainscot is a very local species in Surrey being recorded from three areas: Thorpe-Woking, Frensham, and south London. The foodplant, common reed, occurs in all three areas and the moth is probably resident. The south London records are mostly very recent and may represent an overspill from the colonies on the Essex side of the Thames estuary.

RECORDS – **Rushmoor**, 23-26.7.84 (PAD); **Elstead**, 20.7.85 (4) (DWB); **Thundry Meadows**, 24.6.93 (2) (AMD); **Bramley**, 5.8.77 (RFB); **Thorpe**, 1985, 86 (PJB); **Woking**, 5-25.7.86 (SCP); **North Cheam**, 3-7.7.91 (2) (RFMcC); **Richmond Park**, 28.7.95 (1) (MP); **Wimbledon**, 21.8.77 (JVD);

Mitcham, 16.7.92 (4) (DC), 12.8.93, 10.7.94 (GAC), 8.7.95, 18.7.96 (DC); **Lambeth**, 16.6.89 (Rfmcc); **Barn Elms**, 26-29.7.94 (MRH).

Mythimna impura (Hübner, 1808)　　　　　Smoky Wainscot

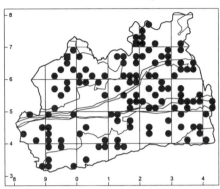

Resident; commons, heathland, open woodland; widespread and common.

Univoltine; July to mid-August.

Foodplant – grasses.

A common species everywhere. In suburban south London this is the commonest *Mythimna*, greatly outnumbering *pallens*, but further away from built-up areas the relative numbers decrease and, especially in the vicinity of wetlands, *pallens* is the more numerous. The larvae are usually common when sweeping grasses in the spring.

Mythimna pallens (Linnaeus, 1758)　　　　Common Wainscot

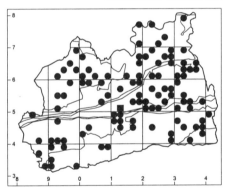

Resident; commons, wetland; widespread and common.

Bivoltine; July, and mid-August to early October.

The Common Wainscot is found throughout Surrey, but only lives up to its vernacular name in the more rural areas. The numbers would appear to be reinforced by migration, especially in the second brood.

Mythimna favicolor (Barrett, 1896)　　　　Mathew's Wainscot

Vagrant; one record.

An example of this coastal saltmarsh species was taken at Chiddingfold, 13.7.1952, by R. Mere, and confirmed by the British Museum (Natural History).

Mythimna unipuncta (Haworth, 1809)　　　　White-speck

Migrant; rare.

The White-speck is one of the least common of the migrant Wainscots but, as with several other species, appears to be turning up more regularly. It was unrecorded in Surrey prior to 1962, but has been recorded six times during the survey period.

[1953 – **Camberley**, 10.7 (*Ent.* **87**:63) refers to Farnborough, North Hants].

1962 – **West Norwood**, 1.8 (BS).
1966 – Surrey , September (1) (French, *Ent.* **104**:209).
1971 – **Thorpe**, October (PJB).
1972 – **Leigh**, 6.10 (RF).
1975 – **Ewhurst**, 28.10 (SFI).
1978 – **Selsdon**, 14.10 (EHW); **Horsell**, 1.11 (CGMdeW); **Oxted**, 14.11 (TD).
1981 – **Addiscombe**, 1.10 (KGWE).
1982 – **Rushmoor**, 18.9 (PAD).
1985 – **Wimbledon**, 1.10 (JVD).

Mythimna obsoleta (Hübner, 1803)   Obscure Wainscot

Status uncertain; possibly resident.

June and July.

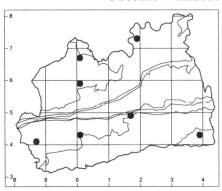

Only ten examples of this species have been noted during the survey period and thus it is difficult to be certain about its status. Most of the records are from areas which may be potential breeding sites and the species is resident along the Thames estuary on the Essex side (Plant, 1993); conversely nearly all the Surrey records are of single specimens. There are no records in Evans (1973), and Bretherton (1957) commented that an area near Sheerwater where it was observed annually from 1947 to 1952 had been largely destroyed. Wetland is one of the scarcest habitats in Surrey and probably one of the most vulnerable; discovery of a breeding colony would be most welcome.

RECORDS – **Rushmoor**, 10.7.83, 11.7.85 (PAD); **Bramley**, 22.7.79 (RFB); **Thorpe**, 25.6.86 (PJB); **Woking**, 15.7.86 (SCP); **Dorking**, 27.6.86 (DAT); **Richmond Park**, 6.6.92 (1) (MP); **Lingfield**, 21.6.94, 16-30.6.95 (JC).

Mythimna comma (Linnaeus, 1761)   Shoulder-striped Wainscot

Resident; commons; widespread and fairly common.

Univoltine; June and July.

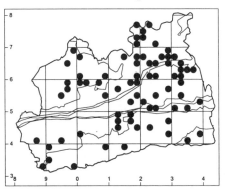

The Shoulder-striped Wainscot is rather widespread in Surrey but in general only fairly common. The commons of south London seem particularly liked by the moth as the following trap counts show: Banstead Downs, 1989 (24), 90 (18), 91 (4) (DC); Mitcham, 1981 (70), 82 (32), 83 (11) (RKAM). However at South Croydon, only a few miles distant, no more than one a year is recorded.

Mythimna loreyi (Duponchel, 1827)   Cosmopolitan

Migrant; very rare.

The Cosmopolitan is our rarest migrant Wainscot, recorded on only three occasions, all during the survey period.

1983 – **Leigh**, 29.8 (RF).
1992 – **Lingfield**, 21.9 (JC).
1994 – **Buckland**, 6.11 (CH).

Cucullia absinthii (Linnaeus, 1761)   Wormwood Shark

Notable/Nb

Resident; waste ground, commons; local and uncommon.

Univoltine; mid-July to mid-August.

Foodplant – mugwort, wormwood.

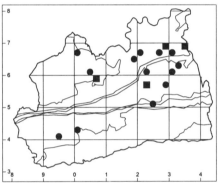

Until the middle of the current century the Wormwood Shark was essentially a coastal species, but in the late 1940s it was found commonly on waste ground in the midlands and then London, often associated with bomb sites. It was first recorded from Surrey in 1954 when it appeared at Weybridge on 23rd July, and again the next year when it was also taken at Wallington, Ewell, Worcester Park and Putney. It appeared to flourish for a number of years before going into decline. In the mid-1970s further waste ground was created in north-west Surrey by the construction of the M3 and M25 motorways and again larvae were common for a few years on wormwood (Baker, 1986). During the survey period the moth has been generally uncommon, but is clearly resident as larvae have been found at several sites. The distribution in Surrey is still mainly northern although several specimens have been seen in the south-west in the last few years.

RECORDS – **Milford**, 24.7.92, 24-31.7.95 (2) (DWB); **Bramley**, 23.7.83, 11.7.86 (RFB); **Thorpe**, 1976-83 (PJB); **Byfleet**, 12.7.80 (AJH); **Wisley**, 14.8.88 larva (GAC); **Surbiton**, 14.8.85 (JTS); **Tolworth**, 3.8.89 (JTS); **Reigate**, 7.77 (RAC); **Walton Downs**, 2.9.94 larva (GAC); **Banstead**, 18.7.96 (SWG); **Hooley**, 2.8.79 (CH); **Mitcham Common**, 27.7.78 (PAM), 21.9.78 larvae (JP), 4.9.79 larvae on mugwort (BC), 24.7.80, 30.7.82 (RKAM); **Mitcham**, 7.8.94 (DC); **Purley**, 5.8.77 (PMS); **South Croydon**, 24.7.83, 19.7.90 (GAC); **South Norwood**, 15.9.85 larvae on mugwort (GAC).

Cucullia chamomillae ([Denis & Schiffermüller], 1775) **Chamomile Shark**

Resident; waste ground, fields; fairly widespread but uncommon.

Univoltine; late April and May.

Foodplant – scentless mayweed.

The Chamomile Shark is found fairly widely in Surrey although there is a distinct concentration of records in the London area. As with most of the Sharks the larva is more easily found than the adult, and systematic searching of the foodplants should reveal it to be more common than the map suggests.

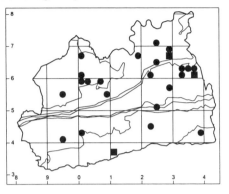

Cucullia umbratica (Linnaeus, 1758) **Shark**

Resident; commons, downland, gardens; fairly widespread but uncommon.

Univoltine; mid-June to July.

The distribution of this species is rather similar to that of the last – fairly widespread but more often recorded in the London area. Unlike most of its congeners, it is the adult stage that is most often recorded, usually at light traps, while the larva does not appear to have been noted during the survey.

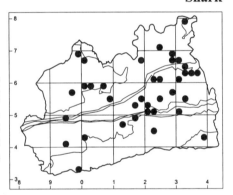

Cucullia asteris ([Denis & Schiffermüller], 1775) **Star-wort**

Notable/Nb

Status uncertain; temporary resident and vagrant.

July.

Foodplant – golden-rod.

The *VCH* recorded this Shark from Haslemere and Croydon. Bretherton (1957) was able to add only one record: Weybridge, 28.6.1952; and further examples occurred at Addiscombe, 24.7.1971 (KGWE); Bramley, 6.7.1965 and 15.8.1972 (1) (RFB); Wormley, six examples 1961 to 1973 (JLM); and

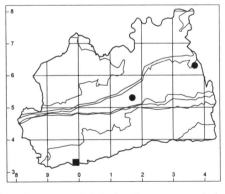

Thorpe, 14.6.1974 (PJB). Two further adults have been recorded during the survey period, and in 1993 several larvae were found in the Chiddingfold area. This latter record seems to

be the only evidence of breeding and is suggestive of temporary residency, the other instances probably being vagrants – those in the west from woodland colonies in Sussex, while those in the east are more likely to arise from the saltmarsh race inhabiting the Thames estuary (see Plant, 1993).

RECORDS – **Oaken Wood**, 4.9.93 larvae (DWB/GAC); **Juniper Hall**, 7.85 (R. Softly (per CWP)); **Addington**, 1979 (BS).

Cucullia gnaphalii (Hübner, 1813)   Cudweed
ssp. *occidentalis* Boursin, 1945
Extinct; not seen for at least 70 years.

A specimen of the Cudweed is stated to have been taken flying at dusk at Witley in 1892 by Miss Ada Evans (Barrett, 1900). Larvae were also taken between Witley and Grayswood by the same lady, and one at Chiddingfold in about 1911 by A.E. Tonge (*Ent. Rec.* 36:75). It is not clear whether the latter refers to a larva or the adult – a rather unsatisfactory record of such a rare species. A further incomplete record is of larvae exhibited by Storey at a meeting of the South London Entomological Society held on 13.8.1925, said to be from "Surrey". Pratt (1992) considers this an unquestionable Surrey record, but in the absence of an actual site one must have certain reservations. It is clear however that the moth has not been seen in Surrey for at least nearly 70 years and possibly nearer 100. The moth is in all probability extinct in England, being lost from West Sussex and Kent in the 1960s and last seen in East Sussex in 1979 (Pratt, *loc. cit.*).

Cucullia lychnitis Rambur, 1833   Striped Lychnis
Extinct.

The claim to Surrey status for the Striped Lychnis is based on five published records: Reigate, 19th century (*VCH*); Box Hill, larvae on mullein (West, *Ent. Rec.* **18**:230), 9.7.1904, larvae on white mullein (Turner, *Proc. SLENHS* **1905-06**); Clandon, 15.7.1905, larvae "commonly" (Carr, *Proc. SLENHS* **1905-06**); and Banstead, 1953 at mvl (Gardner in de Worms *L.N.* **35**:59). Not all these records may be correct; white mullein is not recorded from Box Hill by Lousley (1976), nor would one expect larvae of *lychnitis* in early July, and it is likely that some refer to *verbasci*, just as supposed records of *C. scrophulariae* feeding on figwort certainly do; the Banstead record is not supported by a voucher specimen. However, there are specimens from Box Hill in the British Museum: five from Box Hill in 1907 (Sharp, coll. H. Jeddere-Fisher), and three reared from larvae collected there on 5.8.1912 in Glasgow museum. Like most of the Sharks, the Striped Lychnis is most easily found as a larva, the adults being reluctant to visit light traps, but it does not appear to have been found in this stage in Surrey for over 80 years. Recent field work, in connection with the Joint Nature Conservation Committee's work on the rarer British moths, has failed to rediscover the species in Surrey and it must be considered extinct.

Cucullia verbasci (Linnaeus, 1758) — Mullein Shark

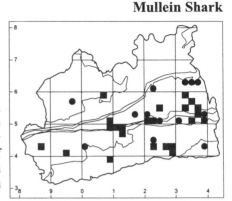

Resident; chalk grassland, open woodland; restricted but fairly common.

Univoltine; mid-April to mid-May.

Foodplant – great mullein, dark mullein, water figwort, buddleia.

In Surrey the Mullein Shark is fairly common on the chalk, local south of it and rare to the north. The adult, like most Sharks, is only rarely taken at light and the great majority of records refer to the conspicuous larvae which can utilize various foodplants depending on the habitat.

Calophasia lunula (Hufnagel, 1766) — Toadflax Brocade

Vagrant; a single example.

An example of this coastal species was recorded at Bookham Common on 13.7.1970 (Sokoloff, *Ent. Rec.* **83**:325).

Brachylomia viminalis (Fabricius, 1777) — Minor Shoulder-knot

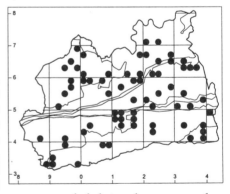

Resident; commons; widespread and fairly common.

Univoltine; July.

Foodplant – grey sallow.

A fairly common species in much of Surrey, but scarce on the chalk. Many of the static traps produce annual counts of only single figures, although when in the vicinity of its breeding grounds much higher counts can be obtained, for example: Bramley, 1985 (69), 86 (104) (RFB), and even at the Rothamsted trap at Pirbright, 1981 (56) (ED). Melanic forms, mostly referable to f. *obscura* Staudinger, occur regularly but are less common than the pale typical form.

Brachionycha sphinx (Hufnagel, 1766)   Sprawler

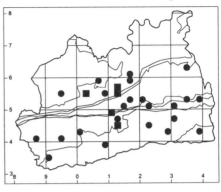

Resident; woodland; fairly widespread and fairly common.

Univoltine; mid-October to November.

Foodplant – oak, sloe, sallow, (elm).

The Sprawler is probably overlooked due to its late flight period, but it does seem to be absent from the north of the county as well as much of the chalk. I have found the larvae at several sites where the adult remains undetected. When light traps are run in its immediate locality, quite good numbers can be expected, although the moth usually flies late in the night.

Dasypolia templi (Thunberg, 1792)   Brindled Ochre

Vagrant; one record only.

In southern England this is a strictly coastal species, and so a specimen recorded from Pyrford on 28.10.1970 (JACG) was a considerable distance from its known haunts.

Aporophyla lutulenta ([Denis & Schiffermüller], 1775)   Deep-brown Dart

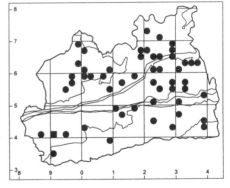

Resident; commons, heathland; widespread but uncommon.

Univoltine; late September to mid-October.

The Deep-brown Dart occurs in suitable habitat over much of the county, but is rarely common. Many of the static traps record it annually, the only one where good numbers occur being at Milford: 1992 (36), 93 (12), 94 (12) (DWB).

Aporophyla nigra (Haworth, 1809)   **Black Rustic**

Resident; commons, heathland, gardens; widespread and common.

Univoltine; mid-September to October.

Foodplant – dock.

The Black Rustic is a common autumn species everywhere in the county. Comparison with trap counts in Evans (1973) suggests that, at least in north-east Surrey, the species has increased considerably during the survey period as the following counts show: Milford, 1992 (300) (DWB); Bramley, 1985 (178), 86 (77) (RFB); Mitcham, 1981 (14), 82 (14), 83 (56) (RKAM); South Croydon, 1983 (261), 84 (83), 85 (44) (GAC); Selsdon, 1972 (2), increasing to 1979 (50), 80 (70) (EHW).

Lithomoia solidaginis (Hübner, 1803)   **Golden-rod Brindle**

Migrant; two examples.

Two examples of this species were noted in 1954, part of a migration from the continent, of which nearly 20 individuals were recorded between 26th August and 2nd September in the south-eastern and midland counties.

1954 – **Sheerwater**, at mvl, 27.8 (Wakely, *Ent. Rec.* **66**:255); **Chiddingfold**, 1.9 (Mere, *Ent. Gaz.* **5**:231).

Lithophane semibrunnea (Haworth, 1809)   **Tawny Pinion**

Resident; commons, open woodland; fairly widespread but uncommon.

Univoltine; late September and October, and after hibernation, March and April.

In Surrey the Tawny Pinion occurs mainly in the east and north of the county, but is nowhere common. As well as coming to light it has also been noticed on ivy and blackberries in the autumn and at sallow blossom in the spring. An example was found hibernating indoors at Reigate on 11.1.1977 (RAC).

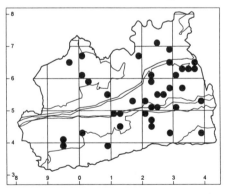

Lithophane hepatica (Clerck, 1759)   Pale Pinion

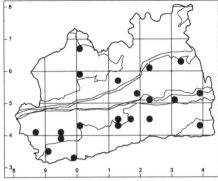

Resident; woodland; restricted and scarce.
Univoltine; late September and October,
     and after hibernating, March
     and April.
Foodplant – (sallow).
Until the last few years the Pale Pinion was
more or less restricted to the south of the
county where it was scarce, but since about
1990 it has been emulating the Grey Shoulder-
knot (*q.v.*) and has been taken in many new
localities in the north and east of the county.
Overall it is still probably rarer than
semibrunnea and it will be interesting to see whether the situation changes in the coming
years.

Lithophane ornitopus (Hufnagel, 1766)   Grey Shoulder-knot
ssp. *lactipennis* (Dadd, 1911)

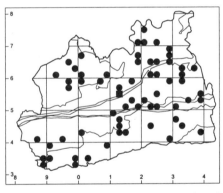

Resident; woodland, wooded commons;
     widespread and fairly common.
Univoltine; late September and October,
     and after hibernating, March
     and April.
Foodplant – oak.
During the present century this species has
undergone a cycle of decline and, in the last
ten years, a rapid increase. The *VCH* described
it as occurring "nearly everywhere" in the
county, but by the 1950s it was scarce in north-
west Surrey (Bretherton, 1957 and 1965), and
in the north-east only three sites were known (Evans, 1973), although the *VCH* mentioned
Surbiton and Worcester Park. In 1983 it turned up at Mitcham (RKAM) and Wimbledon
(JVD), and in the next couple of years it spread throughout the London area, up to half a
dozen specimens a year being taken in many traps. Currently the position seems to be
stable and the species should be found in most oak woods in the county.

Lithophane lamda (Fabricius, 1787)   Nonconformist

Vagrant.
A single specimen of this moth was taken by the Hon. Spencer Canning at sugar on a young
elm between Dorking and Guildford in October 1866. Five specimens were recorded from
north-west Kent in the second half of the nineteenth century and it may have been a temporary
resident at that time; the Surrey specimen may have originated from the same area or may
have been a migrant. The moth has not been recorded in Britain for over 50 years.

Lithophane leautieri (Boisduval, 1828) ssp. *hesperica* Boursin, 1957

PLATE 15 **Blair's Shoulder-knot**

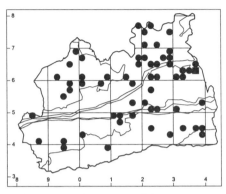

Resident; gardens; fairly widespread and common.

Univoltine; late September and October.

Foodplant – Leyland cypress, Lawson's cypress.

Blair's Shoulder-knot was first taken in this country in 1951, since when it has spread across most of the south of England and is still increasing its range. The first record for Surrey was at Leigh, 2.10.1960 (RF), and odd examples were seen over the next two decades. By the early 1980s a further expansion occurred, the moth being found across the county, often as one of the commonest autumn species: South Croydon, 1985 (207) (GAC); Banstead, 1990 (120) (SWG); and Milford, 1992 (111) (DWB). The foodplants are mainly ornamental trees of larger gardens and hence the moth is more widespread in the north-east than in western Surrey. For an account of finding wild larvae, see Skinner, 1985.

Xylena vetusta (Hübner, 1813)

Red Sword-grass

Vagrant; possible former resident.

There are records of only two examples of this species during the survey period, and indeed during most of the present century it has only been seen at a rate of one or two a decade. At the end of the nineteenth century it was known from Wimbledon Common (1898 list and *VCH*), Tooting (1898 list), Reigate and Haslemere (*VCH*), and "included in Mr Kaye's and Major Ficklin's lists for Surrey". These records suggest that it may have been resident at the time. More recently recorded from: Dormansland, 18.9.1919 (coll. H. Jeddere-Fisher); Egham, 1932 and 1934, and Ottershaw, 16.4.1952 (Bretherton, 1957); Leigh, 20.3.1956, and Ranmore, 11.1956 (RF); Reigate, 22.4.1963 (DAT); and Givons Grove, 28.3.1965 (JDH).

RECORDS – **Pyrford**, 1976 (JACG); **Hog's Back**, 24.3.1991 (M&JH).

Xylena exsoleta (Linnaeus, 1758)

Sword-grass

Extinct; former status uncertain.

This species has been recorded as follows: Dulwich Wood, 1842, *or* West Wickham Wood (Kent) *(Ent.* 1:309); Wimbledon and Reigate (*VCH*); Warlingham, three in 1929 (Bell in de Worms, *L.N.* 35). It has always been scarcer than *vetusta* and seems to have declined drastically throughout the country in recent years.

Xylocampa areola (Esper, 1789)   **Early Grey**

Resident; woodland, commons;
    widespread and common.
Univoltine; mid-March to May.
Foodplant – honeysuckle.
A very common spring species found in suitable habitat throughout the county, especially domestic gardens where the larva feeds on cultivated honeysuckle.

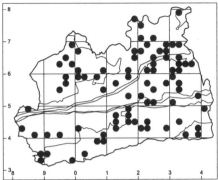

Allophyes oxyacanthae (Linnaeus, 1758)   **Green-brindled Crescent**

Resident; woodland, commons,
    hedgerows; widespread and
    common.
Univoltine; October.
Foodplant – sloe, hawthorn.
A widespread and common species throughout the county, the adults being recorded at light and at ivy bloom, and the larvae being one of the commoner species found when beating the foodplants in the spring. Trap counts at Bramley show: 1985 (69), 86 (60) (RFB). Such abundance is

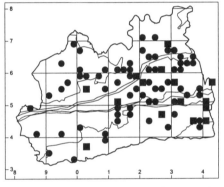

unusual with annual counts from most static traps scarcely reaching double figures. The melanic ab. *capucina* Millière is of frequent occurrence; in some London traps almost all specimens are of this form whereas in rural areas the type is commoner.

[*Valeria oleagina* ([Denis & Schiffermüller], 1775)   **Green-brindled Dot**

Doubtful.

Barrett (1897) summarizes the Surrey records of this moth as follows: five specimens in the collection of J.F. Stephens taken by another collector from Richmond Park; one in the collection of P.B. Mason labelled as being taken by Edwin Shepherd on a paling at Richmond; a further specimen bred from a pupa dug up by Plastead at Battersea Fields [around 1800]. He also gave records from Bristol, Scotland, and Wales, adding that not all may be genuine. P.B.M. Allan (1943) considered many of Plastead's records to be fraudulent and Stephens to have been one of his chief dupes, concluding that *oleagina* was unlikely to have ever occurred in a wild state in this country. There have been no additional records in over 150 years.]

Dichonia aprilina (Linnaeus, 1758) PLATE 8 Merveille du Jour

Resident; woodland; fairly widespread but uncommon.

Univoltine; October.

Foodplant – oak.

Although occurring over much of the county, the Merveille du Jour does seem to be absent from areas of central western Surrey and in the London area, where it is recorded regularly no closer to the metropolis than at Banstead and South Croydon. It is usually recorded in very small numbers, 19 at Milford in 1991 (DWB) being exceptional. A specimen with reduced black markings and ground colour bluer than usual was taken at South Croydon, 18.9.1991 (GAC).

Dryobotodes eremita (Fabricius, 1775) Brindled Green

Resident; woodland; widespread and common.

Univoltine; late September and October.

Foodplant – oak.

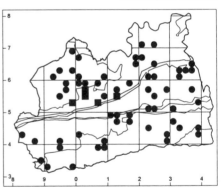

The Brindled Green is a rather common species, especially in rural areas, and although infrequent in the London area it is nevertheless widespread there. Specimens with a grey ground-colour and little trace of green have been recorded from Purley (PJS), and South Croydon and Bookham (GAC).

Mniotype adusta (Esper, 1790) Dark Brocade

Extinct; not seen for nearly 30 years.

There are very few records of the Dark Brocade in Surrey, and it has not been taken for nearly 30 years. The *VCH* gives Reigate. More recently it has been recorded from: Chipstead, 1946 (4) (de Worms, *L.N.* **34**); Westhumble, 1947 (Cole); White Downs, 31.5.1948 (3) and Weybridge trap, 5.7.1958 (JLM); Box Hill, 26.5.1952, South Norwood, 22.6.1954, and Addiscombe, 6.6.1968 (Evans, 1973). Plant (1993) states that it is regular in his garden at Bishop's Stortford but is unable to give any recent London records.

Polymixis flavicincta ([Denis & Schiffermüller], 1775) Large Ranunculus

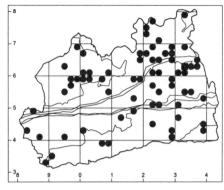

Resident; gardens; fairly widespread and fairly common.

Univoltine; mid-September to mid-October.

Foodplant – rosebay willowherb, sow-thistle.

The Large Ranunculus is fairly widely distributed in Surrey, for the most part at a low density, although it is currently much commoner in the London area. This would appear not to have always been the case, as Evans (1973) mentions only singletons from such places as Addiscombe and Selsdon. At the latter site annual counts increased from one in 1972 to 28 in 1980 (EHW), and at nearby South Croydon, 1983 produced no fewer than 78 examples (GAC). Conversely from being a "fairly common moth" at Westhumble in the 1940s, records dwindle to singletons from Box Hill in 1972, 81 and 82, although a larva was found in 1980 (AJH).

Antitype chi (Linnaeus, 1758) Grey Chi

Vagrant; admitted with reserve.

The record of this species from Givons Grove, 6.9.1961 (Holloway, in Evans, 1973), remains the only record for Surrey. In view of the circumstances of the record, it was accepted with reserve and I see no reason to dispute this opinion, although it is not unknown for this species to turn up as a vagrant far to the south and east of its normal range.

Eumichtis lichenea (Hübner, 1813) Feathered Ranunculus

ssp. *lichenea* (Hübner, 1813)

Vagrant; two examples only.

Specimens of this normally coastal species were taken at Wormley, 26.9.1962 (JLM), and Addiscombe, 26.10.1969 (KGWE).

Eupsilia transversa (Hufnagel, 1766) Satellite

Resident; woodland, commons, heathland; widespread and common.

Univoltine; October and November, and March and April.

Foodplant – oak, hawthorn, English elm, wych elm, (lime, hazel).

The Satellite is a widespread and, at least in well-wooded localities, a rather common species. The adult hibernates, probably flying in mild spells during the winter, and has been noted at sugar and ivy blossom as well as at light.

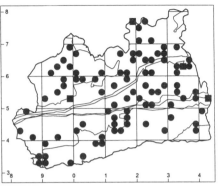

Jodia croceago ([Denis & Schiffermüller], 1775) PLATE 1 Orange Upperwing

RDB2

Resident, possibly extinct; woodland, very local and rare.

April to early May.

Foodplant – (oak).

The Orange Upperwing is a species that has declined seriously in recent years, both locally and nationally, and as it has not been recorded in Surrey for over ten years could quite possibly be extinct. Earlier records suggest that it was certainly far more widespread, including: Sanderstead, 1865 (*Ent. Ann.*

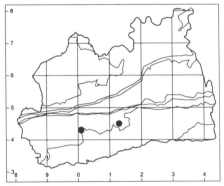

1865:119); Clapham and Croydon, 1868 (*Ent. Ann.* **1868**:116); Haslemere, Box Hill, and Reigate (*VCH*); Caterham, 1927 (Bell in de Worms, *L.N.* **35**:56). More recently larvae were found at Durfold Wood on 25.5.1952, and moths on sallow catkins on 3.4.53, 11.4.53, and 3.4.54 (RFB), and several series of reared specimens were exhibited at the 1955 annual exhibition of the BENHS originating from a female taken near Chiddingfold in 1954. Attention then turned towards the woods around Abinger Common, where in 1961 numbers were taken at sugar, sallow catkins and mvl, e.g. 17.3.1961 (3), 26.3.1961 (8) (RF), and up until the mid-seventies it was still possible to see several examples in one night – for example, 18.4.1971 four at Friday Street (PMS). By the next decade it had declined so that only one example was noted from here in 1983, and despite much field work it has not been seen there since. This record, and the one from Bramley the year after, are the last recorded instances of its occurrence in the county and its future must be in grave doubt. A possible reason for its decline may be due to changing woodland management. The woods at Abinger were maintained for the local leather-tanning industry at nearby Gomshall, tannin being extracted from the bark of coppiced oak trees. The industry has now gone and the woodland has not been coppiced for many years. The moth emerges in the autumn, hibernates, and reappears in the spring, when it was most often encountered.

RECORDS – **Friday Street**, 12.4.77 (3) (Châtelain per BS), 5.5.83 (CH); **Bramley**, 21.4.84 (RFB).

Conistra vaccinii (Linnaeus, 1761)   Chestnut

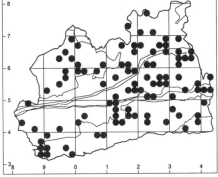

Resident; woodland, commons, heathland; widespread and common.

Univoltine; October, and March and April.

Foodplant – (oak, hazel, ash, honeysuckle).

The Chestnut is a very common species occurring throughout the county, and in some woodland localities approaches abundance. Like several of its relatives it hibernates as an adult, flying in mild spells through the winter.

Conistra ligula (Esper, 1791)   Dark Chestnut

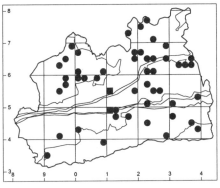

Resident; commons, woodland; widespread and fairly common.

Univoltine; October, and February and March.

Foodplant – oak.

Although recorded from most of the county the Dark Chestnut is very much less common than the Chestnut; indeed at most localities where trap counts have been kept *ligula* occurs at less than ten percent of the numbers of *vaccinii*. There are slight habitat preferences, *ligula* preferring more open habitats such as commons and hedgerows. The adult hibernates but usually dies earlier in the spring than *vaccinii,* although occasional examples survive until March or even April.

Conistra rubiginea ([Denis & Schiffermüller], 1775)   Dotted Chestnut

Notable/Nb

Resident; heathland, woodland; restricted
        and uncommon.

Univoltine; October, and March and April.

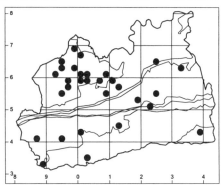

Although generally rather uncommon, the
Dotted Chestnut occurs most regularly on the
heaths of the Bagshot beds, and less
commonly on other heaths and woodland in
central and south-western Surrey. Occasional
examples appear further east and may
represent attempts to increase the species'
range; certainly it appears to be commoner in
north-west Surrey than at the time of Bretherton's list. The early stages remain unknown in
Surrey.

Agrochola circellaris (Hufnagel, 1766)   Brick

Resident; commons; widespread but
        uncommon.

Univoltine; late September and October.

Foodplant – poplar catkins, wych elm
        seeds, (sallow catkins).

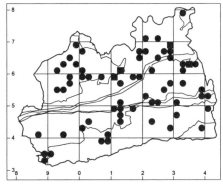

The Brick has been recorded widely across
the county, but is generally rather uncommon,
especially at light traps where it is only
recorded in ones and twos. The only exception
is at Bramley where the counts were: 1985
(18), 86 (32) (RFB). Other lures appear to be
at least as attractive as light and include sugar,
ivy bloom, and ripe blackberries. Larvae can often be found in large numbers in collected
poplar catkins or beaten wych elm seeds, so the moth is probably commoner than at first
sight appears.

Agrochola lota (Clerck, 1759)   Red-line Quaker

Resident; commons; widespread and fairly common.

Univoltine; October.

Foodplant – sallow catkins, [willow].

A fairly common species of open ground, the larvae of the Red-line Quaker feed when small in sallow catkins and consequently the moth is probably least common on the chalk. There are also relatively few records for heathland, but this is likely to be because this type of habitat is poorly worked at the time when the moth is on the wing. The adult is one of the species to be found feeding on ripe blackberries.

Agrochola macilenta (Hübner, 1809)   Yellow-line Quaker

Resident; woodland, wooded commons; widespread and fairly common.

Univoltine; October and early November.

Foodplant – (hybrid black poplar catkins).

The Yellow-line Quaker occurs in similar numbers to the preceding species but prefers more wooded habitats. The moth occurs regularly at light but is also attracted to ivy blossom.

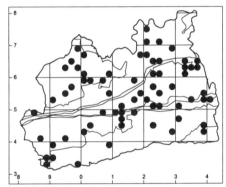

Agrochola helvola (Linnaeus, 1758)   Flounced Chestnut

Resident; wooded commons; widespread but uncommon.

Univoltine; October.

Foodplant – oak.

The Flounced Chestnut is the least common member of the genus and rarely seen in any numbers. Evans (1973) considered that it had increased greatly during the period of his survey, but more recently several observers state that it has declined: Leigh, decreasing (RF); Thorpe, not since 1979 (PJB); and at Wisley RES not seen since 1973. At Bramley,

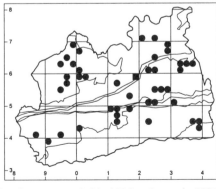

where many species abound, it was scarce with only two recorded in 1985 and none in 1986

(RFB). Bretherton (1957) regarded it as generally scarce, except for Horsell where it was very much more common, and today there are a few sites such as Blindley Heath and Ashtead Common where it is very locally common. The exact habitat requirements remain uncertain.

Agrochola litura (Linnaeus, 1761) **Brown-spot Pinion**

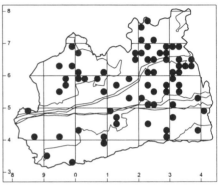

Resident; woodland, wooded commons; widespread and common.

Univoltine; September to mid-October.

The Brown-spot Pinion is a widely distributed and common species, especially so in the north-east of the county. Trap counts at Bramley, where it is very common, show 1985 (75), 86 (69) (RFB); however in the south London suburbs, counts are even greater: Mitcham, 1981 (41), 82 (112), 83 (159) (RKAM); South Croydon, 1983 (402), 84 (143), 85 (133) (GAC).

Agrochola lychnidis ([Denis & Schiffermüller], 1775) **Beaded Chestnut**

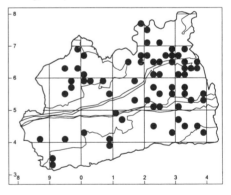

Resident; commons; widespread and common.

Univoltine; late September and October.

Foodplant – (tufted hair-grass).

The Beaded Chestnut shares a similar distribution to the preceding species – rather widespread but commoner in the north-east. Most recorders obtain similar numbers of this and *litura*, although at South Croydon it is very much the scarcer species. There appears to be a preference for more open habitat than is the case for *litura*.

Atethmia centrago (Haworth, 1809)

Centre-barred Sallow

Resident; woodland, commons, hedgerows; widespread and fairly common.

Univoltine; late August and September.

Foodplant – ash.

A fairly common species in the vicinity of ash trees. The larva feeds on the flowers of its foodplant in the spring, resting by day at the base of the tree, and they have been found by turning back vegetation in such situations.

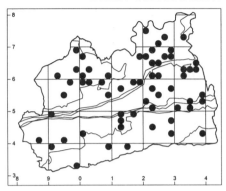

Omphaloscelis lunosa (Haworth, 1809)

Lunar Underwing

Resident; commons; widespread and common.

Univoltine; September and early October.

The Lunar Underwing is one of the commonest of the autumnal moths, occurring across the county. At Leigh, on 29.9.1990, over 950 examples of this species were recorded in one night (RF). Such an occurrence is exceptional, more typical annual counts being: Milford, 1992 (630) (DWB); Bramley, 1985 (410), 86 (130) (RFB).

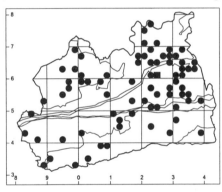

Xanthia citrago (Linnaeus, 1758)

Orange Sallow

Resident; commons, gardens; fairly widespread but uncommon.

Univoltine; September.

Foodplant – lime.

The Orange Sallow occurs throughout the county, but because of its foodplant is found mainly in suburban areas where limes have been planted. Results from trapping would suggest that the moth is scarce, but larvae are not difficult to find in some numbers and it is evident that the adult is not strongly attracted to light. Sugar and honeydew on limes would provide a better lure.

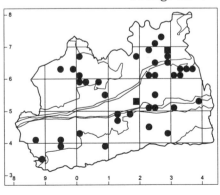

Xanthia aurago ([Denis & Schiffermüller], 1775)　　Barred Sallow

Resident; woodland, wooded commons; widespread and fairly common.

Univoltine; mid-September to mid-October.

Foodplant – field maple, (beech).

The Barred Sallow occurs in small numbers throughout the county, perhaps more commonly on the chalk but still quite regularly off it.

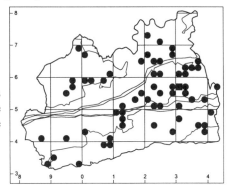

Xanthia togata (Esper, 1788)　　Pink-barred Sallow

Resident; commons, open woodland; widespread and common.

Univoltine; mid-September to mid-October.

Foodplant – sallow catkins.

Although slightly less common than the Sallow, this species is nevertheless found throughout the county, often in good numbers. It is one of the species found regularly at ripe blackberries.

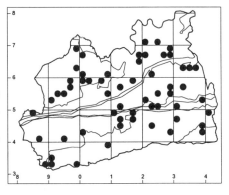

Xanthia icteritia (Hufnagel, 1766)　　Sallow

Resident; commons, open woodland, heathland; widespread and common.

Univoltine; September to mid-October.

Foodplant – sallow catkins, poplar catkins.

The Sallow occurs in similar habitats to the previous species but usually in even larger numbers, and can usually be reared in plenty from collected sallow catkins.

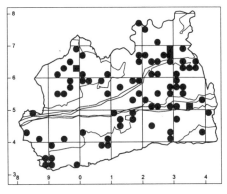

Xanthia gilvago ([Denis & Schiffermüller], 1775) Dusky-lemon Sallow

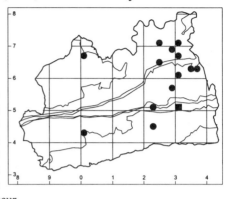

Resident; commons, gardens; local and rare.

Univoltine; late September and early October.

Foodplant – wych elm seeds.

The Dusky-lemon Sallow would appear to have always been scarce in Surrey and is currently rare, not having been recorded since 1991. The reasons for this are not clear; certainly wych elm has suffered less from the effects of Dutch elm disease than the English elm, and there are a number of sites where mature, heavily flowering wych elms still occur.

RECORDS – **Thorpe**, scarce, 1978, 81, 83, 86 (PJB); **Bramley**, 24.9.76 (1) (RFB); **Buckland**, 16.10.81, 6.10.83 (CH); **Leigh**, 1984 (RF); **Nutfield**, 19.9.76, 1.10.79, 12.9.90, 30.4.91 larva on wych elm (PAC); **North Cheam**, 1.10.83, 24.9.85 (RFMcC); **Wimbledon**, 8.10.83, 29.9.84 (JVD); **Mitcham Common**, 27.9.77 at sugar (JP), 21.9.78 (PAM), 1983 (2) at blackberries (RKAM); **Hooley**, 10.10.79 (CH); **Purley**, 21.9.76, 22.9.77 (PMS); **Norbury**, 27.9.84 (BC); **Selsdon**, 1980 (1) (EHW); **Addington**, 1986 (BS).

Xanthia ocellaris (Borkhausen, 1792) Pale-lemon Sallow

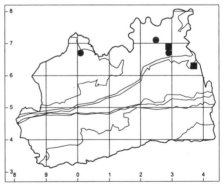

Notable/Na

Resident; commons; very local and rare.

Univoltine; late September and early October.

Foodplant – hybrid black poplar catkins.

The Pale-lemon Sallow is a very local species associated with the commons of south London and the banks of the Thames. Indeed it was first found in Britain at Wimbledon Common in 1893. The *VCH* described it as "that great rarity . . . which has been taken two or three times in Surrey", but gives no further details. Bretherton (1957) gave two sites for north-west Surrey, but considered that the moth had been lost from both as a consequence of felling the old poplars. Its status is certainly precarious and suitable trees should be preserved.

RECORDS – **Thorpe**, scarce; 1976, 78, 80, 82, 85, 87, 92 (PJB); **Wimbledon**, 2.10.78, 1979, 7-14.10.84 (JVD); **Mitcham Common**, 18.9.76 (PAM), 27.9.77 (5) at sugar (JP), 4.78 larvae (GAC), 25.9.79 (CH), 1981 (1), 83 (1) (RKAM), 9.10.91 (DCL); **Addington**, 5.10.85, 14.5.86 larvae in poplar catkins (BS).

Acronicta megacephala ([Denis and Schiffermüller], 1775)   **Poplar Grey**

Resident; commons, woodland,
        widespread and fairly common.

Univoltine; late June and July.

Foodplant – poplar, aspen, (willow).

The Poplar Grey is a widely distributed species, though nowhere common, whose greatest populations probably occur on the commons of south London.

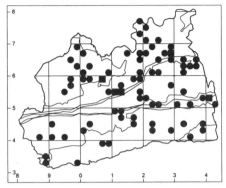

Acronicta aceris (Linnaeus, 1758)   **Sycamore**

Resident; commons, gardens; widespread
        and fairly common.

Univoltine; June and July.

Foodplant – sycamore, horse-chestnut,
        oak, (field maple, cherry,
        service-tree).

This species, rather like the last, is somewhat of a suburban moth associated with trees planted in parks and gardens. In rural areas it is uncommon, for example at Bramley: 1985 (1), 86 (5) (RFB), while at South Croydon counts show: 1983 (59), 84 (37), 85 (12)

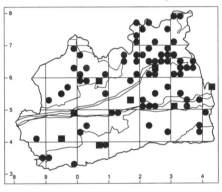

(GAC). Melanic examples occur, especially in the north-east.

Acronicta leporina (Linnaeus, 1758)   **Miller**

Resident; commons, heathland;
        widespread and fairly common.

Univoltine; mid-June to July.

Foodplant – birch, (alder, willow, oak).

The Miller is another widespread moth, although more even in its distribution than the previous two species. It is probably the commonest of the genus on heathland.

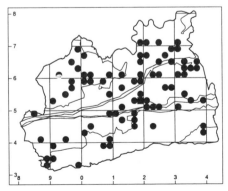

Acronicta alni (Linnaeus, 1767)   Alder Moth

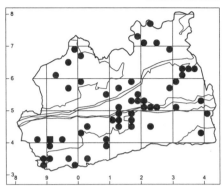

Resident; wooded commons, woodland; fairly widespread but uncommon.

Univoltine; June to mid-July.

Foodplant – (birch, pear, sallow, willow, beech, [oak]).

The Alder Moth is fairly widely distributed although there are several rather large areas from which it remains unrecorded. Although this species has been shown, by the use of mercury vapour light, to be more common than once thought, there would also appear to have been a genuine increase in recent years. Bretherton (1957) could only give three records for north-west Surrey and in his supplement (1965) added only three more. Evans (1973) had only six records from 1950 to 1964, whereafter there were many more. This was no doubt partly due to increased fieldwork in connection with his survey, though it is interesting that mercury vapour lights were in use for some 20 years before the increase became apparent. During the period of this survey, numbers seem to have been stable with many of the static traps recording several individuals each year. Melanics, referable to ab. *suffusa* Tutt, have been noted from Bookham and Headley (GAC), and Nutfield (PAC).

Acronicta tridens ([Denis & Schiffermüller], 1775)   Dark Dagger

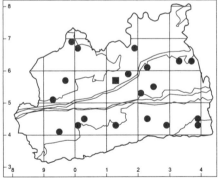

Resident; commons; local but fairly common.

Univoltine; June to mid-July.

Foodplant – sloe, (sallow).

The adults of this species and the next can only be separated by examination of the genitalia, although their larvae are distinctive. As most lepidopterists seem reluctant to do this, and many rely on light traps rather than searching for the early stages, this species is undoubtedly under-recorded. The available evidence suggests that it is local but locally fairly common. Trap counts at South Croydon show: 1983 (3), 84 (4), 85 (1), the corresponding figures for *psi* being: 1983 (89), 84 (59), 85 (32) (GAC). At Ashtead however, the majority of Daggers at sugar were *tridens*.

Acronicta psi (Linnaeus, 1758)   **Grey Dagger**

Resident; wooded commons, downland, heathland; widespread and common.

Univoltine; June to August.

Foodplant – birch, rose, apple, (oak, beech, lime, sallow, plum).

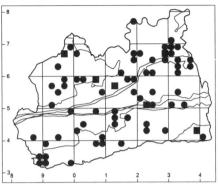

Although frequently not distinguished from the previous species (*q.v.*), the Grey Dagger would appear to be much the commoner and more widespread of this species pair.

Acronicta auricoma ([Denis & Schiffermüller], 1775)   **Scarce Dagger**

Extinct; not recorded this century.

The Scarce Dagger was formerly known from: "Richmond Park and Coombe Wood, common, especially in 1816" (Stephens); Weybridge, bred 1895 (RCK coll.); and two labelled "Surrey 1895" (RFB coll.). An undated record from Kingston in Buckell and Prout (1898) is queried by Prout and dismissed by Plant (1993); this record may be the same as the one of several individuals noted in the collection of Dr. H.N. Kane by his cousin W.F.deV. Kane and taken in the Kingston area prior to 1893 (*Ent.* **26**:61.) – as both Coombe Wood and Richmond Park are immediately adjacent to Kingston there is no justification in dismissing the record out of hand.

Acronicta rumicis (Linnaeus, 1758)   **Knot Grass**

Resident; commons, heathland, woodland; widespread and common.

Bivoltine; mid-May to mid-June, and July and August.

Foodplant – sallow, rose, heather, bird's-foot trefoil, water-pepper, birch, oak, violet, soft rush, (knotgrass, dock, creeping thistle, crab apple).

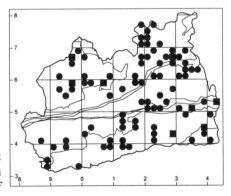

The Knot Grass is found in suitable habitat throughout the county, and the larva, which has been recorded from a very wide range of plants, is frequently encountered.

Craniophora ligustri ([Denis & Schiffermüller], 1775)   **Coronet**

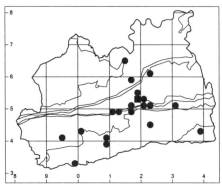

Resident; wooded downland, woodland; local and uncommon.

Univoltine; July.

Foodplant – wild privet, (ash).

The Coronet is distinctly local in Surrey, being recorded from a few areas south of the chalk and in woods on the downs. It is only on the scarp of the North Downs that it is found in any frequency, and at these sites the melanic ab. *coronula* Haworth is the commoner form.

Cryphia domestica (Hufnagel, 1766)   **Marbled Beauty**

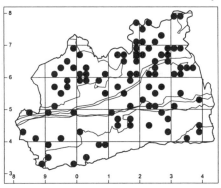

Resident; gardens, commons; widespread and locally common.

Univoltine; July and August.

The Marbled Beauty is a widespread species in Surrey, but is strongly associated with built-up areas where it may be very common. Trap counts from south London show: South Croydon, 1983 (202), 84 (84), 85 (46) (GAC); Mitcham, 1981 (230), 82 (209), 83 (181) (RKAM); Banstead, 1988 (71), 89 (97), 90 (95), 92 (124) (SWG). Counts from the rural south-west, however, are much lower: Bramley, 1985 (3), 86 (19) (RFB); Milford, 1992 (15) (DWB). Despite its frequency in towns, the larva has only been reported on a couple of occasions.

Cryphia muralis (Forster, 1771)   **Marbled Green**

ssp. *muralis* (Forster, 1771)

Extinct; not recorded for nearly 80 years.

Although principally a coastal species, the Marbled Green occurs inland in several localities. The following published records refer to Surrey: 1820s "occurred profusely on the canal bridge in the Old Kent Road" (Newman, *Ent.* **2**:37); Kingston area, prior to 1892 (Kane, *Ent.* **26**:61); Dulwich, 1897 (*Ent. Rec.* **7**:301); Coombe Wood, 1918 (W.J. Cox in de Worms, *L.N.* **34**:70). The first record clearly suggests residency but the others are less certain. It is not clear why this species should have long vanished whilst *domestica* thrives in the urban environment with its associated air pollution.

Amphipyra pyramidea (Linnaeus, 1758) Copper Underwing

Resident; woodland, commons;
   widespread and common.

Univoltine; August and September.

Foodplant – oak, sloe, English elm, wych
   elm, sallow, honeysuckle,
   rose, (lime, hazel, lilac,
   cherry).

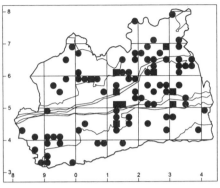

The following species was only separated from *pyramidea* in 1968, and so the only reliable records before then are those for which a voucher specimen exists. The characters on which most entomologists rely for distinguishing the two species are rather subjective and each individual recorder will probably favour one species, only assigning to the other species those specimens which show the particular characters very strongly. I believe, from larval records, that this species is by far the commoner although there has been no genitalic examination of adult catches to categorically confirm this. At South Croydon, trap counts suggest that only 10% are *berbera* (GAC), while at Bramley, roughly equal numbers were recorded (RFB). Further work is needed to determine whether there is a subtle difference in the ecology of the two species.

Amphipyra berbera Rungs, 1949 Drab Copper Underwing

ssp. *svenssoni* Fletcher, 1968

Resident; woodland, commons;
   widespread and common.

Univoltine; late July to early September.

Foodplant – oak, birch, sloe, English elm,
   alder buckthorn, (lilac).

The Drab Copper Underwing occurs in broadly similar habitat to the preceding species (*q.v.*), but is generally less common. Both species are seen in greater numbers at sugar than at light, and both are virtually absent from the Rothamsted trap captures.

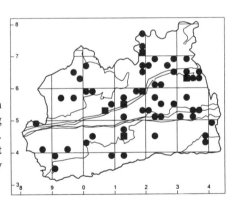

Amphipyra tragopoginis (Clerck, 1759)   **Mouse Moth**

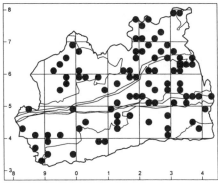

Resident; commons, gardens; widespread and common.

Univoltine; August and September.

Foodplant – common nettle.

The Mouse Moth, although found in most areas of the county, is considerably more common in the suburban areas of south London. The largest numbers recorded in a rural area are from Bramley: 1985 (61), 86 (38) (RFB), while typical numbers from the north-east are: Mitcham, 1981 (54), 82 (98), 83 (85) (RKAM); Carshalton, at acl, 1988 (118), 89 (71), 90 (31) (DC); South Croydon, 1983 (134), 84 (331), 85 (205) (GAC). Like many members of this group, it is only weakly attracted to the Rothamsted traps.

Mormo maura (Linnaeus, 1758)   **Old Lady**

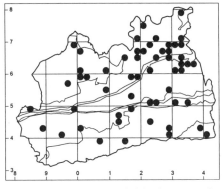

Resident; commons, gardens; widespread but uncommon.

Univoltine; mid-July to August.

Foodplant – sloe, bramble, ivy, rhododendron, (hazel, sycamore, honeysuckle).

The relative paucity, and the distribution, of records of the Old Lady is due principally to the dependence of most entomologists on the light trap, a method which is singularly ineffective in attracting this species. A number of records relate to the adults' habit of hiding by day in such places as outbuildings and under dustbins, and this is probably the reason for the apparent concentration of records in the London area. The best method of attracting the moth is the use of sugar, and if more use was made of this technique then the Old Lady would probably prove to be much more common than the current records suggest.

Dypterygia scabriuscula (Linnaeus, 1758) — Bird's Wing

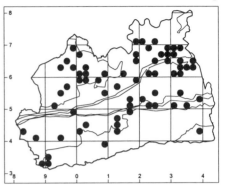

Resident; commons, downland; fairly widespread and fairly common.
Univoltine; mid-June to mid-July.

The Bird's Wing is fairly widely distributed across Surrey with the exception of the weald, from where it has only been recorded at a single site: Ewhurst, 14.7.1978, 7.7.1981 (SFI), and the Hastings beds, where only two individuals have been noted: Lingfield, 10.7.1992, 17.6.1995 (JC). The reason for this apparent scarcity in the south of the county is not clear; it is certainly a common species on the London clay.

Rusina ferruginea (Esper, 1785) — Brown Rustic

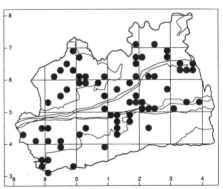

Resident; wooded commons; widespread and fairly common.
Univoltine; mid-June to mid-July.

The Brown Rustic is a fairly common species in suitable habitat throughout the county, although, like the previous species, it is poorly recorded from the south-east.

Thalpophila matura (Hufnagel, 1766) — Straw Underwing

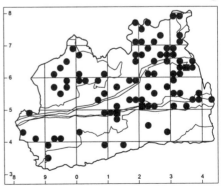

Resident; commons, downland; widespread and locally common.
Univoltine; late July and August.
Foodplant – grasses.

The Straw Underwing is an inhabitant of open grassy areas throughout the county, where it can be rather common. The larvae have been found on several occasions, always very early in the year.

Trachea atriplicis (Linnaeus, 1758)   Orache Moth

Migrant; one record only.

The Orache Moth was a former resident of several eastern counties which became extinct around 1915. In recent years several migrant examples have turned up, including one for Surrey.

1989 – **Woking**, 5.7 (SCP).

Euplexia lucipara (Linnaeus, 1758)   Small Angle Shades

Resident; commons, woodland;
    widespread and fairly common.

Univoltine; mid-June to July.

Foodplant – (bindweed, wormwood).

The Small Angle Shades occurs in suitable places throughout the county, but is rarely more than just fairly common.

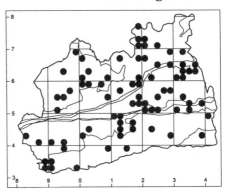

Phlogophora meticulosa (Linnaeus, 1758)   Angle Shades

Resident; woodland, commons, heathland,
    downland; widespread and
    common.

Bivoltine; mid-May to mid-July, and
    August to mid-October.

Foodplant – bramble, creeping thistle,
    white dead-nettle, knotgrass
    (dock, rose, chickweed,
    bracken, oak, primrose,
    groundsel, willowherb,
    sallow).

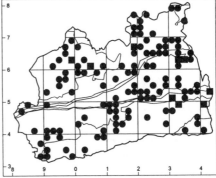

The Angle Shades is a common moth in just about every type of habitat, and, although certainly resident, it is probably also reinforced by immigration. Graphical analysis of all dated records indicates two clear broods, the second considerably larger.

Ipimorpha retusa (Linnaeus, 1761) Double Kidney

Resident; damp woodland, commons; local and scarce.

Univoltine; late July and August.

Foodplant – sallow.

The Double Kidney is a rather local species found in much of the south and west of the county, but virtually absent from the London area and avoiding the chalk. The larvae feed in the terminal shoots of sallow, spinning the leaves together, and may be found by searching.

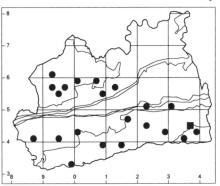

Ipimorpha subtusa ([Denis & Schiffermüller], 1775) Olive

Resident; commons; local and scarce.

Univoltine; late July and August.

Foodplant – aspen.

The Olive is a rather local species, although slightly more widely distributed than its congener *retusa*. Unlike *retusa* it occurs regularly in the London area and is probably commonest there.

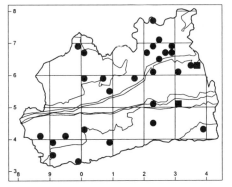

Enargia paleacea (Esper, 1788) Angle-striped Sallow

Migrant; rare.

The Angle-striped Sallow is resident in northern England and Scotland, but occurs in Surrey as a rare migrant. These examples are usually smaller and paler than native ones, and, in the case of my examples, referable to ab. *teichi* Krul.

1956 – **Chiddingfold**, 14.7 (*Ent.* **80**:235).

1958 – **Chiddingfold**, 8.7 (*Ent.* **92**:174).

1964 – **Wormley**, 13-17.8 (3) (JLM); **Reigate**, 15.8 (DAT).

1965 – **Wormley**, 22.7 (JLM); **Chiddingfold**, 11.8 (Mere).

1982 – **South Croydon**, 16.7 (GAC).

1994 – **Pirbright**, 16.7 (GAC).

Parastichtis suspecta (Hübner, 1817)   **Suspected**

Resident; commons, heathland, woodland;
   fairly widespread but
   uncommon.

Univoltine; July.

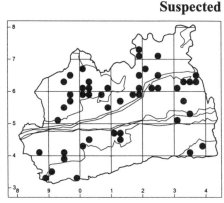

The Suspected occurs through much of Surrey, including as far into London as Richmond Park and Wimbledon, but does seem to be genuinely rare on the weald where it is represented by a single record at Oaken Wood, 30.6.1995 (GAC). It is rarely seen in any numbers; indeed the largest annual count is from South Croydon, 1984 (8) (GAC). Several records are of individuals at sugar and this method is probably as good as any for finding the moth.

Parastichtis ypsillon ([Denis & Schiffermüller], 1775)   **Dingy Shears**

Resident; commons, woodland;
   widespread but uncommon.

Univoltine; July.

Foodplant – willow, hybrid black poplar.

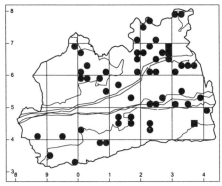

The Dingy Shears occurs in low numbers across much of the county, the gap in the west being almost certainly due to under-recording. The larva feeds on willow; it rests beneath loose bark during the day and can be quite easily found in this situation.

Dicycla oo (Linnaeus, 1758)   PLATE 8   **Heart Moth**

RDB3

Resident; parkland; local and uncommon.

Univoltine; late June to mid-July.

Foodplant – (oak).

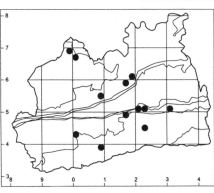

The Heart Moth is one of Surrey's specialities, and is recorded from central southern Surrey, commons around Leatherhead, and the extreme north-west. The feature common to these areas is good numbers of very old oaks in an open situation; at Ashtead it occurs in pasture woodland and at Leigh on farmland where the oaks have been left in and around the fields. Older records from other sites include: Ottershaw, 1950-60 (RFB); Weybridge, 1951-57 (JLM); Lucas Green, 1955-61 (RFB); Cranleigh, 1963, reared from larvae on oak (PAC); and Wormley, 1959-61 (JLM). Despite a number of serious fires at its main locality it still occurs in reasonable numbers. The moth comes to sugar and to light – to the former very early, often before dusk, and to the latter very late, frequently after 1 a.m. Ab. *renago* Haworth occurs at Ashtead.

RECORDS – **Virginia Water**, 4.7.82 (AG); **Thorpe**, 16.7.77, 6.7.79, 12.6.81, 7-9.7.83, 7.7.86 (PJB); **East Horsley**, 27.6-5.7.76 (LJDW); **Ashtead Forest**, 10.7.91 (5), 20.7.91 (6), 28.6.92 (4) (JC); **Ashtead Common**, 7.82 (SHC), 7.7.82 (PMS), 3.7.82, 2.7.83 (sugar), 7-8.7.83 (10+ mvl) (GAC), 26.6.90 (10) (RFMcC), 23.6.92 (20), 26.6.93 (3) (DC), 2.7.93 (4), 9.7.94 (16) (GAC), 5.7.95 (5) (SCP), 9.7.96 (3) (DC); **Bramley**, 24.7.83 (RFB); **Ewhurst**, 24.6.96 (SFI); **Dorking**, 18.7.86 (DAT); **Betchworth**, 2.8.80 (RAC); **Buckland**, 8.7.83, 10.7.85, 20.7.87, 31.7.91 (CH); **Nutfield**, 1.7.76 (PAC); **Leigh**, 1972-79 (15), 80 (2), 82 (7), 83 (5), 84 (5), 85 (5), 86 (8), 87 (5), 88 (9), 89 (4), 10.6-15.7.90 (3), 91 (3), 92 (3), 93 (4), 95 (1), 96 (2) (RF).

Cosmia affinis (Linnaeus, 1767)   **Lesser-spotted Pinion**

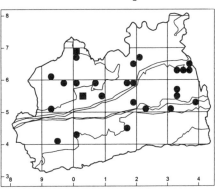

Resident; commons, hedgerows; local and scarce.

Univoltine; July.

.**Foodplant** – English elm.

In contrast to its former status, described as common and generally distributed from the time of the *VCH* to the north-east Surrey survey, this species has been local and rather scarce during the last two decades. No doubt this is due to the loss of elms to Dutch elm disease, although larvae have been found on sucker elms, 15-20 ft high (PJB). Other elm feeders have fared better, in the case of the White-letter Hairstreak, or declined to the point of extinction like *Cosmia diffinis* (*q.v.*). A larger number of records in the last few years suggest that the species may be increasing again.

Cosmia diffinis (Linnaeus, 1767)   PLATE 1   **White-spotted Pinion**

Notable/Na

Resident, possibly extinct; commons, hedgerows; local and rare.

Univoltine; late July and August.

Foodplant – English elm.

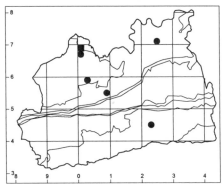

The White-spotted Pinion has declined drastically, and, as it has not been seen in Surrey for nearly 15 years, must be feared to be extinct. The *VCH* regarded it as generally distributed and common in the metropolitan district, but Bretherton (1957) had few records for north-west Surrey, giving: all traps, very scarce to scarce; Egham, 14.8.1931. In north-east Surrey it was described as very local (Evans, 1973) but quite a number of records were given, many from south London, and it was even taken in Camberwell, 7.8.1953 (Wakely, *Ent. Rec.* **66**:71). The larva is said to prefer the epicormic growth found only on mature elms, the only record from the survey period being of larvae between spun leaves from the top of a 60 foot elm (PJB), and it would appear that the moth is unable to utilize the sucker growth which has allowed the White-letter Hairstreak to survive Dutch elm disease.

RECORDS – **Thorpe**, 1975, 78, larva from elm (PJB); **Pyrford**, 1977 (JACG); **East Horsley**, 28.7.76 (LJDW); **Leigh**, 1979 (RF); **Wimbledon**, 15.8.77 (JVD).

Cosmia trapezina (Linnaeus, 1758)   **Dun-bar**

Resident; woodland, commons, hedgerows; widespread and common.

Univoltine; late July to early September.

Foodplant – lime, hawthorn, sloe, oak, field maple, English elm, sallow, hazel, bramble, ash, (birch, aspen, hybrid black poplar, apple, beech).

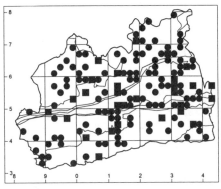

The Dun-bar is by far the commonest member of the genus *Cosmia*, being found throughout the county and occurring at all the static traps in large numbers. The larvae are also very common in the spring on many species of deciduous tree, and as they are cannibalistic should be one of the first species that the novice learns to identify. The melanic ab. *nigra* Tutt occurred at Addington, 25.7.1986 (BS).

Cosmia pyralina ([Denis & Schiffermüller], 1775)   **Lunar-spotted Pinion**

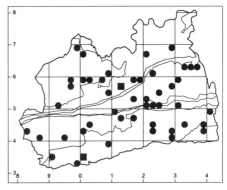

Resident; wooded commons, hedgerows; widespread and fairly common.

Univoltine; July and early August.

Foodplant – English elm, (hawthorn, sloe).

The Lunar-spotted Pinion appears to be a species that is increasing. The *VCH* regarded it as rare, and Evans (1973) considered it to be less common than *affinis*, although in north-west Surrey the situation was reversed (Bretherton, 1957). Currently it is a fairly common species found widely through the county. The wider range of foodplants adopted by the larva mean that it has not been affected by Dutch elm disease in the way that *affinis* and *diffinis* have, although, paradoxically, the only larvae found during the survey period were on elm.

Apamea monoglypha (Hufnagel, 1766)   **Dark Arches**

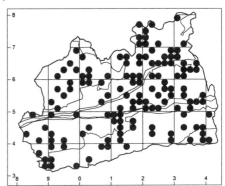

Resident; commons, downland, gardens; widespread and common.

Univoltine; mid-June to August.

The Dark Arches is a very common species throughout the county, appearing in similar numbers in both rural and suburban areas. Melanic forms are very rare, ab. *infuscata* White being noted only once in 15 years at South Croydon (GAC), also from Addington, 17.7.1985 (BS), and Nutfield, 10.7.1991 (PAC).

Apamea lithoxylaea ([Denis & Schiffermüller], 1775)   **Light Arches**

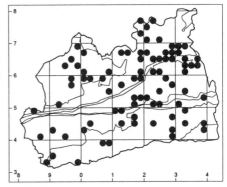

Resident; commons, downland, gardens; widespread and fairly common.

Univoltine; July.

The Light Arches is considerably less common than *monoglypha*, but nevertheless a fairly common moth across the county.

Apamea sublustris (Esper, 1788)　　　　Reddish Light Arches

Resident; chalk grassland, commons;
　　　restricted and scarce.

Univoltine; July.

The Reddish Light Arches is only found with any regularity on the chalk; elsewhere it occurs probably only as a vagrant. Even on the chalk it is usually scarce, static traps producing only a few examples each year, the only exception to this being at Banstead Downs where it has been recorded as follows: 28.6-18.7.1988, 89 (89), 90 (75), 91 (47), 2.6.92 (3) (DC). It appears to be virtually absent from the sandy areas of west Surrey, although nationally it is found on both coastal sand dunes and the Breck district of East Anglia; in this respect it differs from such species as *Agrotis vestigialis* and *Sideridis albicolon*.

Apamea crenata (Hufnagel, 1766)　　　Clouded-bordered Brindle

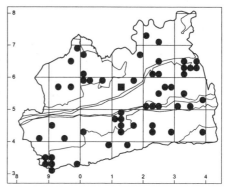

Resident; commons, woodland, downland;
　　　widespread and fairly common.

Univoltine; mid-May to early July.

The Clouded-bordered Brindle is a fairly common species throughout much of the county, although it does seem to have a preference for more rural areas and is scarce in the London area. There are also very few records from the heaths of western Surrey. The melanic f. *combusta* Haworth appears to be more common than the paler typical form.

Apamea epomidion (Haworth, 1809)　　　　Clouded Brindle

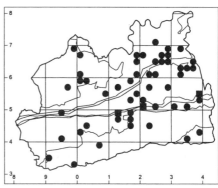

Resident; commons, woodland, downland;
　　　widespread and fairly common.

Univoltine; mid-June to mid-July.

Foodplant – grasses.

The Clouded Brindle is also a fairly widespread species, but unlike *crenata* shows a distinct bias towards the north-east, and in south London it is by far the commoner species. It is also virtually absent from the western heathlands.

Apamea lateritia (Hufnagel, 1766)   Scarce Brindle

Migrant; one example only.

A single specimen of the Scarce Brindle has been taken in Surrey; this was the second British record, the third being seen on the next night just over the county boundary at Bexley, West Kent.

1972 – **West Norwood**, 17.7 (BS).

[*Apamea furva* ([Denis & Schiffermüller], 1775)   Confused
ssp. *britannica* Cockayne, 1950

Doubtful;

De Worms (*L.N.* **39**:105) gives the following record: "several authentic specimens labelled Banstead Downs, July 1904, in the Meldola collection at the Hope Department . . .". Although occurring at Folkestone, the moth is essentially north-western in Britain and this record is almost certainly erroneous.]

Apamea remissa (Hübner, 1809)   Dusky Brocade

Resident; commons; fairly widespread and fairly common.

Univoltine; mid-June to July.

The Dusky Brocade is rather a scarce species in southern and western Surrey, but very much more frequent in the north and east.

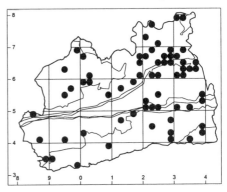

Apamea unanimis (Hübner, 1813)   Small Clouded Brindle

Resident; damp commons; local and uncommon.

Univoltine; June.

The Small Clouded Brindle is a local species which is found in suitable habitat across the county. It shows a distinct preference for damp habitats, often by water, and hence is virtually absent from the chalk and sand formations. Elsewhere it occurs in small numbers and is nowhere common.

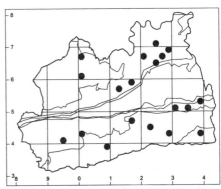

Apamea anceps ([Denis & Schiffermüller], 1775)   **Large Nutmeg**

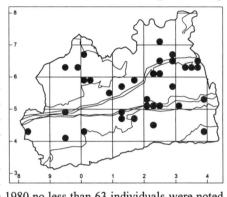

Resident; commons, chalk grassland;
        fairly widespread and mostly
        uncommon.
Univoltine; June to mid-July.
The Large Nutmeg is a fairly widespread
species which seems to show a preference for
drier areas. On the whole it is rather
uncommon, being recorded as singletons or
at the static traps in annual counts never
exceeding single figures. The exception to this
is in the Selsdon area where it is recorded
regularly at South Croydon (GAC) and
commonly at Addington (BS); at Selsdon in 1980 no less than 63 individuals were noted
(EHW).

Apamea sordens (Hufnagel, 1766)   **Rustic Shoulder-knot**

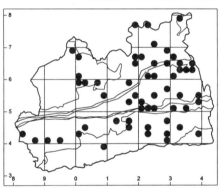

Resident; commons; widespread and fairly
        common.
Univoltine; June to mid-July.
The Rustic Shoulder-knot is a generally
distributed species across the county, but
probably least common on the heaths.

Apamea scolopacina (Esper, 1788)   **Slender Brindle**

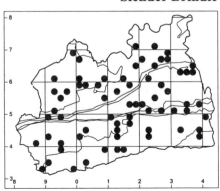

Resident; woodland, commons;
        widespread and fairly common.
Univoltine; July.
The Slender Brindle occurs throughout the
county. It shows a preference for more
wooded localities and in such areas can be
moderately common, although the only site
at which it is recorded in large numbers is at
Bramley: 1985 (42), 86 (82) (RFB).

Apamea ophiogramma (Esper, 1793) — Double Lobed

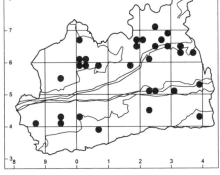

Resident; commons, gardens; restricted and uncommon.

Univoltine; July and early August.

Foodplant – (reed canary-grass).

The Double Lobed occurs in much of Surrey but is more or less restricted to damp areas, especially in river valleys, and so is absent from the chalk. Elsewhere it is found only in small numbers, annual counts from the static traps not exceeding single figures, and it is undoubtedly far less common than earlier this century when ornamental canary-grass was more popular. A melanic example was taken at Nutfield, 14.7.92 (PAC).

Genus *Oligia* – Minors

A genus of four species, three of which (*strigilis*, *versicolor*, and *latruncula*) can only be reliably determined by structural examination of the genitalia. As the only records admitted have been those so made, the exact distribution and relative frequencies of the three species remain unclear. Evidence suggests that both *strigilis* and *latruncula* are widespread and common, whereas *versicolor* is a local and rather rare species.

Oligia strigilis (Linnaeus, 1758) — Marbled Minor

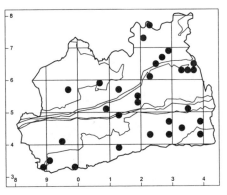

Resident; commons, woodland; widespread and fairly common.

Univoltine; mid-June to early July.

At South Croydon, where all *Oligia* caught between 1983 and 1985 were dissected, the proportion of Marbled Minor was just under 20 percent. Annual counts of *Oligia* species at most static traps run into hundreds, and there is little doubt that this species is both widespread and common, although it is as yet unrecorded from the Bagshot sand area. The melanic form, f. *aethiops* Osthelder, appears to be rare.

Oligia versicolor (Borkhausen, 1792) — **Rufous Minor**

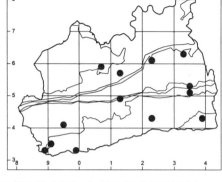

Resident; woodland, commons; local and uncommon.

Univoltine; mid-June to mid-July.

The Rufous Minor is evidently a much scarcer species than its congeners and is probably a woodland species in Surrey, although more work needs to be done to clarify the situation. The presence of a rufous thoracic crest is a good guide to selecting specimens for dissection (PAC, *pers. com.*).

RECORDS – **Haslemere**, 1988 (EE); **Haslemere RES**, 1980 (1) (TGW); **Tugley Wood**, 14.7.90 (GAC); **Oaken Wood**, 20.7.95 (GAC); **Milford**, 10.7.87 (DWB) [det. GAC]; **Wisley RES**, 1986 (7), 87 (8), 90 (1), 91 (1), 94 (3), 20.7.96 (AJH); **Westcott Downs**, 16.6.84 (GAC); **Bookham Common**, 13.7.87 (GAC); **Edolphs Copse**, 16.7.87 (GAC); **Bay Pond**, 14.7.86, 28.7.87 (GAC); **Pilgrim Fort**, 14.7.86 (GAC); **Banstead**, 7.96 (SWG) [det. GAC]; **South Croydon**, 9.6.83, 6.8.84, 1-15.7.85, 25.6-13.7.86, 17.7.95 (GAC); **Lingfield**, 1991 (2) (JC).

Oligia latruncula ([Denis & Schiffermüller], 1775) — **Tawny Marbled Minor**

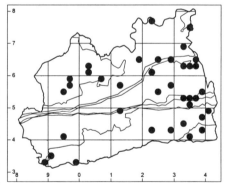

Resident; commons, woodland; widespread and common.

Univoltine; mid-June to July.

Foodplant – (cock's-foot).

The Tawny Marbled Minor is the most prevalent species at South Croydon (about 80% of the group) and also has the largest number of confirmed records. It is highly likely that it really is the commonest species but likely too that there will be some areas where *strigilis* is commoner. Counts in Evans (1973) suggest that this might be the case in more wooded areas, although it is strange that he found no *versicolor* among 238 *Oligia* examined. The Tawny Marbled Minor is usually a slightly smaller species than the others and the proportion of melanics, f. *unicolor* Tutt, is very high, probably in excess of 95% in urban areas.

Oligia fasciuncula (Haworth, 1809)   **Middle-barred Minor**

Resident; commons, woodland;
    widespread and fairly common.
Univoltine; June.
The Middle-barred Minor is immediately
distinguishable from its congeners on wing
markings, and also flies slightly earlier in the
year. It occurs widely in the county but is
usually seen in small numbers, annual trap
counts in single figures being the norm
although at Mitcham it was recorded as
follows: 1981 (99), 82 (38), 83 (143), 84 (41)
(RKAM).

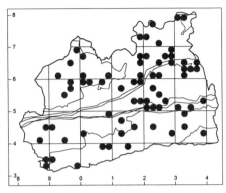

Mesoligia furuncula ([Denis & Schiffermüller], 1775)   **Cloaked Minor**

Resident; commons, gardens; fairly
    widespread and locally
    common.
Univoltine; late July and August.
Although found throughout the county the
Cloaked Minor is apparently scarce in the
south. Towards the north and particularly in
the London area it can be locally common as
the following trap counts show: South
Croydon, 1983 (13), 84 (19), 85 (4) (GAC);
Mitcham, 1982 (23), 83 (72) (RKAM);
Banstead Downs, 1989 (11), 90 (18) (DC).
At Bramley, during the survey period, annual counts averaged only three a year (RFB).

Mesoligia literosa (Haworth, 1809)   **Rosy Minor**

Resident; commons, gardens; fairly
    widespread but uncommon.
Univoltine; late July and August.
Nationally, the Rosy Minor occurs across
much of the country but is very much more
common in coastal localities. In Surrey it is
found at low density in most areas and its
frequency increases towards the north-east,
no doubt influenced by the proximity of the
Thames estuary. Trap counts at Mitcham
show: 1982 (22), 83 (32) (RKAM).

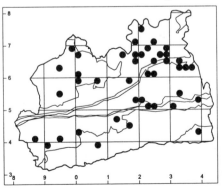

Genus *Mesapamea* – Common Rustics

In 1983 the genus *Mesapamea* was shown to contain two species (Remm, 1983), both of which were present in Britain. Separation is only possible by genitalic examination (illustrated in Jordan, 1986) although some forms are commoner in one species than the other and, in particular, black and red forms are more likely to be *didyma*. All older records unsupported by voucher specimens are of course invalid, but a composite distribution map shows that the species pair is very widespread. Complete counts (of males) have been made at South Croydon, Wisley RES, and Virginia Water, and show that *didyma* is much the less common of the two, although variables of habitat and trap type (mvl against Rothamsted) make it difficult to determine any significant difference between the proportions at each site. Peak emergences of the two species seem to coincide, but larger numbers of *secalis* mean that it appears first and lasts later in the season.

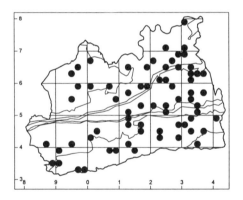

Mesapamea secalis (Linnaeus, 1758)   **Common Rustic**

Resident; commons, woodland, gardens; probably widespread and common.

Univoltine; July and August.

The Common Rustic is undoubtedly a common and widespread species across the county. Examples appear in every sample that has been critically examined, and at the three sites where complete counts were made it was the predominant species.

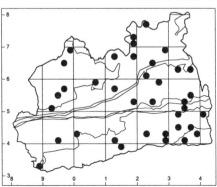

Mesapamea didyma (Esper, 1788)   **Lesser Common Rustic**

Resident; commons, woodland, gardens; probably widespread and fairly common.

Univoltine; mid-July to mid-August.

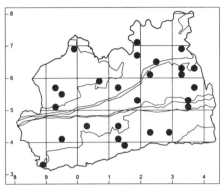

Like its congener, examples of the Lesser Common Rustic appear in most samples critically examined and its distribution is probably equally widespread. Evidence from three sites suggest that it is less common. At Virginia Water (Jordan, *Ent. Rec.* **103**:57) *didyma* formed 29% of the total population (n=181, counted in 1985). At South Croydon the proportions were: *secalis* 83%, *didyma* 17% (n=561, counts in 1988 and 89). At Wisley it was less common still: *secalis* 93%, *didyma* 7% (n=124, counts from 1987-90).

Photedes minima (Haworth, 1809)   **Small Dotted Buff**

Resident; commons, open woodland; widespread and fairly common.

Univoltine; mid-June to July.

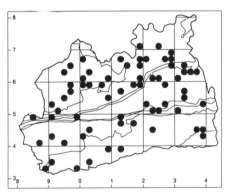

The Small Dotted Buff is found throughout the county. The preferred habitat is grassy commons and woodland, and consequently most static traps, being run in gardens, do not record it commonly. It is, however, regularly recorded in numbers in suitable habitat such as at Ashtead and Bookham Commons.

Photedes pygmina (Haworth, 1809)   **Small Wainscot**

Resident; commons, heathland; local and scarce.

Univoltine; late August and September.

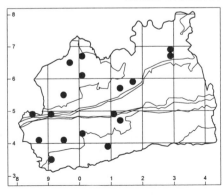

The Small Wainscot is a distinctly local species in Surrey which is unrecorded from the chalk and surprisingly rare on the weald. There is clearly a preference for damper habitats, possibly those that are acidic. Nowhere common, most records are of singletons although reasonable numbers have been obtained at Mitcham, i.e. 1981 (16), 82 (11), 83 (6) (RKAM).

Eremobia ochroleuca ([Denis & Schiffermüller], 1775)   **Dusky Sallow**

Resident; downland, commons; fairly
     widespread but uncommon.

Univoltine; mid-July to mid-August.

Although probably more common on the chalk, the Dusky Sallow has been recorded throughout the county. Most records are of singletons or occasional examples at regularly run traps; however, it was noted commonly by day at Pewley Downs, 8.8.1986 (RFB), and in 1993 considerable numbers were seen at light at Banstead Downs (DC/GAC). Comparison with the previous lists suggests that the moth has increased since about 1970.

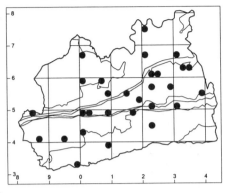

Luperina testacea ([Denis & Schiffermüller], 1775)   **Flounced Rustic**

Resident; commons, heathland, downland;
     widespread and common.

Univoltine; August and September.

The Flounced Rustic is a common early autumn species found in open habitats throughout the county.

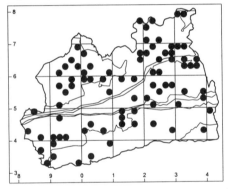

Genus *Amphipoea* – Ear moths

There are four species of Ear moth in Britain, all of which are sufficiently similar to require genitalic examination for accurate identification. Of the two species which have been recorded from Surrey, *fucosa* has rather longer wings, and this character may be used to select suitable specimens for dissection; such examination is essential before records can be accepted. The other species, *crinanensis* and *lucens*, have a more northern distribution and are most unlikely to occur in the county.

Amphipoea fucosa (Freyer, 1830)   **Saltern Ear**
ssp. *paludis* (Tutt, 1888)

Resident; very local and rare.

August.

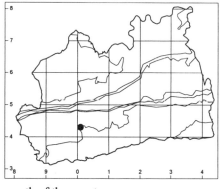

The Saltern Ear, as its name suggests, is principally a coastal species and is rare inland. During the survey period it was recorded from only a single site and confirmed by dissection. Bretherton (1957) mentions several sites in north-west Surrey, especially Weybridge where it appeared regularly, and Evans (1973) gives Putney, Wimbledon and Mitcham. All these sites are close to the Thames, as would be predicted by the moth's usual haunts, and it is possible that it has been overlooked in the north of the county.

RECORDS – **Bramley**, 1977 (1), 80 (1), 81 (1), 83 (1) (RFB).

Amphipoea oculea (Linnaeus, 1761)   **Ear Moth**

Resident; commons, heathland, waste ground; fairly widespread and fairly common.

Univoltine; late July and August.

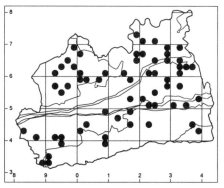

The Ear Moth occurs in fair numbers in suitably open habitat across the county, except perhaps in central western areas, although it might well be under-recorded in this area. Most examples are recorded at light, but the moth will occasionally fly by day and has been observed feeding at the flowers of wild carrot (RDH).

Hydraecia micacea (Esper, 1789)　　　　Rosy Rustic

Resident; commons, waste ground; widespread and fairly common.

Univoltine; September to mid-October.

Foodplant – dock.

The Rosy Rustic is a fairly common autumn species of open areas, possibly more common near water. At the Bramley trap it occurred in large numbers: 1985 (52), 86 (58) (RFB); and at Bay Pond in October 1986 it was also found commonly in an area of recently disturbed ground which had become overgrown with dock (GAC). Although dock is the only foodplant recorded for Surrey, it is highly likely that other plants are used, as elsewhere.

Hydraecia petasitis Doubleday, 1847　　　　Butterbur

Status uncertain; no recent record.

De Worms (*L.N.* **34**:88) says "reported from Burford Bridge, Box Hill", but gives no date or other reference. Apart from this very unsatisfactory record the only other instance of its occurrence in Surrey is of one taken at Worplesdon Hill, at light, 26.8.1946 (Howell, *Ent. 80*:47). Repeated visits to nearby butterbur failed to reveal traces of moths or larvae (Bretherton, 1957), and further attempts to relocate this species at Box Hill (KGWE), and more recently at Eashing (DWB) and Godstone (GAC), have also been unsuccessful. The species is resident in Hampshire and Berkshire, and in view of its retiring habits may still await rediscovery in Surrey.

Gortyna flavago ([Denis and Schiffermüller], 1775)　　　　Frosted Orange

Resident; commons; fairly widespread but uncommon.

Univoltine; September to mid-October.

Foodplant – marsh thistle, creeping thistle, (burdock).

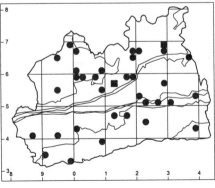

The Frosted Orange occurs across much of the county but appears to be absent from the chalk, where conditions may be too dry. Most static traps record it in only small numbers but it can be more common when light traps are run well into its habitat, for example at Bookham Common where the marsh thistle abounds.

Celaena leucostigma (Hübner, 1808) PLATE 13 **Crescent**

ssp. *leucostigma* (Hübner, 1808)
Resident; wetland; local but locally
   common.

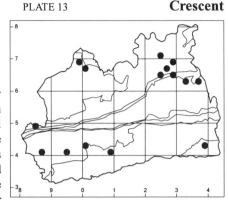

Univoltine; late July and August.
The Crescent is a rather local moth in Surrey
and many records refer to wanderers from
local colonies. In the north-east occasional
examples had turned up over the years in the
Croydon/Mitcham area, and in 1989 it was
found to be locally very common in disused
cress beds adjacent to the River Wandle. The
situation is likely to be similar in the other
corners of the county where the moth has been recorded. The species is said to be polymorphic
throughout its range, but I have not seen any examples of f. *fibrosa* Hübner in Surrey.

RECORDS – **Rushmoor**, 22.8.84 (PAD); **Milford**, 27.7.90 (DWB); **Bramley**, 1980-86
(10) (RFB); **Ewhurst**, 18.7.88 (MR); **Rowhills**, 8.93 (JKH); **Virginia Water**, 19.7.83
(AG); **Thorpe**, 15.8.76, 19.8.87 (PJB); **South Croydon**, 30.7.83, 20.8.96 (GAC);
Addington, 1983 (BS); **North Cheam**, 16.8.89 (RFMcC); **Carshalton**, 1989 (1) (DC);
Mitcham, 29.7.82, 8.8.83, 26.7.84 (RKAM); **Mitcham** (River Wandle), 23.7-2.9.89
(28), 7.7-10.8.90 (139), 5-19.8.91 (20), 16.7-17.8.92 (6) (DC), 12.8.93 (GAC), 11.7-
22.8.94 (20), 31.7.95 (4), 10.8-7.9.96 (5) (DC); **Wimbledon**, 18.8.95 (JVD); **Lingfield**,
26.8.91, 24.7.92, 20.7.96 (JC).

Nonagria typhae (Thunberg, 1784) PLATE 13 **Bulrush Wainscot**

Resident; wetland; widespread and common.

Univoltine; August.

Foodplant – bulrush.

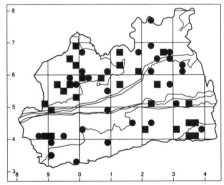

Based on light trap records of adults, the
Bulrush Wainscot would appear to be a local
and scarce species. However, by searching for
the early stages, this impression is shown to
be entirely false and larvae and pupae can be
found in almost any patch of the foodplant in
the county, often in some numbers. The pupa
is to be found head downwards, in contrast to
those of Webb's and the Rush Wainscot. Many
males are quite dark, but I have only come
across the melanic ab. *fraterna* Treitschke once amongst many adults reared: Wire Mill,
1996 (GAC); it was also taken at Nutfield, 24.7.1976 (PAC).

Archanara geminipuncta (Haworth, 1809) Twin-spotted Wainscot

Resident; reed beds; very local and rare.
Univoltine; August.
Foodplant – common reed.
There are records of the Twin-spotted
Wainscot from only five sites in the last 20
years, although two of these are indicative of
breeding colonies. The other records suggest
the presence of undiscovered colonies,
possibly in the Frensham area. Reed beds are
one of the county's most threatened habitats,
and the future of this species must be in doubt.

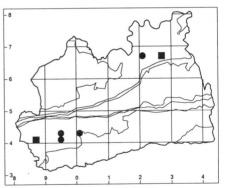

RECORDS – **Thorpe**, 22.8.86 (PJB);
Sheerwater, 20.7.80 pupa (AJH); **Send**, 24.6.95 larvae (GAC), 29.7.95 (6) (SCP);
Bramley, 26.8.84 (RFB); **Rushmoor**, 31.7.83 (PAD).

Archanara dissoluta (Treitschke, 1825) Brown-veined Wainscot

Resident; reed beds; very local and scarce.
Univoltine; late July to early September.
Foodplant – common reed.
The Brown-veined Wainscot is marginally
less rare than *geminipuncta* although still
restricted to a very small number of localities,
but evidently breeding at several of them. Both
species are possibly under-recorded and there
is a need for more field-work in suitable
habitats. Specimens from Mitcham are of the
form *arundineta* Schmidt.

RECORDS – **Frensham Little Pond**,
1.8.85 (DWB), 30.6.95 larvae (GAC); **Rushmoor**, 25.7.83, 5.8.83, 8.7.84 (PAD);
Milford, 4-8.8.94, 15.8.96 (DWB); **Milford House**, 17-26.8.85, 23.7.89 (DWB);
Bramley, 1.10.86 (RFB); **Tolworth**, 6-9.9.85 (2) (JTS); **Mitcham**, 23.7.89, 24.7.90,
5.8.91, 10.7.94 larvae, 31.7.95 (DC/GAC).

Archanara sparganii (Esper, 1790)   Webb's Wainscot

Notable/Nb

Resident, or temporary resident; wetland; very local but fairly common.

Univoltine; late July to August.

Foodplant – bulrush, yellow iris, [(bur-reed)].

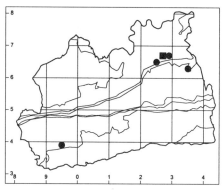

There is currently one established colony of Webb's Wainscot in north-east Surrey, from which odd specimens have been taken nearby. Two further specimens, from widely separated sites, were taken in 1976, a year in which considerable movements of moths occurred. The only previous record is of larvae and pupae from Bookham Common, which were present in 1934, scarce in 1935 and absent after that (Finnigan, *Ent.* **72**:22). These records are consistent with spread from suitable areas of the north Kent marshes and the establishment of temporary colonies, although introduction with the foodplant cannot be ruled out. The fate of the Mitcham colony remains to be seen, although it is still flourishing after seven years.

RECORDS – **Wormley**, 3.8.76 (JLM); **Selsdon**, 23.8.76 (EHW); **Mitcham**, 23.7-12.8.89 (11), 19.8-3.9.91 (8), 1-17.8.92 (21), 26.7-22.8.94 (29), 31.7-14.8.95 (33), 10.8-7.9.96 (23) (DC), 10.7.94 larvae in bulrush and yellow iris (DC/GAC); **Beddington**, 30.7.95 (DC); **North Cheam**, 3.8.94, 3.8.95 (10) (DC).

Archanara algae (Esper, 1789)   PLATE 13   Rush Wainscot

RDB3

Resident; wetland; very local but fairly common.

Univoltine; August.

Foodplant – bulrush.

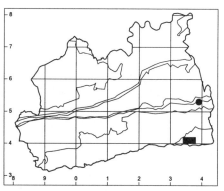

The Rush Wainscot has recently been found to be resident at two lakes on the Surrey/ Sussex border, no great distance from the better-known Sussex haunts of the moth. Several specimens have also been taken at Oxted, an area where there are several potentially suitable lakes, but searches for the early stages there have proved unsuccessful. A further record, of larvae from Reigate Heath on 28.4.1957, is given in Evans (1973), but considered doubtful – a conclusion with which I would concur.

RECORDS – **Oxted**, 17-18.8.75, 1.9.84, 1988 (TD); **Hedgecourt**, 14.6.90 larva, moth reared, 30.6.95 many larvae and pupae, 2.8.96 pupae (GAC); **Wire Mill**, 2.8.96 pupae (GAC).

Rhizedra lutosa (Hübner, 1803)   **Large Wainscot**

Resident; local and scarce.

Univoltine; September and October.

The frequency of records from several sites suggests that the Large Wainscot is resident in the county, although the exact breeding grounds remain undetected. It is clearly also a wanderer, several examples turning up in 1973, 1976, and notably 1990 when it occurred at three new sites within a period of four days. It was formerly described as abundant in reed beds at Sheerwater and Chertsey Meads (Bretherton, 1957), but these sites are now more or less destroyed.

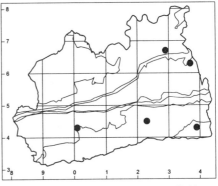

RECORDS – **Rushmoor**, 3.11.82, 3.11.83, 9.10.84 (PAD); **Hindhead**, 24.10.84 (JTS); **Milford**, 19.10.86, 90 (2), 8.10.92, 24.10.96 (DWB); **Bramley**, 1973-86 (20) (RFB); **Thorpe**, 1977, 82, 85 (PJB); **Wisley RES**, 10.76 (1) (AJH); **Buckland**, 1.11.84, 28.10.93 (CH); **Leigh**, 20.10.90 (RF); **Lingfield**, 16.10.90, 16.10.95 (JC); **Nutfield**, 2.10.95 (PAC); **Oxted**, 30.10.82 (TD); **Banstead**, 20.10.90 (SWG); **Mitcham**, 13-14.10.78 (PAM); **Selsdon**, 29.8.76, 1979 (EHW); **Addington**, 1980 (BS).

Arenostola phragmitidis (Hübner, 1803)   **Fen Wainscot**

Vagrant; five recent records.

The frequency of records of the Fen Wainscot suggest that it is merely a vagrant in the county, those in the London area at least probably coming from the Thames estuary. There is no evidence of it breeding in the areas that are home to the other reed-feeding Wainscots. Older records from north-west Surrey support this view: Weybridge trap, 3.8.1954; Horsell, 27.7.1955; Pirbright, before 1940 (Bretherton, 1957). It was also taken at Wormley, 26.7.1967 (JLM).

RECORDS – **Bramley**, 11.7.82 (RFB); **Leigh**, 7.7.89 (RF); **Addington**, 24.7.83 (BS); **Mitcham Common**, 31.7.91 (DCL); **Lingfield**, 27.7.95 (JC).

Oria musculosa (Hübner, 1808)   **Brighton Wainscot**

Migrant; one recent record.

Only a single example of this moth has been recorded during the survey period, a small pale example taken at Bramley, 4.7.1976 (RFB); one was also taken in South Hampshire on the same night. The earliest occurrence of this species in Surrey appears to be one recorded 23.7.1925 at Wormley (*Ent. Rec.* **40**:39). In an article on the moth, Cockayne and Kettlewell (1940) were convinced that the species was not migratory, but were unable to explain the origin of this particular record. More recent records are as follows: New Haw trap, 10.8.1951; Weybridge trap, 6.8.1953; Hook Heath, 27.7.1956; Weybridge, 7.8.1956 (Bretherton, 1957 and 1965); also Thorpe, 10.7.1970 (PJB) and Wormley, 17.7.1971 (JLM). The north-west Surrey records were considered by Bretherton to be strays from the chalk downs, presumably of North Hampshire where it was established at the time. The more recent records may be primary migrants although it could be significant that all the records are from the west of the county.

Coenobia rufa (Haworth, 1809)   **Small Rufous**

Resident; wetland, damp heathland; local but locally fairly common.

Univoltine; mid-July to mid-August.

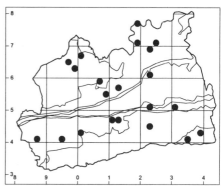

The Small Rufous is an inhabitant of wet areas and in Surrey occurs in the vicinity of water and on the wetter heaths. Such areas tend to be underworked and the moth is probably more widespread than the records suggest; certainly it can be locally quite common. It is far more restricted in the London area where it has been recorded as follows: Kew, 27.7.1990 (DCL); Wimbledon, 2.8.1994 (JVD); Richmond Park, 6.8.1994 (GAC); and Raynes Park, 31.7.1995 (MP).

Charanyca trigrammica (Hufnagel, 1766)   **Treble Lines**

Resident; commons, woodland, downland; widespread and common.

Univoltine; June.

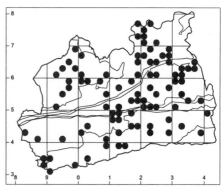

The Treble Lines is found in diverse habitats throughout the county, often very commonly as the following trap counts show: Bramley, 1985 (607), 86 (198) (RFB); Milford, 1992 (489), 93 (240) (DWB). The melanic form, ab. *bilinea* Haworth, has occurred at Woking (J.Pontin), Purley (PJS), Nutfield (PAC), Addington (BS), and South Croydon (GAC).

Hoplodrina alsines (Brahm, 1791)   **Uncertain**

Resident; commons, gardens; widespread and common.

Univoltine; late June to early August.

Foodplant – rotting leaves in a compost heap.

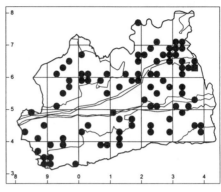

The separation of this species and the next is very subjective, relying as it does on subtle differences of ground colour and texture, and strictly speaking they should be placed in that group for which structural examination should be used. This has not been done, but it is clear that both species are widespread and common. Bretherton considered the numbers of each species at Bramley to be roughly equal, but at many other sites *alsines* would appear to be the commoner.

Hoplodrina blanda ([Denis & Schiffermüller], 1775)   **Rustic**

Resident; commons, gardens; widespread and common.

Univoltine; late June to early August.

The Rustic is a widespread species but probably less common than *alsines* (*q.v.*).

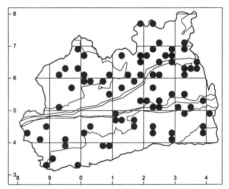

Hoplodrina ambigua ([Denis & Schiffermüller], 1775)   **Vine's Rustic**

Resident; commons, gardens; widespread and common.

Bivoltine; June and early July, and August and September.

Vine's Rustic is currently a widespread and very common species in much of Surrey, but is a relatively recent addition to the county's fauna. Apart from an example at Worcester Park in 1899, the moth was unknown in north-west Surrey prior to 1949 (Bretherton, 1957), and first recorded from the north-east of the county in 1951. The rapid spread has probably been as a result of natural spread and migration.

Spodoptera exigua (Hübner, 1808)   Small Mottled Willow

Migrant; scarce.

The Small Mottled Willow is a migrant species which appears in Surrey every few years and was particularly frequent in 1996. In the other years of the survey period it was probably less frequent than it was in the 1950s and 60s.

1976 – **Bramley**, 4.7 (RFB).

1979 – **Pirbright RES** (ED).

1980 – **Leigh**, 19.9 (RF); **Addiscombe**, 21.9 (KGWE).

1982 – **Bramley**, 11-20.7 (4), 9-19.9 (2) (RFB).

1985 – **Rushmoor**, 25.7 (2) (PAD); **South Croydon**, 25.7 (GAC); **Leigh**, 2.8, 11.10 (RF).

1988 – **Leigh**, 25-27.10 (2) (RF).

1994 – **Nutfield**, 5-26.8 (2) (PAC); **Tolworth**, 7.8 (JTS); **Buckland**, 12.11 (CH).

1995 – **Milford**, 31.7 (DWB); **Banstead**, 10.10 (SWG).

1996 – **Buckland**, 9.6, 3.7, 3-14.8 (3) (CH); **Carshalton**, 9-18.8 (2) (DC);   **Nutfield**, 9-15.8 (2) (PAC); **Milford**, 13-17.8 (6) (DWB); **Lingfield**, 24.8 (JC).

Caradrina morpheus (Hufnagel, 1766)   Mottled Rustic

Resident; commons, gardens; widespread and common.

Univoltine; mid-June to July.

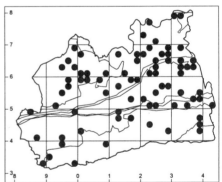

The Mottled Rustic is a common species right across the county, including well into the urban area. Trap counts include: Bramley, 1985 (103), 86 (57) (RFB); Ashtead, 1987 (69), 88 (35), 89 (33) (GG); Mitcham, 1981 (80), 82 (178), 83 (111) (RKAM); South Croydon, 1983 (36), 84 (73), 85 (47) (GAC). A second-brood example was taken at South Croydon, 1.10.1994 (GAC).

Caradrina clavipalpis (Scopoli, 1763)   Pale Mottled Willow

Resident; gardens, commons; widespread and common.

Probably **bivoltine**; May to October; peaks in July and September.

Foodplant – (wormwood).

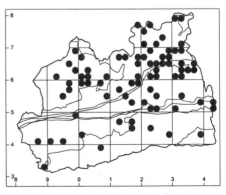

Although the Pale Mottled Willow has been found in most of Surrey, it is rather an uncommon species in rural areas; at Bramley it only occurred as follows: 1985 (3), 86 (6) (RFB). In contrast, in the gardens of south London it can be abundant: South Croydon,

1983 (556), 84 (435), 85 (317) (GAC); Mitcham, 1981 (204), 82 (315), 83 (486) (RKAM); Carshalton, at actinic trap, 1988 (740), 89 (1197), 90 (956) (DC).

Chilodes maritimus (Tauscher, 1806)   Silky Wainscot

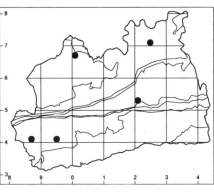

Notable/Nb
Status uncertain; possibly resident.
Mid-June to mid-August.
In view of the lack of recording done in the county's few reed beds, it is difficult to decide whether the handful of records received represent overlooked colonies or merely vagrants from outside the county. The Silky Wainscot is not mentioned in the *VCH*, and Bretherton (1957) considered it scarce even in the reed beds at Sheerwater. It was formerly known from Esher Common, but this site does not seem to have been worked recently.

RECORDS – **Rushmoor**, 29.7.82 (PAD); **Milford**, 29.7.80, 1.8.83 (DWB); **Thorpe**, 25.6.83 (PJB); **Dawcombe**, 27.7.91 (DC); **Wimbledon**, 19.8.76 (JVD).

[*Athetis pallustris* (Hübner, 1808)   Marsh Moth

Erroneous.
A record of this species, given as being local, is published in Oldaker (1951). The intended species was *Photedes minima* (Small Dotted Buff), and there is no evidence, or indeed likelihood, that the Marsh Moth has ever occurred in Surrey.]

Stilbia anomala (Haworth, 1812)   Anomalous

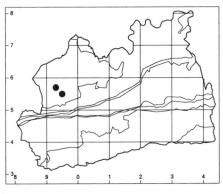

Status uncertain; probable resident.
According to Barrett (1899) the Anomalous was to be found on the heaths of Surrey and other southern counties, although the *VCH* published just a few years later mentions only that it had been reported from Croydon by Mr Sheldon (this presumably refers to Addington Hills). Until recently the only other Surrey record was of one taken at light at Wormley, 28.8.1961 (JLM), but in 1995 it was discovered independently at two sites, no great distance from each other, suggesting that an overlooked colony exists in that area. Further field work is needed on this species.

RECORDS – **Bisley Ranges**, 19.8.95 (MRH); **Pirbright**, 2.9.95 (GAC).

Elaphria venustula (Hübner, 1790)   Rosy Marbled

Notable/Nb

Resident; open woodland, commons, heathland; restricted but fairly common.

Univoltine; June to mid-July.

With the exception of Limpsfield Chart, which is possibly no longer suitable for this species, the Rosy Marbled is confined to central and western Surrey where it is a fairly common species – for example at Ashtead, 6.6-7.7.1992 (27) (DC). On account of its small size it is easily overlooked but, once the observer becomes familiar with it, it is readily recognizable.

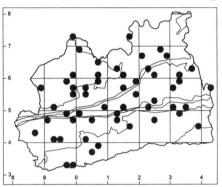

Panemeria tenebrata (Scopoli, 1763)   Small Yellow Underwing

Resident; grassland, road verges; widespread and fairly common.

Univoltine; mid-May to early June.

Perhaps because of its small size and habits, many lepidopterists consider this day-flying moth to be scarce, as indeed do several of the adjacent counties' local lists. It is in fact a very widespread and frequently rather common species, probably occurring in grassy areas throughout the county.

Pyrrhia umbra (Hufnagel, 1766)   Bordered Sallow

Resident; commons, downland; fairly widespread but scarce.

Univoltine; June and July.

Foodplant – restharrow, cross-leaved heath, *Pelargonium*.

The Bordered Sallow is fairly widespread in Surrey and as often recorded off the chalk as on it. It is, however, rather scarce, most records being of singletons and annual trap counts rarely exceeding two or three examples. In addition to restharrow, the larva has been noted on cross-leaved heath at Chobham

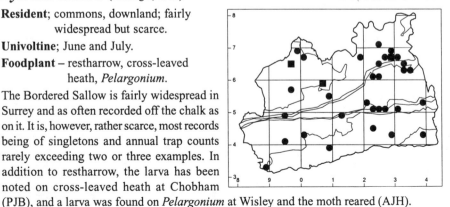

(PJB), and a larva was found on *Pelargonium* at Wisley and the moth reared (AJH).

Heliothis armigera (Hübner, 1803)   Scarce Bordered Straw

Migrant and importation; scarce.

The Scarce Bordered Straw is a more or less infrequent migrant which appears to be becoming more regular, having been recorded virtually every year of the present decade. It is highly likely that all records of the adult relate to primary migrants, although in the past larvae have also been imported with food produce.

1947 – **Streatham**, a larva on Italian tomatoes; **Tooting Bec Common**, 10.10 (Christie in Evans, 1973).

1950 – **New Haw** trap, 24.8 (Bretherton, 1957).

1951 – **Chiddingfold**, 6.9 (Mere, *Ent. Gaz.* **3**:179).

1961 – **Wormley**, 10.10 (JLM).

1967 – **Tattenham Corner**, 29.9 (Wallis in Evans, 1973).

1969 – **Bramley**, 3.8 (RFB); **Virginia Water**, 10.10 (CGMdeW).

1977 – **Addiscombe**, 22.10 (KGWE).

1978 – **Purley**, 13.10 (PMS).

1979 – **Addiscombe**, 1.12 (KGWE).

1980 – **Bramley**, 29.9 (RFB).

1988 – **Wimbledon**, 22.10 (JVD).

1990 – **Banstead**, 16.10 (SWG).

1991 – **Wisley RES**, 8.10 (AJH).

1992 – **South Croydon**, 28.9 (GAC).

1994 – **Lingfield**, 4.9 (JC).

1995 – **Lingfield**, 12.10 (JC); **Banstead**, 15.10 (SWG).

1996 – **Buckland**, 15.8, 5.9 (CH); **Banstead**, 17.8 (SWG); **South Croydon**, 24.10 (GAC).

Heliothis viriplaca (Hufnagel, 1766)   Marbled Clover

Vagrant; single record.

This species and the next were not recognized as separate taxa in Britain until 1938, and consequently earlier records of this species without vouchers must be disregarded (although the record in the *VCH* probably refers to *maritima*, as no doubt does that from Frensham, 27.7.1954 in Perrins (1959)). A single example of this species was recorded from the Horsell trap, 27.8.1952 (CGMdeW in Bretherton, 1957), possibly a vagrant from North Hampshire where it was apparently resident at that time.

Heliothis maritima (Graslin, 1855)   PLATE 11   **Shoulder-striped Clover**
ssp. *warneckei* Boursin, 1964

RDB3

Resident; damp heathland; very local and
   scarce.

Univoltine; late June and July.

Foodplant – cross-leaved heath.

The Shoulder-striped Clover is a species of
damp heathland where there is a good growth
of cross-leaved heath. During the survey
period it was found at only two sites, as adults
by day and larvae by night and by day.
Examples were taken at light traps at Thorpe,
8.7.1970 (PJB), and at Bramley, 13.7.1970

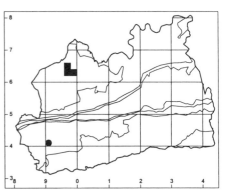

(RFB). Older records from Surrey are: Whitmoor Common, 16.7.1973 (DWB); Lucas Green,
11.7.1955 (RFB); Horsell Common, 11.7.1954 (JLM); Bagshot Heath, 14.7.1937 (Morley,
Proc. SLENHS **1938-9**:110), and Egham, 18.7.1933 (CGMdeW). Although the larvae
continue to be taken regularly at Chobham, I have been unable to find them at any other site
and further work is clearly required on this species.

RECORDS – **Thursley Common**, 27.6.82 (DWB); **Chobham Common**, 23.9.77 larvae
(RFB), 4.9.82 larvae (SHC), 9.7.83 (AJH), 8.9.84 larvae, 14.9.85 larvae (RFMcC),
13.7.85, 17.9.88 larvae, 19.9.91 larvae, 4.9.93 larvae (GAC).

Heliothis peltigera ([Denis & Schiffermüller], 1775)   PLATE 7   **Bordered Straw**
Migrant; scarce.

Foodplant – (marigold).

The Bordered Straw is a migrant species which is generally scarce in Surrey, although it
was recorded in many years of the survey period. 1996 was an exceptional year, as it was
for several other migrant species, with over 50 examples recorded from early June to the
end of September, suggesting that local breeding occurred.

1977 – **Leigh**, 2-4.3 (2) (RF).

1980 – **Wormley**, 5.6 (JLM); **Wisley RES**, 18.6 (AJH); **Nutfield**, 13.8 (PAC);
   Addiscombe, 18.9 (KGWE).

1982 – **Rushmoor**, 11.7 (PAD); **Mitcham**, 12-16.7 (RKAM); **Leigh**, 21.7 (RF);
   Buckland, 4.8 (CH); **Addiscombe**, 18.9 (KGWE).

1984 – **Oxted**, 3.7 (TD).

1986 – **Horley**, 30.6 (JBS); **Compton**, 6.7 (DWB); **Rushmoor**, 10.7 (PAD); **Wisley
   RES**, 29.8 (AJH).

1987 – **Horley**, 7.7 (JBS).

1988 – **North Cheam**, 21.9 (RFMcC).

1989 – **Thursley Common**, 20.8, feeding by day on heather (DWB).

1990 – **Wisley RES** (1) (AJH).

1991 – **Wotton**, 14.9 (JDH).
1992 – **Thorpe** (PJB); **Milford**, 4.6 (DWB); **Oxted**, 3.7 (TD); **Nutfield**, 2.8 (PAC); **North Cheam**, 5.8. (RFMcC).
1994 – **Wisley RES** (1) (AJH); **Oxted**, July (TD); **Buckland**, 2.7-7.8 (CH); **Wimbledon**, 7.8 (JVD); **Nutfield**, 22.8-4.9 (7) (PAC); **Milford**, 3.9 (DWB); **Camberwell**, 17.10 (GM).
1995 – **Buckland**, 30.7 (CH).
1996 – **Headley Warren**, 7.6 (GAC); **Banstead**, 8.6. (6), 11.6 (2), 13.6, 19.6, 10.8, 19.8, 21.8 (2), 2.9 (SWG); **Buckland**, 8-16.6 (3), 18-26.8 (2) (CH); **Leigh**, 8.6 (RF); **Oxted**, 8-9.6 (3) (TD); **Lingfield**, 8.6 (2) (JC); **South Croydon**, 9-17.6 (2), 2.9 (GAC); **Nutfield**, 9.6, 2.7, 13.8 (PAC); **Woking**, 10.6 (J. Pontin); **Tolworth**, 10-12.6 (4) (JTS); **Carshalton**, 11.6 (2), 9.8 (DC); **Ewhurst**, 11.6 (SFI); **Milford**, 12-14.6 (2) (DWB); **Wisley RES**, 14.6 (AJH); **Chessington**, 12.8-29.9 (3) (JP); **Wimbledon**, 16.8 (JVD); **Wotton**, 18.8 (JDH); **Thursley Common**, 31.8 (2) (GAC); **Rowhills**, 2.9 (JKH).

Protoschinia scutosa ([Denis & Schiffermüller], 1775)   Spotted Clover

Migrant; a single example only.

A specimen of this rare migrant was found sitting on heather bloom at Holmbury St. Mary on 24.8.1969 (Renshaw, *Ent. Rec.* **81**:335). The site is in south Surrey and not the north as indicated in the title of the note (*loc. cit.*).

Eublemma parva (Hübner, 1803)   Small Marbled

Migrant; rare, no recent record.

1953 – At least 40 individuals of this species were seen across southern England during 1953, including from Surrey: **Dunsfold**, 23.5 (Minnion, *Ent. Rec.* **65**:256); **Ottershaw** trap, 24.5 (Bretherton, 1957); **Chiddingfold**, 25.5 (Mere, *Proc. SLENHS* **1953-4**:37); **Dulwich**, 17.8 (Edwards, *Ent. Rec.* **65**:216).
1959 – **Wormley**, 20-24.7 (2) (JLM).
1968 – **Bramley**, 9.7 (RFB); **Reigate**, 10.7 (Rudland, *Ent.* **106**:262); **Leigh**, 10.7 (RF).

Protodeltote pygarga (Hufnagel, 1766)   Marbled White Spot

Resident; woodland, wooded commons; widespread and fairly common.

Univoltine; June and July.

The Marbled White Spot occurs in suitable habitat in much of the county, including well into London at such places as Wimbledon and Richmond Park. In the more built-up areas it is perhaps just a wanderer. Examples captured at Bookham Common on 28.9.1985 represent a partial second brood, a phenomenon more well-known on the continent (Heath, 1983).

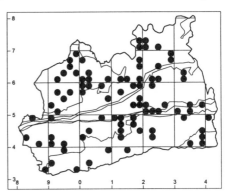

Deltote deceptoria (Scopoli, 1763)   **Pretty Marbled**

Migrant; two examples in the same period.

1952 – **Reigate**, June (Rudland in de Worms, *L.N.* **35**:14); **Leigh**, 13.6 (RF).

Deltote uncula (Clerck, 1759)   **Silver Hook**

Resident; damp heathland, acid grassland; very local and rare.

Univoltine; June to mid-July.

The Silver Hook is a species of wet habitats and in Surrey is associated with acidic areas. It would appear to have always been scarce and local and it is difficult to say whether its status has changed, although it still manages to exist in the London area, being taken recently at Richmond Park.

RECORDS – **Oaken Wood**, 30.6.95 (GAC); **Rushmoor**, 19.7.83, 4.7.85 (PAD); **Thursley Common**, 21.6.80 (GAC), 29.6.85 (DWB); **Milford**, 5.7.85, 13.7.94, 11.7.95 (DWB); **Bramley**, 27.6.76, 10.6.80 (RFB); **Pirbright RES**, 1979 (1) (ED); **Chobham Common**, 9.6.93 (RFMcC); **Woking**, 31.5.92 (SCP); **Wisley Common**, 26.6.86 (JP), 3.7.86 (AJH); **Richmond Park**, 5.7.95 (1) (MP); **Mitcham**, 3.8.81, 7.6.82 (RKAM); **South Croydon**, 20.6.84 (GAC).

Emmelia trabealis (Scopoli, 1763)   **Spotted Sulphur**

Migrant; not seen this century.

The Spotted Sulphur was resident in Britain in the Breck district of East Anglia where it became extinct around 1960. Odd specimens occurred in other areas, mostly last century, and their presence is considered to be due to migration. Surrey records are: Dulwich, a scorched specimen in a gas light in 1858 or 59 (Barrett, 1900); Wandsworth 1871 (Barrett, *loc. cit.*), given as "at light, July 26th" in South (1907) although this detail is not in Barrett as implied.

Earias clorana (Linnaeus, 1761) Cream-bordered Green Pea

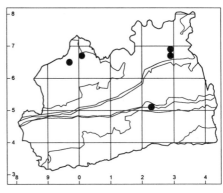

Notable/Nb
Resident; very local and rare.
Univoltine; June and early July.
Foodplant – (willow, osier).
The Cream-bordered Green Pea is a surprisingly local insect in Surrey, recorded recently from only three areas, a distribution very similar to that given in the *VCH* which lists "south London suburbs and parks, and swamps near Redhill". It is probably another declining relict marshland species although there is still plenty of potentially suitable habitat throughout the county from which it remains unrecorded.

RECORDS – **Chobham Common**, 9.6.93 (RFMcC); **Thorpe**, 1976 (1), 79 (1) (PJB); **Buckland**, 6.7.84 (CH); **Mitcham**, 5.7.83, 17-19.6.84 (2) (RKAM); **Mitcham Common**, 30.5.90, 31.5.91, 12.7.92 (DCL).

Bena bicolorana (Fuessly, 1775) =*prasinana* (Linnaeus, 1758) Scarce Silver-lines

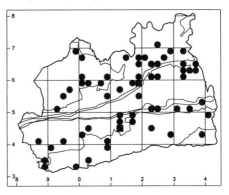

Resident; woodland; widespread and fairly common.
Univoltine; July.
Foodplant – oak, (Turkey oak, birch).
The Scarce Silver-lines is a rather widespread species, although certainly less common than the next species. It is nevertheless found in small numbers in well-wooded areas throughout the county.

Pseudoips prasinana (Linnaeus, 1758) =*fagana* (Fabricius, 1781) Green Silver-lines
ssp. *britannica* (Warren, 1913)

Resident; woodland, commons;
    widespread and common.
Univoltine; June and early July.
Foodplant – oak, birch, beech.

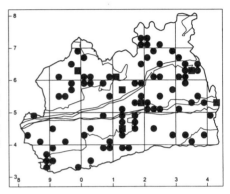

The Green Silver-lines is a common species
everywhere in Surrey, including the more
wooded parts of London. The larva, which
feeds on a variety of deciduous trees, is a
common sight when beating in the late
summer.

Nycteola revayana (Scopoli, 1772)   Oak Nycteoline

Resident; woodland, wooded commons;
    widespread and not uncommon.
Probably **bivoltine**; late March to October;
    peaks April and July.

Foodplant – oak.

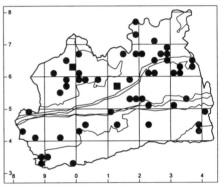

The Oak Nycteoline occurs widely
throughout the county, but is possibly to some
extent overlooked due to its resemblance to a
tortricid, especially in its unicolorous grey
form typical in the London area – f. *nigrescens*
Shelden. It is traditionally regarded as
univoltine in Britain, with the exception of
the Scilly Isles where it is bivoltine, but in recent years the peak emergence has been in
July, both in Surrey and several neighbouring counties, and the conclusion would seem to
be that it is becoming double brooded (Collins, 1993).

Colocasia coryli (Linnaeus, 1758)

Nut-tree Tussock

Resident; commons, woodland, heathland; widespread and fairly common.

Bivoltine; mid-April to mid-June, and mid-July to August.

Foodplant – birch, beech, (hazel).

The Nut-tree Tussock is a fairly common species found in a range of habitats across the county. The melanic f. *melanotica* Haverkampf, a regular form in some areas, has been recorded from Friday Street and Horsell, but is clearly just a rare aberration in Surrey.

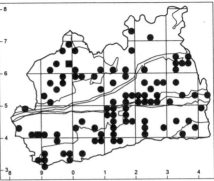

Chrysodeixis chalcites (Esper, 1789)

Golden Twin-spot

Migrant; a single record.

This species and the next have been subject to much confusion in the past, many older records of *acuta* being in fact *chalcites*, as are both illustrations in Skinner (1984). Both species have been taken more frequently in recent years, and there is one record of the Golden Twin-spot from Surrey.

1988 – **Bramley**, 10.11 (RFB).

Chrysodeixis acuta (Walker, 1858)

Tunbridge Wells Gem

Migrant; a single record.

The Tunbridge Wells Gem is a rare migrant species, subject to confusion with the previous one, and prior to the present decade hardly known from this country. There is one Surrey record, the specimen having been critically examined.

1955 – **Horsell**, 5.11 (de Worms, *Ent.* **89**:146).

Trichoplusia ni (Hübner, 1803)

Ni Moth

Migrant; rare.

19th century – **Norbiton**, May 1896 (Richards in Barrett, 1900).

1922 – **East Sheen**, 17.9 by Worsley Wood (*Ent.* **57**:68).

1953 – **Chiddingfold**, 12.8 (Mere, *Ent. Rec.* **65**:364).

1958 – **Dorking**, 10.8 (French, *Ent.* **92**:175); **Ranmore Common**, 23.8 (*loc. cit.*).

1959 – An example taken flying by day near **Dorking**, 10.8 (M.W. Harper, *Proc. SLENHS* **1959**:36) [same as previous?].

1962 – **Wormley**, 2.7 (JLM).

1992 – **South Croydon**, 19.7 (GAC).

1996 – **Buckland**, 3.8 (CH); **Woking**, 9.8 (SCP); **Addington**, 21.8 (BS).

Diachrysia orichalcea (Fabricius, 1775)   Slender Burnished Brass

Migrant; a single record.
1987 – **Addington**, 25.8 (BS); the first and only Surrey record.

Diachrysia chrysitis (Linnaeus, 1758)   Burnished Brass

Resident; commons, woodland, gardens;
widespread and common.

Bivoltine; June to early August, and mid-
August to September.

The Burnished Brass is a common species
throughout the county, occurring in a variety
of habitats and as frequent on the London
commons as in rural areas. The second brood,
occurring from mid-August to September, is
only partial, considerably smaller numbers
being involved than in the main brood.

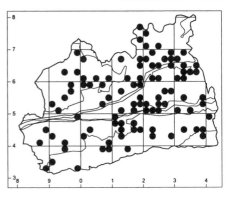

Macdunnoughia confusa (Stephens, 1850)   Dewick's Plusia

Migrant; two examples only.
1955 – **Chiddingfold**, 30.8 (Mere, *Ent. Rec.* **68**:25).
1992 – **Buckland**, 20.8 (CH).

Polychrysia moneta (Fabricius, 1787)   PLATE 15   Golden Plusia

Resident; gardens; fairly widespread and
fairly common.

Univoltine; June and July.

Foodplant – larkspur, monk's-hood,
(mugwort).

The foodplants of the Golden Plusia are
garden plants and the moth is more or less
restricted to this habitat, and consequently
most widespread and common in the south
London area. Very occasional examples of a
partial second brood are recorded, such as:
South Croydon, 8.9.1985, 8.9.1988 (GAC);

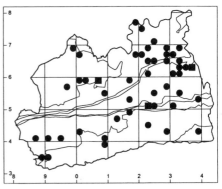

Mitcham, 29.8.1982 (RKAM). A melanic specimen, ab. *maculata* Lempke, was taken at
Hook Heath, Woking, 13.6.1968, and is illustrated (Batten, *Proc. BENHS* **2**:part 2).

Plusia festucae (Linnaeus, 1758)   PLATE 13   Gold Spot

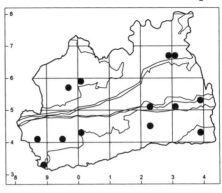

Resident; local and rare.
Bivoltine; June, and August.
Foodplant – (yellow iris).

The Gold Spot is currently a local and rare species which had apparently declined considerably during the start of the survey period but has, in the past few years, been recorded again more widely. The frequency of records from the south-west suggest that it is resident there, although no actual breeding site has been located. In the north-west it was once fairly regular (Bretherton, 1957 and 1965), but has only recently been recorded there again, and in the north-east it has only been seen once since 1977 but was apparently quite frequent in 1969-70 (Evans, 1973). It has also been recorded fairly widely in the south-east, again mainly in the last few years.

RECORDS – **Woking**, 9.81 (J.Pontin), 27.8.95, 30.8.96 (SCP); **Rushmoor**, 24.7.83 (PAD); **Haslemere**, 14.6.89 (EE); **Milford**, 3.8.82 (DWB); **Bramley**, 4.8.83, 9.6.89, 5.8.89 (RFB); **Leigh**, 8.10.96 (RF); **Buckland**, 2.8.94 (CH); **Nutfield**, 5.6.83 (PAC); **Oxted**, 6.8.94 (TD); **Lingfield**, 2.8.90, 27.7.95 (JC); **Beddington**, 5.8.94 (DC); **Mitcham**, 10.8.77 (PAM).

Autographa gamma (Linnaeus, 1758)   Silver Y

Migrant; regular and often abundant
Foodplant – (bramble, knapweed, wormwood).

The Silver Y is a regular migrant, seen every year, which can occur in large numbers. The last few years in particular have seen massive migrations – in open habitats adults taking wing at every few steps of the observer, and in Nork Park, 9.6.1996, over 2000 individuals were estimated to be present (SWG). Several examples of the melanic f. *nigricans* Spuler have been noted, but it is clearly a very rare aberration.

Autographa pulchrina (Haworth, 1809)   Beautiful Golden Y

Resident; commons, woodland, downland;
    widespread and common

Univoltine; late June and July.

The Beautiful Golden Y is a rather common species in much of the county, but shows a preference for more rural areas where it outnumbers *jota*. Trap counts show: Milford, 1992 (16) (DWB); Bramley, 1985 (35), 86 (42) (RFB); South Croydon, 1983 (11), 84 (4), 85 (3) (GAC); Selsdon, 1980 (16) (EHW).

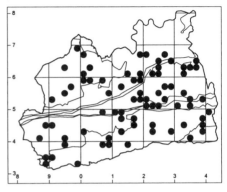

Autographa jota (Linnaeus, 1758)   Plain Golden Y

Resident; commons, woodland, downland;
    widespread and common.

Univoltine; July.

Foodplant – (knapweed).

Like the previous species, the Plain Golden Y is of frequent occurrence all over the county; it is however commoner than *pulchrina* in urban areas and is found further into London. Trap counts show: Milford, 1992 (3) (DWB); Bramley, 1985 (6), 86 (11) (RFB); South Croydon, 1983 (39), 84 (11), 85 (9) (GAC); Selsdon, 1980 (130) (EHW).

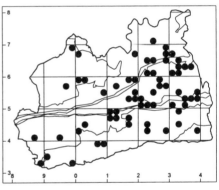

Syngrapha interrogationis (Linnaeus, 1758)   Scarce Silver Y

Migrant; very rare.

The Scarce Silver Y is a resident species in northern and western Britain, but occurs very occasionally in the south-east due to migration. These migrant examples are usually of a different form to native ones.

19th century – An early and rather unsatisfactory record is "occurring near **Reigate**" (Webb, *VCH*).

1955 – **Carshalton Beeches**, 13.8 (J.D. Collins in Evans, 1973).

1964 – **Bramley**, 15.8 (RFB).

1976 – **Bramley**, 10.8, one of a "central European" form (RFB).

Abrostola triplasia (Linnaeus, 1758) =*trigemina* (Werneburg, 1864) **Dark Spectacle**

Status uncertain; very local and rare.

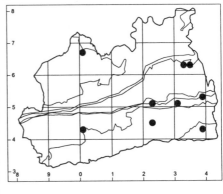

The exact status of the Dark Spectacle is difficult to determine, not least due to considerable confusion in the nomenclature; see Plant (1993) for a discussion of the synonymy, but note that the names have been switched again since! The records received for the survey period are too few and scattered to indicate whether it is a resident, at a very low density and possibly declining, or a migrant, and its past history cannot reliably be determined unless all records are checked against voucher specimens. There is a specimen from Sutton, 1905 (Meldola, Hope coll.) and a series of ten specimens taken at Weybridge between 1952 and 1958 in the Messenger collection. There are also six examples from Wimbledon, 1958-68 (coll. JVD).

RECORDS – **Thorpe**, 1977, 79, 80, 83, 85, 88, 91 (PJB); **Bramley**, 1977 (2) (RFB); **Buckland**, 22.6.93 (CH); **Leigh**, 1977 (1) (RF); **Nutfield**, 25.6.89, 5.7.91 (PAC); **Oxted**, 17.8.84 (TD); **Selsdon**, 1977, 79 (EHW); **South Croydon**, 8.8.96 (GAC); **Lingfield**, 3.6.92, 8.7.93 (JC).

Abrostola tripartita (Hufnagel, 1766) =*triplasia* (Linnaeus, 1758) **Spectacle**

Resident; commons, woodland, downland; widespread and common.

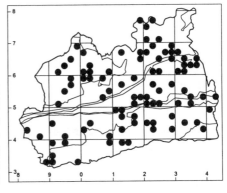

Bivoltine; May to mid-June, and July and August.

Foodplant – (common nettle).

The Spectacle is a frequently encountered moth in many habitats within the county, and is common at the static traps. The adults have been recorded from late April to mid-September, probably as two overlapping broods. The melanic ab. *plumbea* Cockayne has been recorded from Nutfield, 14.8.1995 (PAC).

Catocala fraxini (Linnaeus, 1758) **Clifden Nonpareil**

Migrant; rare.

The Clifden Nonpareil is a migrant species which became temporarily established in east Kent during the middle years of this century. There is nothing to suggest that the few Surrey records are other than primary migrants; indeed it was unrecorded from Surrey during the period of establishment. Only one example was noted during the survey period, attracted to a lighted window in central Croydon.

19th Century – **Richmond Park**, 1852 (Hawkins coll., de Worms, 1954-58). **Sutton**,
  1875 and 18.7.1887 (*Ent.* **20**:325).
1901 – **Norwood**, 10.9 (Swain, *Ent. Rec.* **13**:333).
1933 – **Reigate**, 19.9 (*Ent.* **66**:244).
1937 – **Walton-on-Thames**, 15.9 (*Ent.* **70**:249).
1941 – **Charterhouse, Godalming**, 12.8 (*Ent.* **75**:60).
1965 – **Reigate**, 22.9 (DAT).
1983 – **East Croydon**, 21.9 (Pearson per DCL).

Catocala nupta (Linnaeus, 1767)   Red Underwing

Resident; fairly widespread but uncommon.

Univoltine; mid-August to early October.

Foodplant – Lombardy poplar, willow, (hybrid black poplar, sallow).

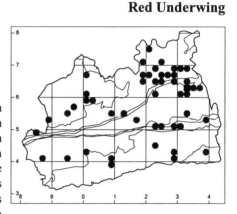

The Red Underwing is fairly widespread in Surrey but noticed mainly in the south London area where it is associated with poplars grown in parks and recreation grounds. Counts from light traps are rather low, but the adult is more attracted to sugar than light and the moth is probably more common than the records indicate. Ab. *brunnescens* Warren, in which the red of the hindwing is replaced by brown, was recorded from Mitcham, 27.8.1892 (Frohawk, *Ent.* **25**:243) and from Esher, August 1935 (*Ent.* **69**:48).

Catocala promissa ([Denis & Schiffermüller], 1775)   Light Crimson Underwing

Vagrant; two records this century.

The Light Crimson Underwing was recorded from Leatherhead, very rarely (Barrett, 1900), and more recently: Chiddingfold, 2.9.1954 (Mere, *Ent. Gaz.* **5**:231), and Wormley, 15.7.1964 (JLM). Although the woodlands of the south-west do provide suitable habitat, considerable search has failed to reveal any other examples and it is therefore likely to be only a vagrant in Surrey.

Catocala sponsa (Linnaeus, 1767)   Dark Crimson Underwing

Extinct; not recorded this century.

A specimen was recorded at sugar from Surrey on 22.8.1892 by Waldegrave (*Ent. Rec.* **3**:236), and although the site is not explicitly stated it may be inferred to be at Bookham Grange near Stoke D'Abernon. Barrett (1900) gives Richmond Park and Leatherhead (possibly referring to the 1892 record). The *VCH* mentions a specimen reported from Croydon in a footnote, possibly implying some doubt as to its accuracy.

Callistege mi (Clerck, 1759)   **Mother Shipton**

Resident; grassland, heathland; fairly
     widespread and fairly common.
Univoltine; mid-May to June.

Although found through much of the county,
the Mother Shipton is only at all regular on
dry soils such as the chalk and Bagshot sands.
Even here it is only fairly common, and
certainly less numerous than *glyphica*.

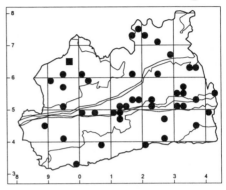

Euclidia glyphica (Linnaeus, 1758)   **Burnet Companion**

Resident; grassland; widespread and
     common.
Univoltine; mid-May to June.

The Burnet Companion occurs throughout
Surrey but favours the chalk where it can be
common.

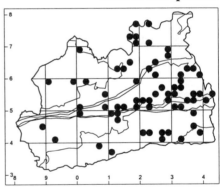

Tyta luctuosa ([Denis & Schiffermüller], 1775)   PLATE 1   **Four-spotted**

RDB3

Resident, possibly extinct; commons; very
     local and rare.

Late May to early August.

During the survey period the Four-spotted has
been recorded only from East Horsley and the
Croydon area; strangely the *VCH* of 1902 also
gives near Croydon and Horsley. No examples
have been seen for nearly ten years now and
it is quite possibly extinct. Between the two
wars a series was obtained from the downs at
Albury (C. Mackworth-Praed coll.). In the

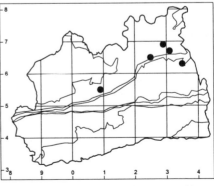

years after the second war it became relatively common, being recorded from: Brockham,
1947 (RF); Coulsdon, 22.5.1948 (ASW); Croham Hurst, 1948 (EHW); and Colley Hill,

13.5.1950 and 17.5.1953 (PAC); Westhumble 1951-53; Reigate Hill, 1953; Addington, 1953 (Evans, 1973). In north-west Surrey a few examples turned up at most of the static traps between 1952 and 1958 (Bretherton, 1957 and 1965), including Weybridge, 22.7.1952, 10.6.1953, 3.7.1957 and 15.7.1958 (JLM), and were attributed to strays from the chalk although they might well have been breeding more locally. After this period the species declined rapidly and in addition to the records below was noted only from Ranmore, 11.6.1965 (SFI), and Addiscombe, 13.7.1969 and 5.7.1971 (KGWE).

RECORDS – **East Horsley**, 4.7.76 (LJDW); **North Cheam**, 18.7.84 (RFMcC); **Mitcham**, 15.8.75, 1.8.77 (PAM), 31.5.83 (RKAM); **Selsdon**, 1.8.77 (EHW).

Lygephila pastinum (Treitschke, 1826)   Blackneck

Resident; commons, verges; widespread but uncommon.

Univoltine; July.

Foodplant – (vetch).

The Blackneck occurs throughout Surrey with no apparent preference of geology, but it is nowhere common, even the static traps recording no more than two or three examples a year. The adult is often put up by day, and the colourful larva can be swept at night.

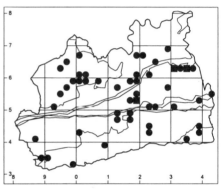

Scoliopteryx libatrix (Linnaeus, 1758)   Herald

Resident; wooded commons, woodland, heathland, widespread and fairly common.

Bivoltine; mid-July to mid-August, and October and after hibernation from April to mid-June.

Foodplant – sallow, aspen, (poplar, willow).

The Herald is a fairly common species found in most of Surrey; the apparent absence from some of the west is probably due to under-recording. There are probably two broods, the summer one larger, with larvae found in June and August. The adult has often been found hibernating in the old forts and pill-boxes of the North Downs (Morris and Collins, 1991).

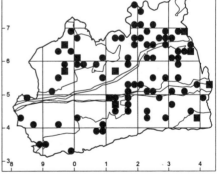

Phytometra viridaria (Clerck, 1759) — Small Purple-barred

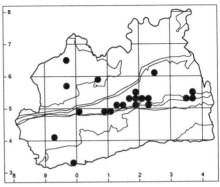

Resident; chalk grassland, heathland;
restricted and uncommon.

Univoltine; mid-May to July.

In Surrey the Small Purple-barred occurs in two distinct habitats: chalk grassland and heathland. Most records are of specimens flying during the day, but it has also been noted at light. On the chalk it is fairly widespread but never very common, and on the heaths it has been recorded from only three sites but is probably overlooked: Witley Common, 5.6.1983 (DWB); Chobham Common, 25.7.1989 (GAC), 28.6.92 (RFMcC); Wisley Common, 10.7.1982 (AJH). It was also recorded from heathy woodland at Oaken Wood, 20.7.1995 (GAC).

Colobochyla salicalis ([Denis & Schiffermüller], 1775) — Lesser Belle

Extinct; possibly temporary resident last century.

The Lesser Belle has only been resident at a single site in Kent during this century, and is probably now extinct there. Last century it was recorded from a number of localities including for Surrey: Dulwich, one on a gas lamp in 1858 (Barrett, 1900); and at Haslemere, where Barrett took several specimens from 1862 to 1866.

Laspeyria flexula ([Denis & Schiffermüller], 1775) — Beautiful Hook-tip

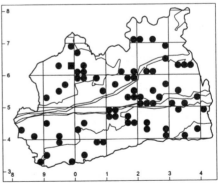

Resident; commons, woodland;
widespread and fairly common.

Univoltine; mid-June to July.

Foodplant – lichens on sloe, (lichens on yew and hawthorn).

The Beautiful Hook-tip is widely distributed in Surrey, and in rural wooded areas can be common: for example, Bramley, 1985 (40), 86 (57) (RFB). In other areas it is only fairly common but, despite its larva being a lichen feeder, occurs as far into London as Wimbledon and Richmond Park.

Rivula sericealis (Scopoli, 1763) — Straw Dot

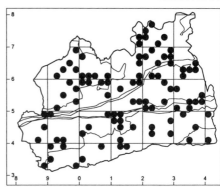

Resident; commons, widespread and fairly common.

Late May to early October; peaks in June and early August.

The Straw Dot is currently a very widespread and rather common species in Surrey. There is evidence of a massive population crash during the late 1970s, possibly as a result of the drought of 1976. At Bramley annual counts of some 200 individuals were recorded in the period immediately before the survey; from 1976 to 1978 the counts were in single figures and no moths were seen in 1979 and 1980, after which there was an equally rapid increase to 98 in 1986 (RFB). Similarly it was unrecorded at the RES trap at Haslemere between 1977 and 1981, and at the Wisley trap it was absent between 1978 and 1981 but by 1983 over 50 were recorded. The moth is on the wing between the end of May and the beginning of October, probably as two broods.

Parascotia fuliginaria (Linnaeus, 1761) — Waved Black

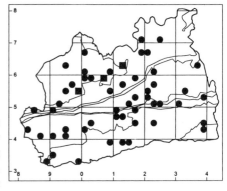

Notable/Nb

Resident; open woodland, heathland; fairly widespread and fairly common.

Univoltine; July and August.

Foodplant – (the fungus *Polystictus versicolor*).

During the last century the Waved Black was considered a very great rarity known mainly from the dockland area of London, including a specimen from Clapham in 1864 (Barrett, 1900), and Bermondsey, 1879 and larvae in 1884. In 1904 it was noted from Camberley and larvae were found there in 1931. By the 1950s it was quite widespread in north-west Surrey (Bretherton, 1957), and a few examples had been seen in the north-east by 1973 (Evans, 1973). The current situation is of a moth that is still extending its range to the east, where it is local, but is firmly established in the west where annual counts from many of the static traps show it to be not uncommon – up to a dozen individuals have been seen at such sites as Bramley, Milford, Windlesham, Wisley and Leigh.

Hypena crassalis (Fabricius, 1787) PLATE 6 **Beautiful Snout**

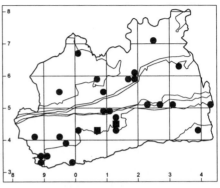

Resident; woodland; restricted but fairly
  common.
Univoltine; June and July.
Foodplant – bilberry.

The headquarters of the Beautiful Snout in
Surrey is the woodland of the greensand
where the bilberry understorey is abundant.
In these woods the moth and its larvae are
often common. Records of a few occurrences
in north-west Surrey suggest that it may be
resident at low density, although it was
unrecorded here during Bretherton's survey,
and at Ashtead Common, where it has been recorded in seven different years, there is no
bilberry nearby. Specimens at South Croydon in 1980 (GAC), and Wimbledon, 27.7.1985
(JVD), may have been wanderers from more distant colonies or, conceivably, primary
migrants. The moth is generally considered to be univoltine, but at Friday Street, 19.8 and
29.8.1993, worn adults were recorded at the same time as fully grown larvae (GAC/DC).

Hypena proboscidalis (Linnaeus, 1758) **Snout**

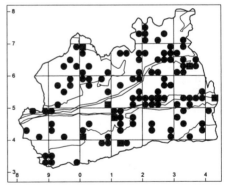

Resident; commons, woodland;
  widespread and common.
Bivoltine; July, and September and
  October.
Foodplant – common nettle.

The Snout is a common species throughout
Surrey, both as adults and as larvae. There
are two broods, the second being smaller, both
physically and numerically.

Hypena obesalis Treitschke, 1828 **Paignton Snout**

Migrant; a single example only.
1969 – **Chobham**, 14.9 (Woollatt, *Ent. Rec.* **81**:336). An example taken at light – at the
  time only the second British specimen. Other migrants occurred in Surrey on the
  same night.

Hypena rostralis (Linnaeus, 1758)　　　　　Buttoned Snout

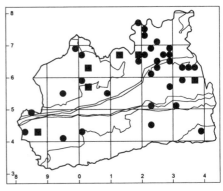

Resident; gardens, commons; restricted and scarce.

Univoltine; July and August, and after hibernation in May and June.

Foodplant – hop.

In Surrey the Buttoned Snout is mainly a species of the London suburbs where it is regularly noted although uncommon. Elsewhere occasional specimens are found but only sporadically. Possibly the adult is not strongly attracted to light and searching for larvae may be a better way of finding the species; they were found commonly in a garden in Surbiton in 1992 (JP). The adult hibernates and has been found in outbuildings such as sheds and air-raid shelters.

Schrankia taenialis (Hübner, 1809)　　　　　White-line Snout

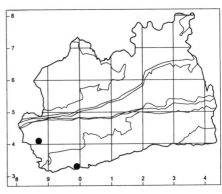

Notable/Nb

Resident; woodland, very local and rare.

Univoltine; mid-July to mid-August.

There are only two records of this elusive moth for the survey period. The *VCH* gives only Haslemere; in north-west Surrey there was an unconfirmed record in 1911 (Bretherton, 1957); and the record in Evans (1973) is highly suspect. However, the moth is very inconspicuous and probably better found at sugar than at light, so it might be expected to turn up in more localities if diligently searched for.

RECORDS – **Rushmoor**, 21.8.84 (PAD); **Tugley Wood**, 14.7.90 (GAC).

Schrankia costaestrigalis (Stephens, 1834)   **Pinion-streaked Snout**

Resident; commons, heathland; local and scarce.

June to mid-September; peak early July. The Pinion-streaked Snout, like the other smaller members of the subfamily, is undoubtedly under-recorded. It is however rather commoner than the previous species and prefers more open habitats, often acidic in nature. There are probably two broods, although the number of records is too small to be certain.

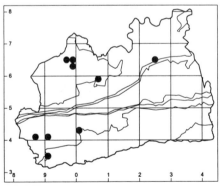

RECORDS – **Haslemere RES**, 1985 (1) (TGW); **Thundry Meadows**, 24.6.93 (3) (AMD); **Thursley Common**, 3-5.8.82 (RFB); **Milford**, 9.8.92 (DWB); **Bramley**, 1982 (5), 83 (4), 84 (3), 85 (2), 86 (8) (RFB); **Pirbright**, 14.7.96 (GAC); **Woking**, 2.7.95 (J. Pontin); **Chobham Common**, 2.7.83 (PJB), 7-28.7.95 (DC); **Thorpe**, 1986, 94 (PJB); **Wisley Common**, 15.7.85 (SCP); **Wotton**, 20.9.76 (JDH); **Buckland**, 4.9.91 (CH); **Nutfield**, 13.7.96 (PAC); **Leigh**, 1979, 83 (RF); **Chessington**, 30.6.96 (JP); **South Croydon**, 6.7.84, 26.6.96 (GAC); **Lingfield**, 25.8.92, 20.9.92, 20.9.93, 11.7.94 (JC).

Hypenodes humidalis Doubleday, 1850   **Marsh Oblique-barred**

Notable/Nb

Resident; heathland, commons; very local and scarce.

Univoltine; July and early August.

The Marsh Oblique-barred is principally a species of the wetter parts of heathland, and can occasionally be fairly common in such localities. The moths have a pre-dusk flight and come much later to light. The species has also been recorded from the marshy part of Ashtead Common, 19.7.1975 (5) (PAC), which site was possibly the origin of a specimen that was identified amongst a sample of microlepidoptera from North Cheam.

RECORDS – **Rushmoor**, 25.7.85 (PAD); **Haslemere RES**, 1983 (1) (TGW); **Thursley Common**, 1.7.82 (10+), 12.7.87 (DWB), 18.7.94 (MH); **Bramley**, 11.7.81 (RFB); **Chobham Common**, 25.7.82 (JP), 10.8.82 (RFB), 25.7.89 (GAC); **Gracious Pond**, 5.7.94 (AMD); **Wisley Common**, 20.7.86, 7.7.89 (SCP); **North Cheam**, 7.88 (RFMcC).

Pechipogo strigilata (Linnaeus, 1758)   **Common Fan-foot**

Notable/Na

Resident, very local and rare.

June.

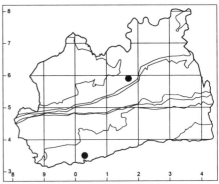

The Common Fan-foot is a species that has declined nationally in recent years and had not been recorded in Surrey for 20 years until examples were taken at two separate sites in 1996. The *VCH* implied that it was fairly generally distributed at the end of the last century, but by the middle of the present one Bretherton had only the following records from north-west Surrey: Ottershaw trap, 20.6 and 12.7.1947, 25.6.1952; not seen otherwise (Bretherton, 1957). The Messenger collection contains four examples taken at Chiddingfold, 27.5.1955. A specimen was reported from Ashtead Common, 14.7.1971 (LKE), one at Selsdon in 1972 (EHW), and another at Bramley, 14.6.1975 (RFB).

RECORDS – **Fir Tree Copse**, 9.6.96 one netted (AMD), 6.6.97 (GAC); **Ashtead Common**, 26.6.96 (K. Redshaw, *pers. com.*).

Herminia tarsipennalis (Treitschke, 1835)   **Fan-foot**

Resident; commons, woodland; widespread and common.

Univoltine; late June to early August.

Foodplant – juniper.

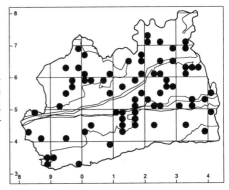

The Fan-foot is a frequently encountered species in suitable habitat throughout the county. The larvae feed on dead and withered leaves, and were beaten from dying juniper at Hackhurst Downs, 23.9.1994 (GAC).

Herminia grisealis ([Denis & Schiffermüller], 1775)   **Small Fan-foot**

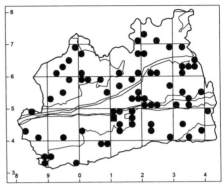

Resident; commons, woodland;
    widespread and fairly common.
Univoltine; June and July.
Foodplant – alder.
The Small Fan-foot is probably as widespread
as the previous species but generally rather
less common.

Macrochilo cribrumalis (Hübner, 1793)   **Dotted Fan-foot**

Extinct; not recorded this century.
According to the *VCH* the Dotted Fan-foot was reported by Mr Webb from Guildford,
Dorking, Nutfield, Gatton and marshes near Redhill. These localities would no doubt have
been suitable habitat at that time, although it is perhaps significant that Barrett (1900), who
was obviously acquainted with Sydney Webb, gives no records for Surrey in his work.

Paracolax tristalis (Fabricius, 1794)   PLATE 10   **Clay Fan-foot**

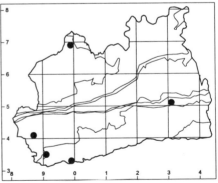

Notable/Na
Resident; woodland; very local and rare.
Univoltine; July.
The Clay Fan-foot is a very local and possibly
declining species in Surrey, only recorded
recently from a very few sites, mostly on the
extreme western boundary of the county. It is
not mentioned in the *VCH*, in Barrett (1900),
or in Bretherton (1957). Other records suggest
that it was once more regular in the east. Evans
(1973) gives: Givons Grove, 13.7.1964;
Caterham, 23.7.1967; and Nutfield, 1967, 69,
70; it has also been recorded from Staffhurst Wood, 20.7.1972 (LKE), and Foyle Riding,
27.7.1973 (PAM). In the south-west it was known from: Wormley, 21.7.1972, 11.7.1973
(JLM), and Bramley, 1973 (2) (RFB), and in mid-Surrey from Ranmore Common, 20.7.1956,
and Leith Hill, 15.7.1958 (RF).

RECORDS – **Rushmoor**, 23.7.84 (PAD); **Haslemere RES**, 1976 (2), 83 (4), 84 (2), 85
(1) (TGW); **Oaken Wood**, 30.6.95 (GAC); **Tugley Wood**, 19.7.95 (DY); **Virginia
Water**, 24.7.83 (AG); **Nutfield**, 16.7.94 (PAC).

APPENDIX 1 – Plant list

alder	*Alnus glutinosa*	Betulaceae
alder buckthorn	*Frangula alnus*	Rhamnaceae
apple	*Malus* spp.	Rosaceae
ash	*Fraxinus excelsior*	Oleaceae
aspen	*Populus tremula*	Salicaceae
barberry	*Berberis vulgaris*	Berberidaceae
bedstraw	*Galium* spp.	Rubiaceae
beech	*Fagus sylvatica*	Fagaceae
bilberry	*Vaccinium myrtillus*	Ericaceae
birch	*Betula* spp.	Betulaceae
bird cherry	*Prunus padus*	Rosaceae
bird's-foot trefoil	*Lotus corniculatus*	Fabaceae
black currant	*Ribes nigrum*	Grossulariaceae
bladder campion	*Silene vulgaris*	Caryophyllaceae
bogbean	*Menyanthes trifoliata*	Menyanthaceae
bracken	*Pteridium aquilinum*	Dennstaedtiaceae
bramble	*Rubus fruticosus* agg.	Rosaceae
broom	*Cytisus scoparius*	Fabaceae
buckthorn	*Rhamnus cathartica*	Rhamnaceae
buddleia	*Buddleja davidii*	Buddlejaceae
bulrush	*Typha latifolia*	Typhaceae
burdock	*Arctium* spp.	Asteraceae
burnet-saxifrage	*Pimpinella saxifraga*	Apiaceae
bur-reed	*Sparganium erectum*	Sparganiaceae
cabbage	*Brassica* spp.	Brassicaceae
cherry	*Prunus* spp.	Rosaceae
chickweed	*Stellaria media*	Caryophyllaceae
clover	*Trifolium* spp.	Fabaceae
cock's-foot	*Dactylis glomerata*	Poaceae
colt's-foot	*Tussilago farfara*	Asteraceae
common bent	*Agrostis capillaris*	Poaceae
common hemp-nettle	*Galeopsis tetrahit*	Lamiaceae
common mallow	*Malva sylvestris*	Malvaceae
common nettle	*Urtica dioica*	Urticaceae
common reed	*Phragmites australis*	Poaceae
common toadflax	*Linaria vulgaris*	Scrophulariaceae
crab apple	*Malus sylvestris*	Rosaceae
creeping soft-grass	*Holcus mollis*	Poaceae
creeping thistle	*Cirsium arvense*	Asteraceae
creeping willow	*Salix repens*	Salicaceae
cross-leaved heath	*Erica tetralix*	Ericaceae
currant	*Ribes* spp.	Grossulariaceae
dandelion	*Taraxacum officinale* agg.	Asteraceae
dark mullein	*Verbascum nigrum*	Scrophulariaceae
dock	*Rumex* spp.	Polygonaceae

dogwood	*Cornus sanguinea*	Cornaceae
Douglas fir	*Pseudotsuga menziesii*	Pinaceae
elder	*Sambucus nigra*	Caprifoliaceae
elm	*Ulmus* spp.	Ulmaceae
English elm	*Ulmus procera*	Ulmaceae
evergreen spindle	*Euonymus japonicus*	Celastraceae
fat hen	*Chenopodium album*	Chenopodiaceae
field bindweed	*Convolvulus arvensis*	Convolvulaceae
field maple	*Acer campestre*	Aceraceae
foxglove	*Digitalis purpurea*	Scrophulariaceae
garden privet	*Ligustrum ovalifolium*	Oleaceae
garlic mustard	*Alliaria petiolata*	Brassicaceae
golden-rod	*Solidago virgaurea*	Asteraceae
gooseberry	*Ribes uva-crispa*	Grossulariaceae
goosefoot	*Chenopodium* spp.	Chenopodiaceae
gorse	*Ulex europaeus*	Fabaceae
great mullein	*Verbascum thapsus*	Scrophulariaceae
great willowherb	*Epilobium hirsutum*	Onagraceae
greater burnet-saxifrage	*Pimpinella major*	Apiaceae
green field-speedwell	*Veronica agrestis*	Scrophulariaceae
grey sallow	*Salix cinerea*	Salicaceae
groundsel	*Senecio vulgaris*	Asteraceae
ground-elder	*Aegopodium podagraria*	Apiaceae
ground-ivy	*Glechoma hederacea*	Lamiaceae
hawthorn	*Crataegus monogyna*	Rosaceae
hazel	*Corylus avellana*	Betulaceae
heather	*Calluna vulgaris*	Ericaceae
hedge bedstraw	*Galium mollugo*	Rubiaceae
hoary ragwort	*Senecio erucifolius*	Asteraceae
hoary willowherb	*Epilobium parviflorum*	Onagraceae
hogweed	*Heracleum sphondylium*	Apiaceae
hollyhock	*Alcea rosea*	Malvaceae
honeysuckle	*Lonicera periclymenum*	Caprifoliaceae
hop	*Humulus lupulus*	Cannabinaceae
horse-chestnut	*Aesculus hippocastanum*	Hippocastanaceae
hybrid black poplar	*Populus* x *canadensis*	Salicaceae
ivy	*Hedera helix*	Araliaceae
jasmine	*Jasminum* spp.	Oleaceae
juniper	*Juniperus communis*	Cupressaceae
knapweed	*Centaurea* spp.	Asteraceae
knotgrass	*Polygonum* spp.	Polygonaceae
laburnum	*Laburnum anagyroides*	Fabaceae
lady's bedstraw	*Galium verum*	Rubiaceae
larch	*Larix decidua*	Pinaceae
large bird's-foot trefoil	*Lotus pedunculatus*	Fabaceae

larkspur	*Consolida* spp.	Ranunculaceae
Lawson's cypress	*Chamaecyparis lawsoniana*	Cupressaceae
Leyland cypress	x *Cupressocyparis leylandii*	Cupressaceae
lilac	*Syringa vulgaris*	Oleaceae
lime	*Tilia* x *vulgaris*	Tiliaceae
lodgepole pine	*Pinus contorta*	Pinaceae
Lombardy poplar	*Populus nigra 'Italica'*	Salicaceae
London plane	*Platanus* x *hispanica*	Platanaceae
marjoram	*Origanum vulgare*	Lamiaceae
marsh bedstraw	*Galium palustre*	Rubiaceae
marsh cinquefoil	*Potentilla palustris*	Rosaceae
marsh ragwort	*Senecio aquaticus*	Asteraceae
marsh thistle	*Cirsium palustre*	Asteraceae
meadow vetchling	*Lathyrus pratensis*	Fabaceae
meadowsweet	*Filipendula ulmaria*	Rosaceae
meadow-grass	*Poa* spp.	Poaceae
Michaelmas daisy	*Aster* spp.	Asteraceae
monk's-hood	*Aconitum napellus*	Ranunculaceae
mugwort	*Artemisia vulgaris*	Asteraceae
nasturtium	*Tropaeolum majus*	Tropaeolaceae
nettle-leaved bellflower	*Campanula trachelium*	Campanulaceae
Norway maple	*Acer platanoides*	Aceraceae
Norway spruce	*Picea abies*	Pinaceae
oak	*Quercus* spp.	Fagaceae
orache	*Atriplex* spp.	Chenopodiaceae
orange balsam	*Impatiens capensis*	Balsaminaceae
Oregon grape	*Mahonia aquifolium*	Berberidaceae
osier	*Salix viminalis*	Salicaceae
Oxford ragwort	*Senecio squalidus*	Asteraceae
pear	*Pyrus communis*	Rosaceae
perforate St. John's-wort	*Hypericum perforatum*	Clusiaceae
petty whin	*Genista anglica*	Fabaceae
plum	*Prunus domestica*	Rosaceae
poplar	*Populus* spp.	Salicaceae
potato	*Solanum tuberosum*	Solanaceae
primrose	*Primula vulgaris*	Primulaceae
privet	*Ligustrum* spp.	Oleaceae
ragwort	*Senecio* spp.	Asteraceae
red bartsia	*Odontites vernus*	Scrophulariaceae
red campion	*Silene dioica*	Caryophyllaceae
red currant	*Ribes rubrum*	Grossulariaceae
reed canary-grass	*Phalaris arundinacea*	Poaceae
restharrow	*Ononis* spp.	Fabaceae
rhododendron	*Rhododendron ponticum*	Ericaceae
rose	*Rosa* spp.	Rosaceae

rosebay willowherb	*Chamerion angustifolium*	Onagraceae
rowan	*Sorbus aucuparia*	Rosaceae
sallow	*Salix* spp.	Salicaceae
scentless mayweed	*Tripleurospermum inodorum*	Asteraceae
Scots pine	*Pinus sylvestris*	Pinaceae
sea campion	*Silene uniflora*	Caryophyllaceae
service-tree	*Sorbus domestica*	Rosaceae
silver birch	*Betula pendula*	Betulaceae
sloe	*Prunus spinosa*	Rosaceae
small balsam	*Impatiens parviflora*	Balsaminaceae
small scabious	*Scabiosa columbaria*	Dipsacaceae
soft rush	*Juncus effusus*	Juncaceae
sow-thistle	*Sonchus* spp.	Asteraceae
spindle	*Euonymus europaeus*	Celastraceae
sweet chestnut	*Castanea sativa*	Fagaceae
sweet William	*Dianthus barbatus*	Caryophyllaceae
sycamore	*Acer pseudoplatanus*	Aceraceae
timothy	*Phleum pratense*	Poaceae
tomato	*Lycopersicon esculentum*	Solanaceae
traveller's joy	*Clematis vitalba*	Ranunculaceae
tufted hair-grass	*Deschampsia cespitosa*	Poaceae
Turkey oak	*Quercus cerris*	Fagaceae
valerian	*Valeriana officinalis*	Valerianaceae
violet	*Viola* spp.	Violaceae
water-pepper	*Persicaria hydropiper*	Polygonaceae
water figwort	*Scrophularia auriculata*	Scrophulariaceae
wayfaring-tree	*Viburnum lantana*	Caprifoliaceae
western hemlock	*Tsuga heterophylla*	Pinaceae
white campion	*Silene latifolia*	Caryophyllaceae
white dead-nettle	*Lamium album*	Lamiaceae
white mullein	*Verbascum lychnitis*	Scrophulariaceae
white poplar	*Populus alba*	Salicaceae
wild angelica	*Angelica sylvestris*	Apiaceae
wild parsnip	*Pastinaca sativa*	Apiaceae
wild privet	*Ligustrum vulgare*	Oleaceae
willow	*Salix* spp.	Salicaceae
wormwood	*Artemisia absinthium*	Asteraceae
wych elm	*Ulmus glabra*	Ulmaceae
yarrow	*Achillea millefolium*	Asteraceae
yellow iris	*Iris pseudacorus*	Iridaceae
yellow loosestrife	*Lysimachia vulgaris*	Primulaceae
yellow rattle	*Rhinanthus* spp.	Scrophulariaceae
yew	*Taxus baccata*	Taxaceae

APPENDIX 2 – Gazetteer of sites

Abinger	TQ1146	
Abinger Forest	TQ1546	
Addington	TQ3663	
Addiscombe	TQ3366	
Addlestone	TQ0464	
Albury Bottom,		
Chobham Common	SU9764	
Alderstead Heath, Chaldon	TQ3055	
Ash Vale/Ranges	SU8953	Army firing range
Ashtead	TQ1758	
Ashtead Common	TQ1759	Corporation of London
Bagshot	SU9163	
Banstead	TQ2360	
Banstead Downs	TQ2560	
Barn Elms	TQ2277	
Barnes	TQ2277	
Barnsthorns Wood, Effingham	TQ0955	
Bay Pond, Godstone	TQ3551	Surrey Wildlife Trust
Beddington Park	TQ2965	
Betchworth	TQ2051	
Bisley	SU9559	
Blackheath, Chilworth	TQ0345	
Blindley Heath	TQ3645	
Bonsey's Bridge, Horsell	TQ0061	
Bookham Common, Leatherhead	TQ1256	National Trust
Borough Farm, Milford	SU9241	
Botany Bay, Chiddingfold	SU9834	Forest Enterprise
Boundstone	SU8343	
Box Hill, Dorking	TQ1751	National Trust
Boxhurst, Dorking	TQ1851	National Trust
Bramley	TQ0143	
Bransland Wood, Bletchingley	TQ3248	National Trust
Brockham	TQ1950	
Brookwood	SU9457	
Buckland	TQ2250	
Buckland Hills	TQ2252	
Burford Bridge, Box Hill	TQ1751	
Burstow	TQ3240	
Bushbury, Brockham	TQ1947	
Butts Wood, Chobham Common	SU9863	
Byfleet	TQ0661	

Camberley	SU8860	
Camberwell	TQ3377	
Canfold Wood, Cranleigh	TQ0839	
Canterbury Copse, Chiddingfold	SU9934	Forest Enterprise
Carshalton	TQ2865	
Caterham	TQ3355	
Charterhouse, Godalming	SU9645	
Cheam	TQ2463	
Chertsey	TQ0466	
Chertsey Meads	TQ0566	
Chessington	TQ1864	
Chiddingfold	SU9635	
Chipstead Valley	TQ2657	
Chobham Common	SU9764	National Nature Reserve
Clapham	TQ2975	
Clasford Common, Guildford	SU9452	
Claygate	TQ1663	
Cobbett Hill, Pirbright	SU9453	
Cobham	TQ1060	
Cockshot Wood, Dorking	TQ1853	National Trust
Colley Hill, Reigate	TQ2452	National Trust
Compton	SU9548	
Coombe Wood, Kingston	TQ2070	
Coulsdon	TQ3059	
Coulsdon Common	TQ3257	Corporation of London
Cranleigh	TQ0638	
Croham Hurst, South Croydon	TQ3363	
Croydon	TQ3365	
Culvers Island, Carshalton	TQ2766	
Cutt Mill, Elstead	SU9145	
Dale Park, Carshalton	TQ2765	
Dawcombe, Betchworth	TQ2152	Surrey Wildlife Trust
Devil's Jumps, Churt	SU8639	National Trust
Dormansland	TQ4041	
Dorking	TQ1649	
Dulwich	TQ3372	
Dulwich Upper Wood	TQ3371	
Dunsfold	TQ0036	
Durfold Wood, Chiddingfold	SU9832	
Earlswood	TQ2748	
East Horsley	TQ0954	

East Sheen	TQ2075	
Edolphs Copse, Charlwood	TQ2342	Woodland Trust
Effingham	TQ1055	
Effingham Park, Copthorne	TQ3339	
Egham	TQ0071	
Egham Wick	SU9869	
Elstead	SU9044	
Enton	SU9540	
Epsom	TQ2060	
Epsom Downs	TQ2158	
Esher Common	TQ1262	
Ewell	TQ2162	
Ewhurst	TQ0940	
Farnham	SU8446	
Farthing Downs, Coulsdon	TQ3057	Corporation of London
Featherbed Lane, Addington	TQ3762	
Fetcham Downs, Leatherhead	TQ1554	
Field Common, Molesey	TQ1367	
Fir Tree Copse, Dunsfold	TQ0235	Surrey Wildlife Trust
Fisherlane Wood, Chiddingfold	SU9832	Forest Enterprise
Foyle Riding, Limpsfield	TQ4149	
Frensham Common	SU8540	National Trust
Friday Street, Dorking	TQ1245	
Frimley	SU8958	
Frith Hill, Frimley	SU9058	
Gatton	TQ2753	
Givons Grove, Leatherhead	TQ1754	
Godalming	SU9743	
Godstone	TQ3551	
Gomshall	TQ0848	
Gracious Pond, Chobham	SU9863	Surrey Wildlife Trust
Grayswood	SU9134	
Guildford	SU9949	
Hackbridge	TQ2866	
Hackhurst Downs, Gomshall	TQ0948	National Trust
Ham Common	TQ1871	
Hambledon	SU9638	
Hankley Common, Tilford	SU8841	
Haslemere	SU9033	
Haslemere RES	SU9034	

Hawks Hill, Leatherhead	TQ1555	
Headley Heath	TQ1953	National Trust
Headley Lane	TQ1853	
Headley Warren	TQ1853	
Hedgecourt, Felbridge	TQ3540	Surrey Wildlife Trust
Hindhead Common	SU8936	National Trust
Hog's Back	SU9248	
Holmbury St. Mary	TQ1044	
Holmwood Common, Dorking	TQ1746	National Trust
Hook Heath, Woking	SU9857	
Hooley	TQ2856	
Horley	TQ2942	
Horsell [Common]	TQ0060	
Horsell Birch	SU9859	
Hydon Heath, Hambledon	SU9739	National Trust
Juniper Bottom, Box Hill	TQ1752	National Trust
Juniper Hall	TQ1752	
Juniper Hill, Reigate	TQ2352	
Kenley Common	TQ3358	Corporation of London
Kew Gardens	TQ1876	
Kingston	TQ1870	
Knaphill	SU9658	
Lambeth	TQ3178	
Leatherhead	TQ1756	
Leigh	TQ2345	
Leith Hill, Dorking	TQ1343	National Trust
Leith Hill Wood, Dorking	TQ1242	National Trust
Lightwater	SU9262	
Limpsfield Chart	TQ4352	
Lingfield	TQ3842	
Longcross, Chobham Common	SU9865	
Lucas Green	SU9360	
Mare Hill Common, Milford	SU9340	
Mayford	SU9956	
Merrow Downs	TQ0249	
Merton	TQ2569	
Mickleham [Downs]	TQ1753	[National Trust]
Milford	SU9441	
Mitcham Common	TQ2868	

Morden Hall Park	TQ2668	National Trust
Motspur Park	TQ2267	
Mugswell	TQ2554	
Netley Heath, Gomshall	TQ0849	
New Haw	TQ0563	
Newdigate	TQ2044	
Newlands Corner	TQ0449	
Norbiton	TQ1968	
Norbury	TQ3169	
Norbury Park, Leatherhead	TQ1653	
Normandy	SU9251	
North Cheam	TQ2465	
North Holmwood	TQ1747	
Nower Wood, Leatherhead	TQ1954	Surrey Wildlife Trust
Nutfield	TQ3050	
Oaken Wood, Chiddingfold	SU9933	Forest Enterprise/Butterfly Conservation
Ottershaw	TQ0263	
Oxshott Heath	TQ1461	
Oxted	TQ3852	
Oxted Downs	TQ3854	National Trust
Pewley Down, Guildford	TQ0148	
Pilgrim Fort, Caterham	TQ3453	
Pirbright	SU9555	
Pirbright Common	SU9254	Army firing range
Pirbright RES	SU9554	
Prince's Coverts, Oxshott	TQ1561	
Purley	TQ3161	
Putney	TQ2375	
Pyrford	TQ0259	
Quarry Hangers, Caterham	TQ3153	
Ranmore	TQ1450	
Raynes Park	TQ2369	
Redhill	TQ2850	
Redlands Wood, Dorking	TQ1545	
Redstone Wood, Redhill	TQ2850	
Reigate [Hill]	TQ2551	
Richmond Park	TQ1972	

Riddlesdown, Purley	TQ3260	Corporation of London
Riddlesdown Quarry, Purley	TQ3359	
Ripley	TQ0556	
Rosehill Park, Sutton	TQ2566	
Roundshaw, Wallington	TQ3063	
Roundshaw Park, Wallington	TQ2963	
Rowhills, Farnham	SU8549	
Run Common, Cranleigh	TQ0341	
Rushmoor	SU8740	
Salfords	TQ2846	
Sanderstead	TQ3361	
Selhurst	TQ3267	
Selsdon	TQ3562	
Send	TQ0356	
Shalford	SU9947	
Sheepleas, East Horsley	TQ0851	
Sheerwater	TQ0260	
Shirley	TQ3665	
Sidney Wood, Dunsfold	TQ0234	Forest Enterprise
Silent Pool, Shere	TQ0648	
Somersbury Wood, Ewhurst	TQ1037	
South Croydon	TQ3363	
South Hawke, Oxted	TQ3753	National Trust
South Norwood	TQ3368	
St. George's Hill, Weybridge	TQ0762	
St. Martha's Hill, Chilworth	TQ0248	
Staffhurst Wood, Limpsfield	TQ4148	
Stoke D'Abernon	TQ1359	
Streatham	TQ3071	
Stringers Common, Guildford	SU9952	
Stroude	TQ0068	
Surbiton	TQ1867	
Sutton	TQ2564	
Sydenham	TQ3472	
Tadworth	TQ2256	
Tandridge Hill, Oxted	TQ3753	
Tattenham Corner	TQ2258	
Thornton Heath	TQ3267	
Thorpe	TQ0067	
Threehalfpenny Wood, Addington	TQ3764	

Thundry Meadows, Elstead	SU8943	Surrey Wildlife Trust
Thursley Common	SU9040	National Nature Reserve
Tilford	SU8743	
Tolworth	TQ2066	
Tooting	TQ2772	
Tugley Wood, Chiddingfold	SU9833	Forest Enterprise
Virginia Water	SU9969	
Vann Lake, Ockley	TQ1539	Surrey Wildlife Trust
Wallington	TQ2964	
Wallis Wood	TQ1238	Surrey Wildlife Trust
Walton Downs, Epsom	TQ2257	
Walton-on-Thames	TQ1066	
Wanborough Wood	SU9149	
Wandsworth	TQ2873	
Warlingham	TQ3558	
West End (Esher)	TQ1263	
West Norwood	TQ3271	
Westcott Downs, Dorking	TQ1349	National Trust
Westhumble, Dorking	TQ1651	
Weybridge	TQ0764	
White Downs, Gomshall	TQ1148	National Trust
White Hill, Caterham	TQ3253	
Whitmoor Common, Guildford	SU9853	
Whyteleafe	TQ3358	
Wilderness Island, Carshalton	TQ2865	
Wimbledon	TQ2271	
Windlesham RES	SU9463	
Winterfold, Cranleigh	TQ0743	
Wire Mill, Felbridge	TQ3641	
Wisley Common/RES	TQ0658	
Witley Common	SU9240	National Trust
Woking	TQ0159	
Woldingham	TQ3756	
Woodham	TQ0362	
Worcester Park	TQ2265	
Wormley	SU9538	
Worms Heath, Warlingham	TQ3757	
Worplesdon	SU9753	
Wotton	TQ1346	
Wyke Common, Aldershot	SU9152	Army firing range

APPENDIX 3 – Rothamsted Experimental Station traps in Surrey

SU9034	**Haslemere**	Mr T. G. Winter	1976-96
SU9554	**Pirbright**	Mr E. Dennison	1976-82
SU9463	**Windlesham**	Mr J. A. Bailey	1976-81
TQ0658	**Wisley** (Royal Horticultural Society)	Dr A. J. Halstead	1976-96

APPENDIX 4 – Organisations

Study societies

British Entomological and Natural History Society
Dinton Pastures Country Park, Davis Street, Hurst,
Reading, Berks RG10 0TH.

Amateur Entomologists' Society
P.O. Box 8774, London SW7 5ZG.

Croydon Natural History and Scientific Society
96a Brighton Road, South Croydon, Surrey CR2 6AD.

Conservation bodies

Butterfly Conservation
Surrey branch – S. Jeffcoate, 5 Elmhurst Drive, Dorking,
Surrey RH4 2BA.
Head office – P.O. Box 222, Dedham, Colchester, Essex, CO7 6EY.

Surrey Wildlife Trust
School Lane, Pirbright, Surrey GU24 0JN.

APPENDIX 5 – References

Allan, P.B.M., 1943.
Talking of moths. Newtown.

Ansorge, E., 1969.
The macrolepidoptera of Buckinghamshire. Bucks
Archaeological Society, Aylesbury.

Baker, B.R., 1994.
The butterflies and moths of Berkshire. Hedera Press,
Uffington.

Baker, P.J., 1986.
Changes in the status of the lepidoptera of a north-west Surrey
locality. *Proc. Trans. Br. ent. nat. Hist. Soc.* **19**:33-42.

Barrett, C.G., 1895.
The Lepidoptera of the British Islands, vol. II. Reeve, London.

Barrett, C.G., 1896.
The Lepidoptera of the British Islands, vol. III. Reeve, London.

Barrett, C.G., 1897.
The Lepidoptera of the British Islands, vol. IV. Reeve, London.

Barrett, C.G., 1899.
The Lepidoptera of the British Islands, vol. V. Reeve, London.

Barrett, C.G., 1900.
The Lepidoptera of the British Islands, vol. VI. Reeve, London.

Barrett, C.G., 1901.
The Lepidoptera of the British Islands, vol. VII. Reeve,
London.

Barrett, C.G., 1902.
The Lepidoptera of the British Islands, vol. VIII. Reeve,
London.

Barrett, C.G., 1904.
The Lepidoptera of the British Islands, vol. IX. Reeve, London.

Bretherton, R.F., 1957.
A list of the macrolepidoptera and Pyralidina of north-west
Surrey. *Proc. S. Lond. ent. nat. Hist. Soc.* **1955**:94-151.

Bretherton, R.F., 1965.
Additions to the list of macrolepidoptera and Pyralidina of
north-west Surrey. *Proc. S. Lond. ent. nat. Hist. Soc.* **1965**:18-30.

Bretherton, R.F., 1983.
Calotephria salicata Hbn.: Striped Twin-spot Carpet again in
Surrey. *Entomologist's Rec. J. Var.* **95**:211.

Buckell and Prout, 1898-1901.
The fauna of the London district: Lepidoptera. *Trans. City of London Entomological and Natural History Society.* **8**:51-63; **9**:66-80; **10**:62-74.

Chalmers-Hunt, J.M., 1962-67.
The butterflies and moths of Kent, **2**. Arbroath and London.

Chalmers-Hunt, J.M., 1968-81.
The butterflies and moths of Kent, **3**. Arbroath and London.

Collins, G.A., 1987.
Capture of the imago of *Synanthedon andrenaeformis* (Laspeyres): Orange-tailed Clearwing. *Entomologist's Rec. J. Var.* **99**:40.

Collins, G.A., 1993.
Further observations on the voltinism of the Oak Nycteoline, *Nycteola revayana* Scop.(Lep.: Noctuidae). *Entomologist's Rec. J. Var.* **105**:117-8.

Collins, G.A., 1995.
Butterflies of Surrey. Surrey Wildlife Trust, Pirbright.

Costen, P.D.M., and Peet, T.N.D., 1986.
Thera cupressata Geyer: A species of geometrid moth new to the Channel Islands. *Entomologist's Rec. J. Var.* **98**:217.

Dandy, J.E., 1969.
Watsonian vice-counties of Great Britain. Ray Society, London.

de Worms, C.G.M., 1954-58.
The moths of London and its surroundings. *Lond. Nat.* **33**:101-146; **34**:66-107; **35**:33-76; **36**:59-99; **37**:136-178.

de Worms, C. G. M., 1979.
A striking form of *Drymonia dodonaea* D. & S. *Entomologist's Rec. J. Var.* **91**:260.

Dickson, R., 1976.
A Lepidopterist's handbook. Amateur Entomologist's Society.

Dyer, J.L., 1993.
Noctua janthina ([Denis & Schiffermüller]) confused with *Noctua janthe* (Borkhausen, 1792). *Entomologist's Rec. J. Var.* **105**:171.

Emmet, A.M., ed., 1991.
The moths and butterflies of Great Britain and Ireland 7:2.
Harley Books, Essex.

Evans, L.K., and Evans, K.G.W., 1973.
A survey of the macrolepidoptera of Croydon and north-east
Surrey. *Proc. Croydon Nat. Hist. Sci. Soc.* **XIV**:273-408.

Goater, B., 1974.
The butterflies and moths of Hampshire and the Isle of Wight.
Classey, Faringdon.

Goater, B., 1992.
*The butterflies and moths of Hampshire and the Isle of Wight:
additions and corrections.* Joint Nature Conservation
Committee.

Goss, H., 1902.
Butterflies and moths. *A history of the County of Surrey,* 3
Zoology. Constable, London.

Heath, J., ed. 1983.
The moths and butterflies of Great Britain and Ireland, 10.
Harley Books, Essex.

Jordan, M.J.R., 1986.
The genitalia of the species pair *Mesapamea secalis* (L.) and
Mesapamea secalella Remm, (Lep.:Noctuidae).
Entomologist's Rec. J. Var. **98**:41.

Kettlewell, B., 1973.
The evolution of melanism. Clarendon Press, Oxford.

Lindley, A., [1985].
Surrey's vanishing wildlife. A habitat survey review 1975-85.
Surrey Wildlife Trust.

Lousley, J.E., 1976.
Flora of Surrey. David & Charles, Newton Abbot.

Mentzer, E. von, Moberg, A., and Fibiger, M., 1991.
Noctua janthina [D. & S.] *sensu auctorum* a complex of three
species (Lep.: Noctuidae). *Nota lepid.* **14**(1):25-40.

Morris, R.K.A., 1984.
The macrolepidoptera of Mitcham Common, north-east Surrey.
Proc. Trans. Br. ent. nat. Hist. Soc. **17**:54-60.

Morris, R.K.A., and Collins, G.A., 1991.
On the hibernation of Tissue moths *Triphosia dubitata* L. and the Herald moth *Scoliopteryx libatrix* L. in an old fort. *Entomologist's Rec. J. Var.* **103**:313.

Morton, A.J., and Collins, G.A., 1992.
Distribution analysis of Surrey Lepidoptera using the DMAP computer package. *Nota lepid.* **15** (1):84-88.

Newman, L.W., and Leeds, H.A., 1913.
Text book of British butterflies and moths. St. Albans.

Oldaker, F.A., 1913.
A list of the Lepidoptera occurring within six miles of Haslemere. Haslemere Natural History Society.

Oldaker, F.A., 1951.
A list of the Lepidoptera occurring within six miles of Haslemere. Revised edition, Haslemere Natural History Society.

Pelham-Clinton, E.C., 1972.
Chloroclystis chloerata (Mabille, 1870), a geometrid moth new to the British list breeding in southern England. *Entomologist's Gaz.* **23**:151.

Perrins, C.M., 1959. in Anon.
Birds Butterflies Moths of the Godalming district. Charterhouse Natural History Society.

Plant, C.W., 1986.
Migratory Lepidoptera in the London area. *Lond. Nat.* **65**:7-29.

Plant, C.W., 1993.
Larger moths of the London area. London Natural History Society.

Pratt, C., 1981.
A history of the butterflies and moths of Sussex. Booth Museum, Brighton.

Pratt, C., 1986.
A modern review of the demise of *Hecatera dysodea* D. & S.: the Small Ranunculus. *Entomologist's Rec. J. Var.* **98**:70.

Pratt, C., 1992.
An historical summary of *Cucullia gnaphalii occidentalis* Bour. (Lep.:Noctuidae) in England. *Entomologist's Rec. J. Var.* **104**:9.

Remm, H., 1983.
New species of Noctuidae (Lepidoptera) from the USSR.
Ent. Obozr. **LXII**:596-600.

Riley, A.M., 1986.
A review of the status of *Eupithecia goossensiata* Mab. (Ling
Pug) and *E. absinthiata* Cl. (Wormwood Pug)
(Lep.:Geometridae). *Entomologist's Rec. J. Var.* **98**:85-89.

Shirt, D.B., ed., 1987.
British red data books: 2. Insects. Nature Conservancy
Council, Peterborough.

Skinner, B., 1981.
Peribatodes secundaria Denis & Schiffermüller in Kent: a
species of geometrid moth new to Great Britain.
Entomologist's Rec. J. Var. **93**:181.

Skinner, B., 1984.
Colour identification guide to Moths of the British Isles.
Viking.

Skinner, B., 1985.
Feral foodplants of *Lithophane leautieri hesperica* Boursin
(Blair's Shoulder-knot). *Entomologist's Rec. J. Var.* **97**:185.

South, R, 1907.
The moths of the British Isles. Warne, London.

Tremewan, W.G., 1980.
On the status of *Zygaena trifolii decreta* Verity in south-east
England. *Entomologist's Gaz.* **31**:143.

Tutt, J.W., 1899.
A natural history of the British Lepidoptera, **1**. Swan
Sonnenschein, London.

Tutt, J.W., 1900.
A natural history of the British Lepidoptera, **2**. Swan
Sonnenschein, London.

Tutt, J.W., 1902.
A natural history of the British Lepidoptera, **3**. Swan
Sonnenschein, London.

Wall, C., 1975.
The biology of the British species of *Chesias*
(Lepidoptera:Geometridae). *Entomologist's Gaz.* **26**:89.

Waring, P., 1992a.
On the current status of the Juniper Carpet moth, *Thera juniperata* L. (Lep.: Geometridae). *Entomologist's Rec. J. Var.* **104**:143.

Waring, P., 1992b.
Moth conservation project, news bulletin 5.

West, B.K., 1988.
Campaea margaritata L. (Lep.:Geometridae) and its second brood. *Entomologist's Rec. J. Var.* **100**:234.

West, B.K., 1996.
Panolis flammea D. & S. (Lep.: Noctuidae): its forms and their incidence in north-west Kent. *Entomologist's Rec. J. Var.* **108**:313.

Wheeler, A.S., 1955.
A preliminary list of the macro Lepidoptera of Bookham Common. *Lond. Nat.* **34**:28.

APPENDIX 6 – Glossary

acl   Actinic light (see Studying moths section).

aposematic   Having coloration, usually reds or yellows, that warns potential predators of danger. In a more general usage, it is also applied to warning scents, sounds and behaviour.

beating   A technique for finding larvae which feed on trees or shrubs (see Studying moths section).

coll.   In the collection of.

cryptic   Hidden, camouflaged by shape or coloration.

dusking   Many species of moth start to fly at or before dusk, often flying along lanes or hedgerows, and can be netted at this time. A few species are more likely to be found thus than at the light trap.

frass   Larval droppings.

gen. det.   Genitalic determination (see Studying moths section).

glabrous   Without hairs.

larva   The caterpillar stage.

mvl   Mercury vapour light (see Studying moths section).

ova   Eggs.

pinacula   Small plates.

RDB status   Red Data Book (see Explanation of species accounts).

RCK coll.   Rothschild-Cockayne-Kettlewell collection of aberrational forms, held at the Natural History Museum, London.

RES   Rothamsted Experimental Station trap (see Studying moths section).

setae   Hairs.

sugar   A method of attracting the adults of moths that feed (see Studying moths section).

sweeping   A technique for finding larvae which feed on low plants (see Studying moths section).

verrucae   Warts.

INDEX – ENGLISH NAMES

Figures in bold indicate plate numbers

INDEX – ENGLISH NAMES (continued)

INDEX – ENGLISH NAMES (continued)

INDEX – ENGLISH NAMES (continued)

INDEX – ENGLISH NAMES (continued)

INDEX – ENGLISH NAMES (continued)

INDEX – ENGLISH NAMES (continued)

INDEX – SCIENTIFIC NAMES

Figures in bold indicate plate numbers

INDEX – SCIENTIFIC NAMES (continued)

INDEX – SCIENTIFIC NAMES (continued)

INDEX – SCIENTIFIC NAMES (continued)

INDEX – SCIENTIFIC NAMES (continued)

INDEX – SCIENTIFIC NAMES (continued)

INDEX – SCIENTIFIC NAMES (continued)

INDEX – SCIENTIFIC NAMES (continued)

25/7/99   SALLOW KITTEN   — WOKING.